THE LONG

AFRICAN DAY

NORMAN MYERS

with photographs by the author

Macmillan Publishing Co., Inc.
NEW YORK

Collier Macmillan Publishers
LONDON

To Dorothy

who kept me going when things were going well
who stopped me from stopping when things were going badly
who gave me a push off again when things were not going
at all and whose idea it all was anyway

Macmillan Publishing Co., Inc.
866 Third Avenue, New York, N.Y. 10022
Collier-Macmillan Canada Ltd.

Library of Congress Catalog Card Number 71-182022

Second Printing 1974

Produced by Chanticleer Press, New York

Printed by Amilcare Pizzi, S.p.A., Milan, Italy

CONTENTS

FOREWORD

This is a story not so much of wild animals as wild communities. Within its formalized framework it aims at telling a tale not only of lions and zebras and plants, but of lions-and-zebras-and-plants. It also aims at telling the tale of Africa.

It has made little sense for a long time to write a book about African wildlife where there is hardly room for the African. Space is getting short in Africa, even in empty Africa: that is where local people have views on their diminishing living-space, which they express as forcefully as people in many other parts of the world. You cannot understand the world of the zebra unless you understand its total world, often a Masai world. And the Masai world is part of a total East African world, with fertile croplands as well as arid stocklands—both crowded in their own way. Unless you look at the entire environment, it is like looking at the black stripes on the zebra and saying that is all there is to it—except that the larger world is not so black and white. The wild lands of Africa are lands of animals and men, men with their hoes and hopes, men with their limited awareness of newer ways but their certain knowledge that the wider world lives better, men of all sorts and conditions: all are one.

It has been the aim of this volume to cover those creatures that contribute most to the workings of the great ecosystems. Everyone knows how elephants are modifying the landscape on every side and altering the habitat, not only for themselves but for many other creatures: rhinos, giraffes, kudus, zebras, wildebeest—hence lions, cheetah, hyenas, vultures; hence plants as much as any. But there is one smaller creature that has had as much influence on the welfare of wilderness areas as any over the past hundred years, and that is the tsetse fly. And another insect that can change the face of a forest as fast as elephants is the termite. Birds do not alter the shape of things in such significant fashion, so far as is known—a flock of a hundred egrets is scarcely to be compared with a herd of a hundred antelopes—although flamingos in their millions are different; so are queleas in their tens of millions. Reptiles similarly exert less effect now that the great era of their dominance has given way to the mammals; similarly, too, less is known about reptiles, except for such as crocodiles, which exert quite an effect on their fellow creatures, or monitor lizards, which exert quite an effect on crocodiles. While all these creatures are of equal interest in themselves, they do not have an equal impact on what goes on around them; hence they attract less attention from investigators. This is not to say, of course, that some insignificant-seeming segment of the system does not contribute some critical factor; but that sort of insight must be held over till Africa has more researchers—and more time.

The reader might bear in mind the range of forces that are deciding the future of wildlife far more forcefully than all the elephants that ever lived. East Africa, like most of the developing world (not to mention the developed world), is under the stress of formidable pressures, especially of people with their rising numbers and rising expectations. In the ebb and flow of shifting patterns, there are few factors that remain constant. They change like the patterns in an African forest where there is little light and dark, but mottlings and mergings and shadings in between. Yet among this mosaic there are a number of factors that are constant and will frequently return throughout these pages. They appear by direct statement at many points and by implication at more. The main point is that these African countries are going their own way. The world can go with them if it wants; but these African countries are going their own way.

Ten years ago this book could not have been written—there weren't the researchers. Five years ago it could not have been written with its present scope—there weren't yet the research results. It could not have been written now without the help of the researchers. It is based on the very generous advice and assistance of over a hundred persons working in the field throughout East Africa and other areas. These men and women have been extremely generous with their time in talking about their work, providing documentary data, even supplying material before their own publication dates. There was once a stage when it was not unusual for people to suggest that data released before publication (in two years' time, five—who knows?) would stop the world turning. Now the attitude is almost invariably the opposite. During a lengthy period I have found these people helpful beyond measure, as will be apparent to the reader on many a page. I hope my attempt to bring this recent research between two covers has remotely matched the spirit of those who supplied it.

The photographs were taken almost entirely in the parks and reserves of East Africa; it is plain what I owe to the National Parks and Game Departments of Kenya, Tanzania, and Uganda, especially to their directors, wardens and other staff members—particularly, I might say, to the many game rangers who proved not only some of the sharpest-eyed men one could encounter but the most cheerful and patient besides. Many wildlife areas now have their research centers, and I received extraordinary help from a range of scientific organizations, even at a time when they get enough callers wanting to "talk about lions." Especially helpful were the Serengeti Research Institute, the Ngorongoro Conservation Unit, the Nuffield Unit for Tropical Animal Ecology, and the Tsavo Research Project.

The reader who wishes to pursue some particular aspect at greater length may consult the bibliography. He will find listings of publications dealing with various topics: on almost every theme there are many times as much material as has been incorporated here. Meanwhile, I wish to express my special thanks to those who have spent hours in discussing their work, many more hours than could fairly have been hoped for—including R. Allsop, J. Ashe, L. H. Brown, G. Clough, I. Douglas-Hamilton, K. E. Eltringham, J. B. Foster, A. Graham, A. M. Harthoorn, D. Hendrichs, D. Hopcraft, P. Jarman, Miss J. U. M. Jarvis, the late F. X. Katete, J. M. King, H. Kruuk, H. F. Lamprey, R. M. Laws, W. Leuthold, F. W. Minot, F. Mitchell, M. L. Modha, J. S. Owen, J. Packard, J. A. Pile, J. Robin, M. A. Rodgers, R. Sachs, M. J. Sawyer, G. B. Schaller, A. R. E. Sinclair, D. Sindeyo, D. W. L. Sheldrick, D. Thornton, R. J. Wheater, and M. H. Woodford. I received help from further afield through the ready letter-writing of W. F. H. Ansell, R. H. U. Bell, K. Curry-Lindahl, G. G. Ganf, M. R. Gosling, K. G. McCullagh, C. A. R. Savory, and U. de V. Pienaar. Finally, there were those people who supplied constant enthusiasm for the whole project from start to finish: and it is not too much to say that a great part of this book is attributable to the especial assistance of only a very few: R. L. Casebeer, R. K. Davis, P. E. Glover, the late J. Goddard, P. Des-Meules, I. S. C. Parker, and D. Western. The final script has been read in part by a number of people who have made many amendments. But none of them bears any responsibility for whatever errors or shortcomings still persist, which belong nowhere but with the one who perpetrated them in the first place. My thanks to J. Ashe, R. M. Bere, R. K. Davis, P. Dolhinow, P. E. Glover, C. J. Hillman, U. de V. Pienaar, T. W. Ransom, M. F. Russell, and J. Walsh. And I am particularly appreciative to H. B. S. Cooke and the *Quarterly Review of Biology* for permission to reproduce the map of Africa during its prehistory evolution, to H. F. Lamprey and the East African Wildlife Society for permission to reproduce the diagram of ecological separation in Tarangire, and to R. M. Laws and the *Journal of Reproduction and Fertility* for permission to reproduce the map showing differentiation among the Tsavo elephant populations.

While almost all the photographs have been taken under natural conditions, there were special facilities generously accorded by S. Din of Secret Valley Safari Lodge, D. Hopcroft, Miss J. Jarvis, R. E. F. Leakey of the National Museum in Nairobi, R. Rickenbacher of Treetops, M. F. Russell, and Miss R. Tauber. The quality of the photographs in the book is entirely the result of the precision processing of Photofinishers in Nairobi, run by Masood Quraishy and his brothers, Jilo and Mehmood.

Sheets of notes by the hundred were typed by Mrs. M. Zola and Mrs. A. Fitch, while the final version of the text was typed by Mrs. E. Girvin. In between times, various drafts were typed by Mrs. A. C. McAdam, who originally expected a manuscript typing of 100,000 words, wound up typing two and a half drafts three times as long, and eventually contributed far more to this book than beating the typewriter.

I could hardly have completed this book without someone as adept with hot coffee and cold compresses, figurative as much as literal, as my wife—especially when there were atmospheric disturbances around the household and the climate ranged from sudden cold spells to outbursts of hot air. Dorothy maintained an environment equable and enduring while the writing was going on, and when the photography was under way she did more than just set record after record as a film-changer.

NORMAN MYERS

THE LONG AFRICAN DAY: 1972

This is the story of the long African day. It tells what happens in the wildlife country of East Africa while the sun sweeps over from one wide horizon to the other. Things change from hour to hour. They make a pattern of events that is always new, always different, always interesting. The creatures vary their activities from one time of day to another, from the freshness of morning to the heat of midday to the cool of evening. A watchful observer can spot as many as a hundred varying sorts in a single day: mammals, reptiles, insects, birds. In some areas he could find two hundred.

A wildlife area is more than a simple collection of creatures that happen to be there. It is a complex community that constitutes a single major ecological system wherever there is enough room for freedom of maneuver—not always easy in developing Africa. The creatures make up an independent community of interdependent beings, as self-sustaining as they are self-regulating. The environment and the forms of animal life it supports establish an ecological equilibrium that is to be found with fecundity of this kind only in wilderness tracts such as in East Africa. Here you watch a scene of evolution at work, as it has been at work for millions of years. Here, in the savannah wilds of Africa, is the last place to see it so easily on this scale.

It is not always apparent to the casual observer what is going on under the surface. There is a network of life, more finely balanced than you might imagine from a passing glance. Just how flourishing and fragile is now being revealed by the people who are taking a long look at it. During the past few years, researchers from all over the world have been coming to Africa to study these great ecosystems. There has been a "knowledge explosion" in East Africa. The savannah's secrets are being uncovered; the code is being broken; yet the mystery of the spectacle remains. Watch a herd of elephants on their way across the bushlands with their air of monumental assurance, and you will see.

Many myths are being challenged; many ideas are being turned inside out, not once but again and again. Some of this research is painstakingly detailed, perhaps unnecessarily so to the passing observer. But unless we find out just what a rhinoceros eats—the precise species of plants—instead of investigating something more exciting, like its sex life, the rhinoceros may end up with no sex life at all.

The safari watcher with time and inclination can reflect upon what happens at different periods of the day. He can begin to sense why the various phases are so important, why the creatures do one thing at morning, another at midday, another by late afternoon. What they do in any one phase affects their well-being over a whole twenty-four-hour cycle, while the day's activities may affect the whole sweep of the season, even a year, occasionally a lifetime. The hippopotamus must be back at the mud wallow soon after sunup to avoid the African sun; its body has hardly any mechanism for resisting heat, although it has special blood adaptations that enable it to submerge for five minutes at a stretch. The eland makes for shade during the midday hours, but only for limited periods; it is better equipped physiologically to withstand heat; an oryx is better adapted than a camel. The leopard is often idle at early morning; it is waiting until later in the day, when the gazelles come down to the streamside and the thicker cover. The cheetah is rarely seen at the water holes; it cannot use its hunting speed among the thicker vegetation, so it keeps to the plains. Wild dogs are out on the hunt at early morning and late evening, and this is the best time to spot them. Why they are so active at these times, nobody knows—yet. Whatever insight has been gained into the community of wild

Africa is nothing compared with the vast number of activities still unknown, still inscrutable, following the same patterns with the same purposes from times in the beginning.

The story revealed by the savannah's secrets shows how much there is to be learned from this world, a world that seems so different from man's. The creatures of the wide, wild landscape have their separate functions in regulating the systems and their workings. The individual species are not altogether competitive, however much they may appear so. Rather, they are complementary, mutually supporting. Over millions of years they have adapted themselves to fit into their own niches among the natural order of things, occupying segments of the wildlife spectrum where they do not conflict with one another. The spectacle here is prolific and variegated as nowhere else, an array orchestrated into a single organic whole.

People from all over the world wonder at the wonder of it. Why are wildebeest not often found without zebras, or Thomson's gazelles without both? Why do Grant's gazelles generally stay in one place all the year round, while Thomson's gazelles may wander from horizon to horizon? Why do lions sometimes appear to be the least competent hunters, and why are they not nearly as significant a factor in Ngorongoro Crater as the hyenas? Why do some elephants knock down more trees than others, some apparently to no purpose? Why do wildebeest generally congregate in big herds and zebras in small ones? Why are there no giraffes in much of Uganda and no kob antelopes in the whole of Kenya, while other creatures that are often seen with them elsewhere fare equally well in both areas? Why do only some lions climb trees? How does a rhino find its way around over miles of terrain when it can hardly see? How many elephants make too many, and how many leopards make too few? Why is the cheetah not in such direct danger of extinction as was once thought, but in much greater danger of disappearing when its total environment is grossly overstrained? Why are there so many more species in Africa—mammals, insects, birds, reptiles, plants—than in most other parts of the world? Why do animal populations vary so much in numbers, even when they are left undisturbed? If African parks twice the size of Yellowstone feature so many animals right now, why is there concern about their future? After all, there are many times more animals in a Yellowstone-sized park than in Yellowstone. How do you look after creatures that have looked after themselves well enough for millions of years before man ever got onto his hind legs? Is the best way of looking after them to leave them alone? Can they be "left alone" in a world crowded beyond measure by a supremely sagacious and savage species that has been called the one "really wild animal"?

These creatures are being looked at by people from the far ends of the earth; this is a new hope for their future. The stream of visitors is rising faster in East Africa than in any other vacation area of its size in the world. They are coming to see the long African day in all its variety and color. These are travelers who get up when the sun gets up, ready to spend a day free from the ticking tyrant on their wrist. Right at dawn the animals begin their activity. The lions are finishing their kill, and the jackals and vultures are waiting for their turn. The cheetah is on the lookout for a chance to hunt. The antelope herds, out on the plains where they have spent the night away from brushwood and ambush, are beginning to make their way to the rivers and water holes. The bat-eared foxes sit outside their holes sunning themselves. The light sparkles on Kilimanjaro's eastern glaciers. Lion cubs sport in the soft warmth. A leopard stretches and looks around. The elephants as usual are eating, just eating. The sun rises. The day begins.

The zebras and wildebeest make their way to the watering places. This is a good opportunity for the lions that have not yet killed. The herds know it, and they may take an hour over the last hundred yards to the water's edge. All their senses are ultra-alert. At last they drink. They wander off—though sometimes they leave one behind on the ground. The elephants arrive. An elephant, with its bulk, runs quite a risk of overheating, and it needs a good splash around as the sun is nearing its height. It drinks its fill, thirty gallons of it, then enjoys a mud bath. Cooled at last, it moves off to find shelter from the noontime sun. At the same water hole, the buffalo are settling in for a long, steady wallow; the full treatment takes several hours. The same goes for the hippos; hull-down, they snooze in sludgy bliss from early morning till late afternoon.

By midday the horizon is dancing with mirages. All is languid; all is oppressive. Many animals are lying up to avoid the heat. Not that there is nothing left to see. On the plains there are a few antelopes left. Some graze and browse, some browse and graze; some do neither. They come in all shapes and sizes, from the thousand-pound eland to the ten-pound dik-dik. Some don't bother to go near the water hole; they can last for months without water. A giraffe herd wafts across the horizon. Crocodiles heave off the sand-banks into the water. Greater bustards strut around, while tiny sunbirds flit here and there, brief flashes of color in the glare. A rhinoceros arrives for a mud soak. It rolls over and over till it is satisfied, then takes another roll just to make sure. It shambles off for a dust-bowl siesta. Kilimanjaro glistens above.

By midafternoon things are stirring again. The lions stroll from their thickets and lie on little knolls to enjoy the breeze. The elephants decide in their ponderous way that now is the time to take up feeding again. With some mass reflex, they all start at once. The larger herds of antelope begin their trek to better grass out on the plain; the area near the watercourses has been beaten to bare earth. Vultures soar in spirals above the savannah, seeking signs of a kill at the morning watering points. Hyenas sit at the entrances to their burrows and sniff the air for the same signs. Jackals emerge with a like mind. The whole community gradually shakes off the stupor of the day's heat as it prepares to resume its diverse activities. By evening the bush is all sounds again. A wart-hog suddenly stops feeding—quite a sacrifice for a warthog—and stands with every nerve alert: a strange shadow has shifted. A gazelle stares fixedly at a thicket: a family of cheetah is on the move. A bird rises startled: a leopard is beginning its prowl. The bush returns to life, exactly as it has done since before man went on his evening prowl. On Kilimanjaro the last light glows soft across the western glaciers. A giraffe sways along the skyline. The shadows become one big shadow. In a land of color and contrast, the sunset is a last wonder of the long African day.

Some of these animals were here when Europe was still a bog, America and Asia were a single landmass (and separate again, and together again), and before Kilimanjaro had erupted above the earth's crust. They represent the main remnant of the golden age of mammals a few millennia ago, a throwback to the most splendid array of animal life the earth has ever seen. East Africa is their last great refuge. They have survived through all the hours of their own long African day; now they may be nearing their twilight. In the middle of the most advanced stage of earth's history they may suddenly vanish. They are being trapped out, shot out, and, above all, elbowed out. One minute they are here, the next gone—and gone forever. They will disappear in the twinkling of a geological eye. Even if man were to live on for millions of years, it is doubtful if he could restore the smallest part of this spectacle. It is as yet beyond him to re-create the simplest living creature.

And these are not simple creatures. They are highly developed beings, adapted to their environment by forces of evolution that man can only vaguely grasp. They took eons to form, and they have survived aberrations of the earth's crust and atmosphere at every stage, with every variation. They have survived all the ages, but they have never come upon an age as dark as this. They have flourished in the face of predators of every shape and size, until they have come up against the most cunning, the most rapacious, the most insatiable predator of all. Man is the only creature who kills incessantly for reasons other than hunger. Animals have been shot by the millions in southern Africa, machine-gunned in north Africa, slaughtered by the thousands to meet the dictates of misguided

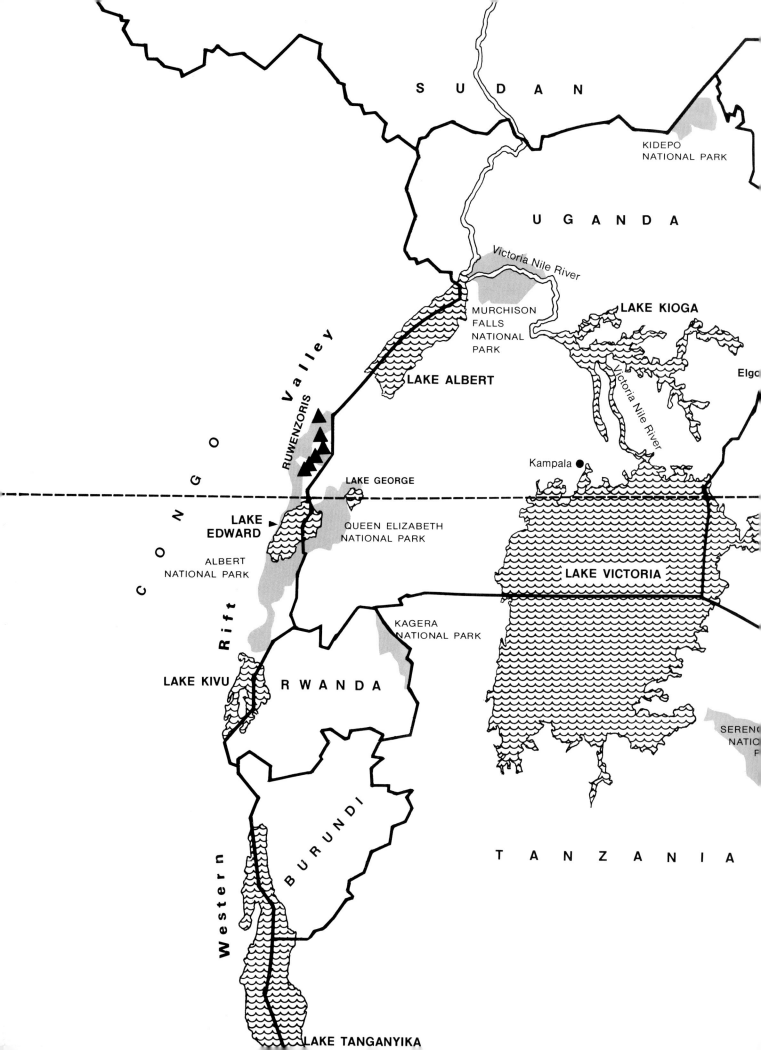

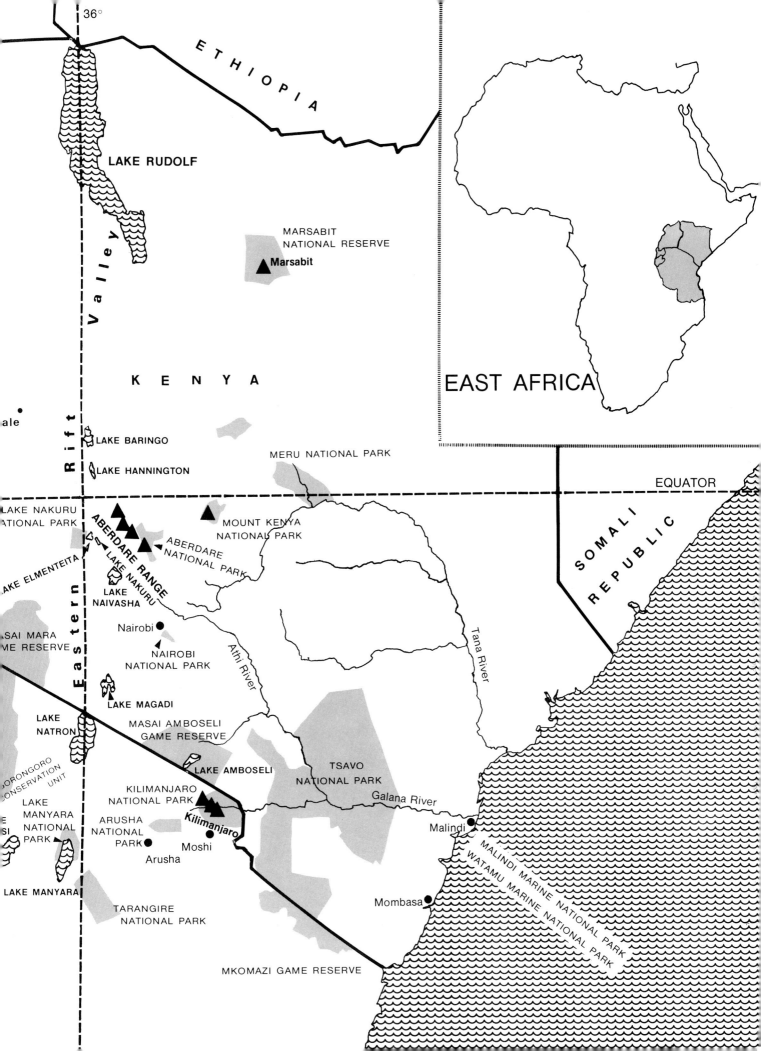

science, poached for fickle fashion trends, crowded to extinction by creeping cultivation, hounded and pursued and butchered everywhere. Now they represent only one twentieth part—perhaps one hundredth—of what they once were. They are largely confined to a few sanctuaries, over half of them in a small part of the continent, East Africa.

There is hope that this long African day is not about to enter the night. More people in more parts of the world are taking more interest. Visitors from overseas are coming to see the spectacle "before it is too late." Precisely because they are coming, it may never be too late. They are coming in their jetloads from every continent, to see these savannahs so remote from mechanized city life. Sometimes urban man wants to break away from the concrete jungle to a more pristine sort of jungle. For him it is a retreat; and it is because of such visitors and the money they bring that the animals are finding a retreat as well.

There is further hope for the wild creatures. Investigators are finding that these savannah areas, some of the "poorest" and the most destructible lands in the world, are proving prolific and productive beyond most finest "managed" grasslands anywhere. Without damage to the wildlife, these arid regions could produce a food supply that may yet plug massive gaps in Africa's food needs. Agricultural countries such as these need powerful persuasion to look after their wildlife. What if they were to view wildlife as a cash crop? To visitors the idea of killing animals is often repugnant; slaughtering the game is surely against all the principles of conservation. But in an overloaded, protein-starved land, this might be the best—as well as the last—chance of saving the game. Nature left to itself is teeming and vigorous beyond measure. This would be the first attempt to benefit from wild nature in such a direct manner and on such a scale, and at the same time it could insure a future for the wildlife as nothing else would. Wildlife would become not so much a source as a "re-source," something to be used time and time again. The wild creatures share a communal secret that matches their mystique for the affluent (not to say well-fed) visitor from overseas. They can provide a raison d'être of their own for the man who looks at them not as a fine subject for a photograph, but as a fine subject for a meal. This is the man who has no inclination to stand and stare; this is the man in whose country the wild animals live and upon whose sufferance they daily depend.

If the time since the great creatures first appeared in ancient Africa is considered as the time from sunrise to sunset, then the earliest mammals were there from the first few hours. But most creatures of the African savannah are comparative newcomers and do not reach their peak until the day is three-quarters done. Even today they are still, relatively speaking, not far beyond the crest of their development, even though they have probably passed their finest hour. It is only six minutes ago that man appeared in his cave, and he was not ready to emerge from it until the last few ticks of the clock. Yet in this brief moment of time, he has destroyed creatures without number, especially in this "civilized" period of history. If the wildlife of Africa is to be saved, it will be not at the eleventh hour, but at half a second to midnight.

Africa is full of passing shadows. This may be only a dark patch before brighter times ahead. For those who look, there may already be strong signs of the light.

The infant elephant, unsure of its feet during the first few hours, will have many hours to spend through its phase of Africa's long day. It will be a period quite unlike any that other elephants, or elephant ancestors, have ever passed through, with more upheavals than in the momentous days of the just-completed Pleistocene. But because of the network of African parks, and the new conservation ideals developed by Africans, it could still hope to live out much of an elephant's normal lifetime, although the prospect of any wild elephants at all in wild Africa by the time its own offspring are producing offspring is far from certain.

THE LONG AFRICAN DAY:
A LOOK A LONG WAY BACK

In the beginning Africa wasn't. It was only one part of a great landmass that included South America and India and Australia. Together they made up the supercontinent of Gondwanaland.

All this was many millions of years back, and it was a state of affairs that lasted millions of years. From the furthest beginnings of the earth there must have been a Gondwanaland, although when those beginnings were nobody really knows. Once people said 1,000,000,000 years was enough for everything to have happened. Then it became 2,000,000,000. With an effort of imagination the estimate was revised to 3,000,000,000. Now the earth is thought to have originated 4,500,000,000 years ago. For much of this time nothing much happened. The planet was settling down. Sometimes it erupted; then

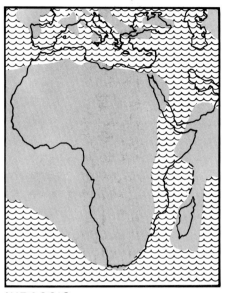

JURASSIC

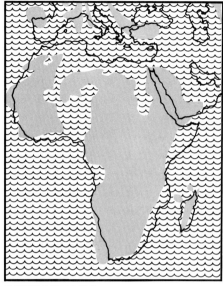

CRETACEOUS

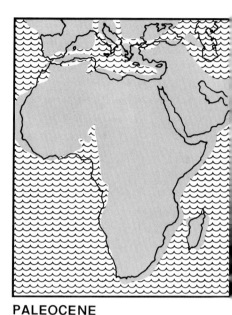

PALEOCENE

Six steps in the emergence of
Africa from the ancient mega-
continent Gondwanaland.

it settled down again. Rocks were formed. They were twisted and bent, they were heated up and became other rocks.

After a while the rains started, coming down in a steady stream that built up the seas. Much later, the first stirrings of life appeared. The fossil remains of life go back only 550,000,000 years, the latest one-eighth of the earth's existence. Life had probably been there a lot longer, perhaps four times longer, mostly in soft single-celled forms that left no traces in the rocks. Not until creatures with shells arrived did life leave its signs, and by then life was probably ancient. The first of these more recent eras, the Paleozoic or "era of ancient life," began 550,000,000 years ago. In the fullness of time it was followed by the Mesozoic ("middle life"), and finally the Cenozoic ("recent life"). The Paleozoic stage marked a parting of the ways for the planet. Suddenly there was an outburst of multiformed life, fossil-forming life in many guises. It arrived with an evolutionary spasm that has hardly ever been repeated. And for primeval times these creatures were far from primitive. At first they all lived in the seas. It was not until 225,000,000 years ago, a stage roughly halfway between those hazy far-back times and the present day, that the great roaming out of the water started to surge to its climax as the reptiles strayed onto the land. Things have not been the same since.

When the Paleozoic gave way to the Mesozoic, the earth caught its breath before taking another stride forward. There was much crunching of the crust. Mountains started to rear into the primordial skies. What had been a surface largely flat and uniform began to develop differences. What had been a climate generally equable began to be more varied. Some areas became arid; others were invaded by ice sheets. This was an epic time in the epochs and the eons, and there was not to be another such archetypal phase until almost the present day.

To some eyes there is a rhythm in these changes of the earth. The continents surge to the surface; they throw up mountains; the oceans are on the retreat. Huge lakes appear, only to evaporate into the skies. What has so far been similar and stable becomes tumultuous. Volcanoes spew out sparks and spread their lava over the landscape. Where there have been tropical forests there are glaciers. New stages bring on new plants and animals with explosive energy. For a short time evolution becomes revolution.

If one such extraordinary episode took place 550,000,000 years ago, and another marked the beginning of the Mesozoic, 225,000,000 years ago, then still another arrived

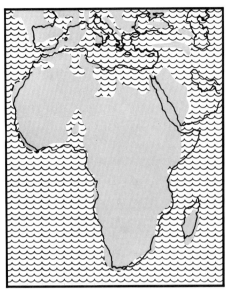

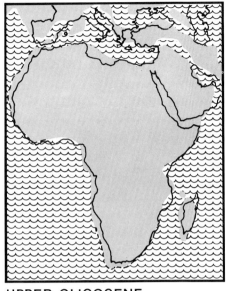

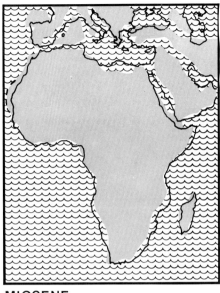

EOCENE   **UPPER OLIGOCENE**   **MIOCENE**

just the other day when the Pleistocene turned the normal shape of things upside down, particularly when ice ages set off a new pattern of cataclysms for land and life. After each such stage, things settle down into a long phase of stability if not tranquillity. The new land shapes are eroded away, the small deep oceans are silted up, and seas spread across landscapes that have become flatter. It is thought a continent can be worn flat in only 25,000,000 years. At such stages, things grow more the same again. Why there should be these dimly discernible cycles is difficult to say, if indeed they exist at all. They seem to last about as long as for our galaxy to turn once around. Perhaps the cause is not to be found far away from the earth, but deep inside it, when hot pressures build up and let loose their energy at cyclic intervals. More probably, there is a buildup of the oxygen level in the earth's atmosphere until it reaches a critical point allowing an "explosion of life" in fresh forms. Whatever the cause, the result is a new scene that supersedes everything that went before, which is why the earth has hardly ever been so diverse as it is now. We are just emerging from the Pleistocene phenomenon. Some say we are still not completely out of it, that its full force could return any time—given a few thousand years.

In many senses Africa is one of the most diverse regions. Until very recently it has enjoyed a fair degree of isolation that has allowed it to get on with evolving into forms more complex, if not more colorful, for scores of millions of years. Every time a convulsion has taken place in North America or Europe there has been a backward shift in the range of life forms. In the long run this could make for a greater scope in land and life forms; but for a time there is a retreat. Africa has generally been able to get on with its affairs in primordial peace. It has enjoyed sufficient interruptions to stimulate change without catastrophe. Although nowadays, for the first time, much of Africa is becoming like much of the rest of the world, there are still few places, such as East Africa, where one can see the old continent as it was, panoramas as pristine and Pleistocene as anywhere. Along the Nile shores where crocodiles swarm, one can even have an experience of Mesozoic dimensions. There is no single time when one can say Africa "arrived"; over the ages its landscapes lurched around, its climate chopped about, its vegetation flourished and faltered, its mammals and birds and reptiles underwent change after change. But if one were to set a point and say that *then* at that moment the first formations revealed themselves as anything like what the continent is today, one might choose the change-of-life phase that marked the world 225,000,000 years ago.

Left: To glimpse a creature that is uniquely African, take a look at a lungfish.

Right: The dawn lights up a leopard returning from a hunt; it must get its prey into a tree as soon as possible, or a flock of vultures, starting to circle the skies, may warn another stronger or more numerous predator that a kill carcass is waiting to be snatched.

Below: In the stillness of the early morning, the goliath heron stalks along smoothly; it does not want to disturb the scene, or it might not spot its food.

The period that followed, the Triassic, marked the breakup of Gondwanaland. Africa emerged as by far the largest chunk. It did not take the shape it reveals today for almost another 100,000,000 years. But at any rate it was on its own and could follow its own life-style, away from hangers-on. There was still an attachment to the Arabia segment, but that area has always been more closely related to Africa than to what the atlas labels Asia. Before the breakup of Gondwanaland, Africa's ancient face had not been submerged beneath the waves for 50,000,000 years. Unlike most land available for living on nowadays, Africa did not have its slate washed clean and lifeless from one era to another (Asia has been under water for most of the time). It kept its face above water, until now we can see a face of unimaginable oldness. Around Lake Victoria there are Kavirondo rocks at least 3,000,000,000 years old. In the Serengeti there are rocks older still. Africa is not only a piece of the earth's crust as ancient as any; it is also enduring. It was not soft enough to be shaped afresh by whatever series of earth-shudders might shake it. During the times of the ancient world, its rocks were battered and buried and disgorged again in grotesque earth movements that left them hardened, often transformed into granite, prepared for permanence. Traveling south from Kenya to Tanzania one can still see what ancient Africa looked like. The plains around Tsavo are a landscape in essence little changed from early times.

Meanwhile, the core of Africa's ancient block has, on occasion, been forcefully altered. These tough rock formations were too old, too hard to bend. Instead they broke, and then they were sheared away around the edges. Sometimes the whole structure was strained until it fractured. These ruptures were worn away by erosion, slowly and steadily. The weather-worn rocks of the remotest beginnings—the quartzites and schists —were burst apart by eruptions of crystalline rocks from inside the earth's hot body. By and large, however, Africa has been shaped by rain and wind. Already in the days of Gondwanaland the processes were under way, if not advanced. Gradually Africa's primitive ridges and wrinkles were smoothed off until there emerged a peneplain, a flattened landscape. The forces for producing this "Africa surface" continued pretty well uninterrupted until well into the Cenozoic, concluding with the peneplain of the Miocene. The continent was still no more than a thousand feet above the seas, except for patches like Rwanda that were already lost lands, lands in the heart of Africa and different from Africa.

During this same phase, life had been spreading across these landscapes. For much of its time Africa had no animals at all. Before the first great cyclic changes 550,000,000 years ago, there was nothing. There were silent scenes. Not a bird sang. There was not a seed nor an insect on the early worldwinds. In the seas, however, there was plenty of life. A group of fishes was soon to throw off the coelacanth, which has recently been dredged up from the depths of the ocean and the depths of prehistory. Another group was near to producing the African lungfish, an archival throwback to early eras. By the time Africa's long day had started 225,000,000 years ago, amphibians were trying to get a hold on the edge of the swampy shores. Then came the reptiles. These rudimentary land-explorers dragged themselves along on their bellies as much as on their legs. Slowly their limbs grew more powerful, until the reptiles developed into dinosaurs and other giants. The plant-eating brachiosaurus, the brawniest and longest (seventy feet) dinosaur ever known, once roamed the coasts of East Africa. Another beast, with a big-dipper back and an armor of sail-shaped plates, strode the lands of Africa under the name of stego-saurus. Alongside these creatures there were already ancestral crocodiles, of suitably ancestral size, in the marshes, together with some lesser four-legged creatures with features that foreshadowed the beings that were to be the glory of Africa, the mammals.

Suddenly the dinosaurs came to an end, 165,000,000 years into the African day, only around 60,000,000 years ago. With the end of this reptile realm there was oppor-tunity for other creatures to exploit the environment. The mammals did just that, with a radiative vigor that has proved the prime spectacle of Africa ever since. It was this age that eventually resulted in the emergence of one particularly precocious mammal. It is an age that may be a little past its peak, or it could be close to its final plunge, a plunge

that is being precipitated with a ruthless energy far surpassing the sudden "great dying" of the reptiles. But for once the normal processes of evolution have little to do with the changes.

It was during the stage of the giant reptiles, in the Jurassic period, 150,000,000 years ago, while the birds were first appearing, that Africa grew more modern in terms of its vegetation. A wet phase swept the continent. There were rivers on every side, meandering their way across flat plains into new lakes. Along the coast there were delta-like areas that made it difficult to say where Africa ended and the seas began. Yet during the Cretaceous period that followed, the shorelines of the continent started on their final shaping. The landmass had become cut off from all others by the oceans, separated, except at Gibraltar, by wide reaches of sea. Instead of a small Mediterranean there was a patch of ocean that stretched from the Atlantic across southern Europe, over the eventual site of the Himalayas, and on to Malaya. Africa's splendid isolation was insured by this ancient sea.

Fifty million years ago the main form of the continent was much as it is now. The mammals were in their heyday. Their main advance, the placental variations allowing an offspring to develop in the body of the mother and to be born in a much more advanced state, had already arrived in the "dawn epoch" of the modern age, the Eocene. This was a time of flowering plants and palms and fish that all looked much as they do now. There were ancestors of elephants and rhinos. All the insect groups the visitor knows (especially at evening time) were already there in abundance. The landscape was undergoing periodic warpings, such as those that formed Lake Victoria's basin. Warm climates continued into the Oligocene, while Africa began to dwindle, possibly as a result of volcanic eruptions that spread fire where there had been none for a long time. Similar rumblings set off the first stages of the eastern Rift Valley, part of the great horseshoe-shaped trough that now cleaves across East Africa sixty miles wide and half a mile deep. To replace the forests there arrived a new phenomenon, grasslands. And across the savannah there spread another phenomenon, grass-eating antelopes. Then came a further phenomenon, antelope-eaters. There the first ape also appeared. Africa was getting closer to its modern miracle, man. It was also getting closer to what awaited these plants and animals as soon as man got his hands on them.

By the Miocene stage there were volcanoes blowing off, as actively in the eastern regions of Africa as in all the rest of the continent put together. The highlands of Kenya were receiving their volcanic coverings, later to decompose into the rich soils of Kikuyuland. Frequent faults were rending Africa from end to end, and what wasn't fractured was often warped by bucklings that caused Africa's climate to become much more varied, and the vegetation with it. Finally came the Pliocene, the last major period of stability before the cataclysms of the Pleistocene. The mountain-building around the world continued, nowhere with such fearful force as in East Africa, where there were surgings as titanic as tectonic. Mount Kenya soared into the skies, 6,000 feet higher than today's 17,000-foot massif, higher even than Kilimanjaro was ever to be. But elsewhere there was erosion as usual, erosion and more erosion. Many mammals began a decline, partly, perhaps, because the manlike ape was coming into his own, and partly because of climatic changes like the drought that lasted through much of the Pliocene. The forests shrank; so did the lakes; so did the water holes on the plains. The elephants continued to prosper with all their evolutionary energy, before their decline in the period following. The hooved creatures thrived, including many of today's antelopes. There were wildebeest, or wildebeest ancestors, together with the forebears of hartebeest and gazelles. Those that could get by in arid Africa survived; those that couldn't leave behind the

Left above: By the time there are no slanting shadows on Kilimanjaro, the elephants are heading for the rivers and swamps.

Right: If you are watching Grevy's zebras you are probably on the fringes of a desert, if not farther into it—and for most of the day you can well believe what is meant in Africa by "hot and dry," all the more when the snows of Mount Kenya are in the background with the equator running almost through the middle of them.

ways of the rainy Tertiary died out. If the interior of Africa was fairly stable, the coast-lines weren't. Sometimes the shores wandered far inland, sometimes they wandered out to sea. Periodically, the sea rose and retreated and rose again. Just now it is low.

This was a time of spectacular formations across the whole of Africa, notably again in East Africa. It lasted only three to four million years, the final stage before the beginning of the ultramodern epoch of the Holocene 10,000 years ago; many people think it includes the "now era" of the Holocene. The Pleistocene opened with heavings of the earth that left Africa uplifted, then tilted, then fractured across the old-order formations. There were strainings as the landmass burst asunder. There were fresh volcanic eruptions. The early cone of Mawenzi on Kilimanjaro had been worn away into a spiky pinnacle, but it was overtopped by the fresh dome of Kibo, rising recent and uneroded nearly 20,000 feet high. It now soars sheer out of the plain, scarcely a foothill, an isolation that has led to Kilimanjaro's own unique forms of life. There are fifty insects and other creatures on the upper slopes that are not to be found anywhere else. As is the way with insects in windy areas, they have tended to dispense with wings. In an environment that swings from the extremes of winter to summer every day, there is probably a greater urge for breeding than in more sedate climates, just as the tropics generally allow more generations in a year than a temperate region. Hence, what has proved especially suitable for Kilimanjaro's dome has spread itself rapidly throughout the insects until, in the short time since Kilimanjaro erupted from the plain, a particular range of creatures has evolved that the mountain has made its own.

The main changes of the Pleistocene, however, were caused not by eruptions in Africa so much as by what went on elsewhere. The northern hemisphere was subjected to sheets of ice that extended right around the globe. Although the glaciers never reached anywhere near Africa, each time the ice extended south—as it did four times—Africa encountered climatic disruptions of an intensity it had hardly experienced so rapidly before. A drop in the temperature of a few degrees on the equator meant less evaporation; hence more moisture from more rain; hence more forests. During the intervals there was less rain. The current dry phase started 10,000 years ago. Nobody is sure whether it is a new stage altogether, or whether it is an interval before another glaciation comes upon us. If things run true to form, the next 10,000 years could see another ice age. This would not mean disaster unlimited: man in his more primitive forms has already survived several ice ages, just as he has come through all manner of volcanic eruptions and earth shudderings. It will merely mean that land prices in New York and San Francisco will hit rock bottom—until they hit sea bottom in the following flood.

The fortunes of Lake Victoria give some idea of what might happen. During the Pleistocene there were times when the lake was 300 feet higher than it is now, and hence vastly bigger. There were times when it threatened to dry up. There were times when it was half swamp. Lake Rudolf was possibly once Greater Lake Rudolf, big enough to link up along the Rift Valley with the Nile in one direction and with Lake Baringo in the other. At other times, it disappeared altogether. The Rift Valley itself was formed by three major cracks, the last one only 500,000 years ago. The valley floor did not suddenly drop into a mile-deep cleft such as one sees outside Nairobi, where the spectacle is at its most striking from Russia to Rhodesia. It generally dropped at a rate of less than six inches in 1,000 years. The hot springs and steam jets of Hell's Gate near Naivasha reveal how the volcanic pressures are still showing plenty of life only a short way beneath the spectator's feet.

As the Rift Valley was forming, so were its lakes. They have varied in extent, depending in part upon glaciers thousands of miles to the north. Quite recently the three lakes at Nakuru, Elementaita, and Naivasha were all one. Now they are slowly dwindling away. Naivasha is only thirty feet deep and Nakuru less than ten. On the other hand, Lake Tanganyika, a true rift lake, is 4,700 feet deep, the deepest in the world. More remarkable

Later in the morning, the cheetah and her cub will be on the move: that is their hunting time. But for a while after sunup they wait for the day to rouse itself.

than its depth is what goes on in the top few hundred feet, where there are around 160 sorts of fish—and over four-fifths of them, along with hundreds of molluscs, crustaceans, flatworms, sponges, and others, are unique to Lake Tanganyika. Just like the whole continent, there are spots within Africa that have enjoyed isolation from their environs and have developed in their own distinctive ways.

By the end of the ice ages, there were roaming across Africa almost all the animals of today's wildlife scene. Africa now includes close to a quarter of the mammals of the world, ranging across more families than any other zoogeographic region. This unique variety has arisen not only because of the continent's size and its position largely within the tropics and astride the equator, but also from its range of vegetation within the landscape patterns, as well as its long prehistory of semiseclusion and stability (while remaining close enough to the other landmasses to "top up" the basic stock from time to time). Having achieved its "biotic maturity," the continent could permit further factors to exert their influence, factors that seem to operate in many parts of the tropics but which would affect the already rich array in Africa more than in most other areas. The variety of creatures, plant and animal, in a landscape depends broadly upon how many niches there are for them, or rather how rich the niches are for the creatures to then adapt into subniches which later may develop into new niches in their own right, or how far a niche supplies forage and *lebensraum*, together with all the other features of this basic ecological concept, in sufficient profusion for creatures to overlap from one niche to another. In equable climates, with little drastic change such as the temperate zones encounter in winter (though a four-month cold spell does not always shut down life much more than a four-month drought season), there is less need for creatures to adapt to a range of

Watch a zebra and you may wonder what good its stripes are as camouflage, unless they are intended as disruptive coloring. But watch a herd with the water hole trees behind and the midday heat shimmer in front: that is how a lion often "sees" them.

environmental pressures, so they can often manage with a smaller niche. The same stability from one season to another produces a greater profusion of food, allowing a smaller niche once again for the species to support itself in. A tropical bird may reveal a less complex life-style than one from North America or Europe, but it forms part of a much more complex array of birds. By extension, the tropics feature many species stemming from remote eras, primitive beings that have become highly specialized; temperate lands on the other hand feature species more recently evolved, fewer of them, more adaptable, hence occupying broader niches and frequently more numerous: in North America there are far fewer species of antelope and deer, but probably well over 10,000,000 deer alone, whereas Africa with its tremendous array of antelope species— at least 40—probably does not match them in total numbers, certainly not in the totals the white-tailed deer alone can muster.

Whatever the causes of this tropical virtuosity, there is a much greater array of creatures in Africa than in any similar-sized region outside the tropics. Taking mammals alone, there are around 850 species in Africa south of the Sahara, which amounts to many more than in the next major realm on earth, Central and South America, where three-quarters are rodents and bats anyway. Preeminent in Africa are the antelopes and other bovids, around 80 altogether, not only the most spectacular array of the world's larger animals but the most readily seen across the open savannahs. Most of these animals have emerged in Africa (rather than strayed in from elsewhere): almost three-quarters of the carnivores, four-fifths of the insectivores, nine-tenths of the antelopes and other hoofed animals, and practically all the primates.

Only a short time ago many of these creatures were sharing Africa with now-extinct animals such as the buffalo-sized sheep and the gorilla-sized baboons of Olduvai. Only a little time before that, they were sharing it with a creature that was learning how to pick up stones and throw them at other animals, especially sharpened stones. This newcomer was also learning how to hack animals to bits with other sharpened stones. His hands were precise enough and powerful enough for both. His build was smaller than a pygmy's and his brain comparatively bigger than any other creature's. By 500,000 years ago, true man had arrived. He was exceedingly clever and exceedingly weak. Pound for pound, there was not another creature so feeble as he. Each new dawning of the long African day brought him the same problem: how to get enough food to stay alive while making sure he did not become food himself. He had lots of intelligence, but he had no claws, no fangs, no hair. He could use his fingers and opposable thumbs for fashioning a spear, but he could not use them to fetch water. Sooner or later each day he had to go down to the same water hole, where he sometimes caught his own prey. He had to bend and drink, just as certainly as the zebras and just as vulnerably. When he lowered that expanded cranium to the water, its gray matter was of no use to him if there were another creature watching. The struggle would be as unequal as it is today, when the same creature goes hunting those same carnivores with his superweapons that "make things equal."

But at that early stage, man still could not dominate the environment sufficiently to multiply his numbers much. Altogether, Africa was home to perhaps 1,000,000 of this manling. Judging by the number of animals on a stretch of savannah now and reckoning that Africa then included 5,000,000 square miles of suitable country out of its total of 11,000,000 square miles, there could have been nearly 2,000,000 lions and four or five hundred million other major animals. Now man has learned a thing or two. There are 350,000,000 of him in Africa and perhaps 10,000,000 of the larger animals—possibly a few more, possibly less. Possibly, there are more wild creatures in North America. Within the lifetime of most people now alive in Africa, there could well be three times as many humans trying to find space in what is no longer "empty Africa."

For most of its time Africa has had no humans at all. It has had rhinos a lot longer than people. It has had crocodiles a lot longer than rhinos. It has had many animals a lot longer than crocodiles—many, many of them. There have been species by the thousands and millions if one counts all the forms of life that Africa ever featured. Almost all of them are gone. They were gone long before man emerged, certainly before modern man arrived. At any one time there has never been more than a fraction of the entire array. They have been following on in an incessant process of flux and renewal. One throng gives way to another. Now this is the last scene so far, and in many respects it is the most singular spectacle that has ever developed. It has taken a long while to build up. There have been many stages to the long African day. Sometimes Africa has been dry, sometimes it has been drenched. Sometimes it has been especially cool, sometimes especially hot—all over. Always, there have been animals in myriad marvels. Every moment of every hour there has been another phase to the procession. The scene is now far different from what it has ever been since its remotest beginnings.

Contrary to common belief, a buffalo is one of the more timid creatures of Africa, and no more likely to cause harm than a gazelle or a monkey. But it is also highly inquisitive, and the patient onlooker can get a closeup view without much difficulty. Whereupon buffalo and safarist can take a long look into each other.

Time-Scale of the Long African Day*

During almost all this time, the most epochal changes have taken a few million years; now they take a few decades.

		LAND AND PLANTS	ANIMALS
		3.75**	
CENOZOIC ("recent life")	PLIOCENE	All continents are now reaching their present shapes. Drier conditions again cause the forests to retreat. Mount Kenya soars above the equator, far higher than today's eroded pinnacle, and Kilimanjaro starts to erupt. Eastern and southern Africa are both upraised as high as 6,000 feet, while the Ruwenzori range surges to 17,000 feet. A huge lake covers the Congo. 7.5**	The mammals start on their decline, though the man-apes flourish: some move upright. A few creatures, such as the white rhinoceros, reach more or less final form. The great cats steadily assume more modern appearance, while the bovids suddenly advance in every direction—antelope, buffalo, cattle—to exploit a still expanding spectrum of plant food. The first true elephants appear. The forerunners of the springbok, impala, and gerenuk branch off from the main gazelle stock.
	MIOCENE	Rains increase, causing further wide-scale erosion. The continent becomes cooler, though not so cold as modern Africa. Madagascar breaks away. A greater part of Africa's flora is much like it is now. The continent's isolation is eventually ended when land-bridges join Africa-Arabia to Eurasia across the Red Sea, via Sicily, and across the Straits of Gibraltar. Extensive tracts of eastern and southern Africa are raised to 4,000 feet, while forests extend again over much of the continent. 26**	Many more herbivores emerge, some of them in huge numbers; still only a few bovids. The first giraffids arrive, deer-sized; the first okapi appears too, already very similar to today's. Rudimentary antelopes evolve. The felids and canids become more differentiated; early stabbing (sabre-toothed) cats emerge. Primitive gazelles are on the spread. Eventually hominids evolve, possibly using simple tools at this early stage, even eating meat.
	OLIGOCENE	The seas recede greatly. Climates grow cooler; drier periods cause forests to give way to grasslands, further stimulated by fire-spreading volcanoes. The Rift Valley starts to sink. Africa becomes a peneplain mostly under 2,000 feet. 40**	Africa makes a brief exchange with Eurasia to acquire new carnivores and primitive ruminants. There is a spectacular surge of grass-eaters, together with forerunners of the felids and canids. Elephants feature four-tusked variants; some are developing trunks, while remaining small—alongside super-rhinoceroses, the largest land mammals ever, twice as tall as present-day elephants. Horses grow two feet high.
	EOCENE	Milder conditions continue. Tropical vegetation spreads far to the south and north. Volcanic outbursts leave the Atlantic and Indian oceans in much their present form. The equator possibly shifts north until it runs along the northern Mediterranean. 60**	There is a major expansion of mammals: early elephants, rhinos, pigs, horses, and a broad spectrum of other hoofed creatures. Hyaenodons develop until they can kill creatures the size of a modern rhino. Rudimentary monkeys and apes evolve. The first true birds emerge, including an ancestral ostrich and primitive pelicans. Insects appear in all their present groups, and most fish would be recognizable today.
	PALEOCENE	The old Gondwanaland plain of Africa is raised up, fracturing as it goes. The seas retreat from the landmasses, allowing Africa-Arabia to be connected to Europe via the Balkans, and to Asia by a land-bridge across to India. 70**	The land-bridges to Eurasia allow Africa to acquire a cross-section of the world fauna, with a rapid differentiation of mammals far beyond the former small insect-eaters. But many in this "trial and error" period prove overspecialized or aberrant, soon to be superseded by a more adaptable array.
MESOZOIC ("middle life")	CRETACEOUS	South America drifts away westward, leaving Africa a free island. Tremendous swamps cover the landscape with vegetation developing luxuriant forms. Eventually the climate cools off, allowing deciduous trees to edge out the conifers. The evolution of insects speeds up, stimulating yet more varied growths among the flowering plants. 135**	Giant reptiles dominate life on land and sea till they disappear in a flash extinction at the close of the period; only the crocodiles are left of the ruling reptiles. A throw-off from the lizards grows into snakes. Mammals remain inconspicuous, but placental forms, allowing the young to develop more before birth, are ready to exploit the new opportunities.
	JURASSIC	Africa splits further away from South America. The seas encroach again, though not as much over Africa as over Europe and Asia. Forests spread across Africa's flattened landscape, as do swamps, lakes, meandering rivers. Flowering plants appear. 180**	Reptiles grow more numerous as they grow larger. Huge creatures roam the East African swamps : crocodiles are now fully developed, some three times as long as today's. Mammals remain small and rudimentary, living in trees. A few reptiles take to the air, some developing scales into feathers.
	TRIASSIC	The ancient mega-continent Gondwanaland starts to break up. Africa drifts away from Eurasia, while the seas retreat from much of its surface. Deserts spread across the land, leaving scanty shrub growths on the mountaintops. Much of the earth is hot and parched. 225**	Reptiles dominate life on land, but mammal-like reptiles proliferate in southern Africa. Mini-dinosaurs appear. The first flies, first termites. Crocodiles emerge. First signs of early mammals.

This stage roughly marks the start of Africa's breakaway from Gondwanaland, to emerge as a separate entity with its own distinctive features: Africa's long day begins.

*This Time-Scale chart is not to scale.

** million years

		LAND AND PLANTS	ANIMALS
PLEISTOCENE	**UPPER**		
		10,000	Late Stone Age.
		12,000 — Africa warms up again, becoming moister.	
		30,000	Middle Stone Age.
		50,000 — Temperatures in Africa fall by at least 10°F. Increased rainfall causes glaciers on East African mountains to extend 3,000 feet lower.	Modern races of man now apparent.
		60,000 — Congo forest almost disappears.	Tool-making starts to vary according to regional variations, with differentiated "tool kits" in different areas.
		70,000 — A worldwide drop in temperature sets off the first glaciation in the northern hemisphere, causing various direct and indirect perturbations in the climate of the tropics.	
		100,000 — A great Rift Valley lake dries up, leaving Lake Nakuru, Lake Naivasha, and others.	Tempo of human culture accelerates very rapidly.
		150,000	Many larger mammals start to disappear (due to man's activities, or climatic changes, or both): ancephaline antelopes, such as wildebeest and hartebeest, drop from 25 species to 12, pig forms from 16 to 4.
		200,000 — The Rift Valley nears its present form. Lake Victoria becomes a swamp.	Eland and kudu as now; possibly wildebeest and steinbok. A very large form of hartebeest.
	MIDDLE		
		250,000 — The process of change speeds up, causing increased oscillation in climate, etc. The Sahara sometimes measures 200 miles narrower than it is now.	Time necessary to evolve a species probably telescopes from well over 1,000,000 years at earlier stages to 50,000 years.
		400,000	Most of today's mammals have emerged by now, but some, such as the bushbuck, have still to assume complete modern-day form.
		600,000	Black rhino, spotted hyena probably much as they are now. Intermediary forms of reedbuck and puku; and outsized klipspringer; possibly present impala; eland and kudu comparable but not identical to today's forms. Homo erectus.
		700,000	Man is possibly using fire; stone-tool technology develops widely as man spreads into Eurasia.
		750,000 — Ruwenzoris possibly surrounded by an extensive lake, including present-day lakes George, Edward, and Albert.	
		1,000,000	East Africa features a nine-foot horned "sheep," a rhino-sized pig, and a gorilla-sized baboon. Hippos feature periscope-like eyes. But more and more of today's creatures are replacing assorted archaic creatures. Africa's bovids expand to around 60 species.
		1.0** — Much eruption along Rift Valley floor as the trench deepens.	
		1.1**	Very rapid expansion of man's brain leads towards rudimentary speech.
	LOWER		
		1.3** — Lake Victoria periodically rises to as much as 300 feet above present level. Other great lakes of eastern Africa slowly forming. Greater Lake Rudolf perhaps stretches along almost the entire Rift Valley in Kenya, three times longer than at present. Ruwenzoris still rising.	
		1.7**	First representatives of modern hyenas.
		1.8**	Hominid hunters and tool-makers well established at Olduvai. Early Stone Age begins.
		2.0**	
		2.4**	Possible emergence of leopard, caracal, zebra (striped?), much like their present-day forms. Sabre-toothed cats are probably on their final phase; several other felids resemble today's cat-carnivores. The giraffe emerges much as now, while another giraffe with broad palmate horns goes extinct.
		2.6** — Sea levels much lower than today.	
		2.8**	Several aberrant rhinos disappear.
		3.0**	Man-apes (ape-men?) manufacturing simple stone tools.
		3.5** — Pleistocene well under way; start of a stage which is to feature greater climatic changes, together with associated upheavals in vegetation, than at any time since modern plants and animals emerged.	

LAND AND PLANTS	ANIMALS
1920 A.D.	Tsetse fly causes the human population to move out of areas which later become Uganda's Queen Elizabeth and Murchison Falls parks.
1900 A.D.	Major alien settlements of eastern and central Africa follow the first white explorers. As man becomes more disruptive to the environment, many areas become more receptive to the tsetse fly, allowing it to spread throughout the following decades, despite massive attempts to curb it, such as game elimination programs and other gross intrusions on the environment.
1890 A.D.	A great rinderpest epidemic spreads south, wiping out up to nine-tenths of the buffalo and other major creatures. The Masai influence is severely reduced following the rinderpest outbreak, a smallpox epidemic, and a series of civil wars.
1840 A.D.	The first white explorers arrive in East Africa.
1820 A.D.	Kikuyu reach the Nairobi region.
1800 A.D.	Masai reach at least as far as the present Kenya–Tanzania border.
1700 A.D.	Boers spread north, shooting out vast areas of savannah country.
1600 A.D.	Masai leave the Lake Rudolf area to start their spread south.
1100 A.D.	Kingdom of Zimbabwe.
700 A.D.	Kingdom of Ghana.
600 A.D.	Arabs start to reduce much of what remains of Africa's wildlife north of the Sahara.
100 A.D.	Romans plundering North Africa's wildlife for their arena spectacles.
200 B.C.	Pastoralists in the East African Rift Valley.
1000 B.C.	Cultivators start to attack the Congo forest.
2100 B.C. Present-Day: Man's spread as a cultivator and pastoralist leads to broad-scale modification of forests and savannahs alike, until his influence becomes as extensive and intensive as a major biophysical upheaval of earlier eras.	
2300 B.C.	Farming settlements in Ethiopia.
2500 B.C. The warmer, moister phase finally ends throughout Africa, as the Sahara reaches its present extent. Rainforests are on the retreat, partly because of the drier environment, partly because of man's fires.	Livestock cultures become less dispersed across Africa, possibly because of spread of the tsetse fly.
3000 B.C. Sahara starts to dry out for the last time.	
5000 B.C. Eruptions from scores of small volcanoes set up an "explosion area" in present-day Queen Elizabeth Park.	First Neolithic cattlemen penetrate deep into the Sahara.
5500 B.C.	Ancient Egyptians establish their civilization.
6000 B.C. The climate warms up again, producing a moister environment. Lake Chad grows to eight times its present size.	Larger animals such as hippos and giraffes roam into the interior of the Sahara.
8000 B.C. Africa grows cooler, and evaporation falls off. Most areas south of the Sahara become more arid.	Man the agriculturalist can now cultivate crops and domesticate animals.

ANIMALS

1972	East Africa is now increasing its human numbers at almost 3.5 percent a year, making this one of the most rapidly expanding regions of the world—and likely to increase more rapidly still, leading to almost twice as many people, with aspirations greater than ever before, by 1990.
1971	FAO starts on a major game-cropping project in Kenya.
1970	Tourism becomes Kenya's leading "export," displacing coffee. Start of rapid dividing-up of Kenya Masailand into private ranches.
1969	Many parks with elephants throughout the continent are undergoing fundamental modification. Kruger Park now has over 10,000 elephants, a fivefold increase in little over a decade.
1968	Research cropping of 300 elephants in Tsavo leads to uproar and suspension of crisis investigations.
1967	Kenya becomes first nation of black Africa to institute official family planning.
1965	The Murchison Falls elephants are initially reduced, twenty years after the herds started to decline; some hippo culling too.
1964	A continued build-up of the Tsavo elephants sets off the need for urgent measures to safeguard the area.
1963	Kenya becomes independent, and sets up its major network of parks and reserves in time for the sudden outburst of tourist interest.
1962	Uganda becomes independent, rapidly increasing its game reserves from three to eleven.
1961	Tanganyika starts independence with one park, increases the chain to ten within the first decade.
1960	Elephants in Uganda have now lost three-quarters of their range over the past 30 years; congestion is increasing at more rapid rates than ever, causing the remaining range to be cut by one-third in only another 10 years.
1959	A series of good rainy seasons sets off a "cattle explosion," increasing the herds to twice what they have ever been in many areas.
1958	Crowding of hippos in Queen Elizabeth Park, with little outlet left for migration, leads to extensive changes in the habitat; large-scale cropping begins. The poaching of Tsavo elephants is brought to a sudden end by a blitz campaign.
1957	Ngorongoro split off from Serengeti.
1955	Livestock overgrazing in many parts of eastern and central Africa becomes more severe; fluctuations in cattle numbers shift into wild oscillations, leaving more degradation of the grazing grounds each time. Many watering points in, for example, Tanganyika Masailand, start to dry up in an impoverished environment.
1952	Uganda starts to establish its parks.
1948	Start of extensive cattle inoculation programs in East Africa lead to great surges in cattle numbers. Serengeti Park in Tanganyika reconstituted.
1947	Nairobi Park established in Kenya, soon followed by Tsavo Park.
1945	Ending of World War II allows public-health programs to be greatly expanded. African populations are now probably twice what they were 50 years earlier, and will almost double again in only another 25 years.

EARLY DAY

Up and about with the dawn. In Africa you get up with the sun because that seems the natural way of doing things. The light sweeps across the plain, in among the thickets, along the stream beds, over the flat-topped thorn trees, into whatever part of scrub or grassland has been used by animals for their overnight security. Out on the savannah a lion is lying, his mane burnished by the early light. He has been active much of the night; soon will be the time for sleeping. The sun works wonders too for the coat of a cheetah, poised on top of a rise, looking out over the plain. Inactive most of the night, the cheetah is now ready to hunt. It does not make for the bush-living antelope that are

emerging from their refuges; rather, it tries to spot a gazelle that has spent the night on the open plain and is likely to remain there.

On every side the savannah is alive with activity. Hundreds of birds are calling. There are rustlings and scratchings around and inside every bush. There is a jackal here, a hyena there, a bat-eared fox farther over, all of them going about their affairs before the day gets too hot. Other creatures are not moving; they are just sitting and waiting. Silhouetted against the sunrise there are trees crowded with birds—vultures must spend a large part of their lives waiting. Soon the pride of lions down below will have finished their kill carcass. The cubs play with the remains while the lionesses laze around, bloated with food and satisfaction. On the opposite horizon is a herd of elephants doing only what they have been doing all night and only what they generally do—collecting their hundreds of pounds of daily food. Over on the fringes of a swamp a herd of buffaloes is

To see the sights you have to be out and about as soon as the animals are. But the Grant's gazelle buck is not "starting a new day"; it is simply moving into a new phase of the one continuum.

grazing, with little of the inexorable if leisured urge of elephants; but buffaloes are ruminants, and need only a fraction as much food in proportion to their size. An elephant is always largely looking for food and largely wasteful with what it finds.

In and about the thickets a rhino goes on its lumbering way. Across by the river groups of zebras and wildebeest are gathering for their morning drink—but they will take an hour or two of cautious edging forward before they find the determination, or the desperation, to approach the water's edge: who knows what other creature may already have arrived at the pool?

Peering over a tree on the far bank is a giraffe, and close by it another group of zebras taking advantage of the giraffe's elevated vision: less chance of a surprise attack with a giraffe around. But the giraffe is not nearly so dependent on daily water as a zebra, and it turns away to join other giraffes that are swaying across the savannah a little way out onto the plain. Although they are a mile off (how close such things seem in Africa!), they are easy enough to pick out, just as a safari onlooker is easy for the giraffe to pick out.

A little way down the track a twitching nose protrudes from a bush, followed by a duiker. Around the corner appears a troop of baboons, picking and scratching at the ground as they go. The duiker freezes. One moment it is there; the next (or the same?), it is gone. A tremor of the bushes, and all is still.

Up above, the snows of Kilimanjaro glisten in the equatorial sun. What will happen beneath their frozen dominance during the easy warmth of the morning? What new patterns will the creatures reveal by the time the ice cliffs are sparkling in the noontime glare? What new scenes will have emerged by the time the sun has swung over to the western glaciers? The icy dome acts as a splendid sundial, marking the phases of the long African day.

The lioness returning from her night's hunting clears a stream on her way to the thicket where she left her cubs in hiding.

Sunup sees the lines of wildebeest trekking across Ngorongoro Crater. They are
moving from their nighttime
resting places to daytime
grazing grounds.

GAZELLES

As the wildlife-watcher moves across the plains in the early morning, he may meet a
herd of gazelles. However gentle their tread, he senses how spring-loaded it is. A single
untoward sound and they generate more energy than one would expect from so slight
a frame. Gazelles are so alive and so delicate, they are something to stare at. Whatever
one may think of tales linking the Garden of Eden with East Africa, a sunlit plain of
gazelles in the morning is like the morning of creation.

They fill the plain. Thomson's gazelles, the smaller of the two sorts, live only in the
grasslands, but wherever you find them they are there in sprightly thousands. The Serengeti has a lot of wildebeest, but there may be just as many Thomson's gazelles. Sometimes they fill the horizon on every side. This is Africa proliferant with a marvelous
abandon. Yet there can hardly be too many. Evolution and Africa make a combination
that is extraordinarily prodigal, and colorful as well.

The gazelles wag their tails incessantly—a newborn fawn can move its tail before it
can move its legs. Possibly the tail acts as a warning device; when one gazelle does not see
any more tails flicking out of the corner of its eye, it is time to be elsewhere. And it is
characteristic of this creature that a part of it that can move unceasingly does move
unceasingly.

The Grant's gazelle is bigger than the Thomson's, but not nearly as numerous. There
are 60,000 in the Serengeti, or one Grant's to every eight or ten "Tommies." Yet in
Nairobi Park they are more or less even, which is possibly a reflection of the disastrous
drought several years ago, when the Grant's gazelles survived more successfully. In

Ngorongoro Crater there are at least 1,500 Grant's and twice as many Thomson's. But since Grant's gazelles weigh three or four times the mere fifty pounds of a Tommy, there are more pounds of them to reckon with. Thomson's gazelles keep to the shortest of short-grass areas, which restricts them to only half the Crater for much of the year and half of that for the rest, while the Grant's range over the entire area. Perhaps the Thomson's gazelle has adapted to a way of life on the short-grass plain where it can see what is going on, while the Grant's gazelle is able to live in areas where the grass is longer, even though drier. The Thomson's gazelle has a dark line down the side of its body, possibly a disruptive color device to deceive an attacker; it is more appropriate on the open plains—but is the coloring a reflection of food habits or a cause of them (or both)? A Tommy's diet is limited, whereas a Grant's gazelle can wander farther into the arid scrublands, and can thrive in places like the Mara Reserve with sixty inches of rain a year. In Kenya's northern deserts, a region the size of California, there are Grant's by the scores of thousands and hardly any Tommies. Nevertheless, the Grant's do not match the Thomson's in overall numbers in East Africa.

Oddly enough, neither gazelle is to be found much in Uganda. They live side by side with hartebeest in Kenya, with topi in Tanzania, and with a whole range of creatures across all three countries. Possibly gazelles once prospered in greater numbers in Uganda but were eliminated by disease or exceptional local competition or unusual predation. But what if they were now to be reintroduced by transporting a few breeding herds? A move of this kind has been suggested for parts of Uganda where the vegetation seems suitable. Would they survive? Uganda kob and other small antelopes failed to survive when they were brought to Kenya. But if the gazelles flourished, would they thereby cause some other creature to fall on hard times? Or would they diversify the ecosystem by merely fitting into other niches already partially occupied? A mechanism with more diverse parts has more parts to go wrong, but, much more important, it has more parts to take the strain of a major upset. The more variegated a spectrum of species, the better. Should man try to improve on nature in this way?

An answer might emerge from investigations in other parts of Africa. Why, for instance, are there no gazelles farther south? There are plenty of common creatures like impala and wildebeest and zebra; yet there is no creature that does the same job as the Thomson's gazelle. There are other grassland creatures like the oribi, which are found in East Africa but never occur in anywhere near the numbers of Tommies. For that matter, these areas far to the south have no gerenuk or dik-dik: what creature there occupies the unusual niche of a gerenuk? In the drier areas of the far southwest there are springbok that look like a remote offshoot of gazelle ancestors. How do the present-day species come to be distributed as they are? Probably the belt of bushland across central Africa has much to do with it, having caused some ancestral "gazelle" to throw off two variations on the one theme in eastern and southern Africa. But much obscurity remains. Quite a problem in ecological detection, which has been much illuminated by the findings of Dr. Fritz Walther and Dr. Richard Estes, who have found, among other things, that a Thomson's gazelle is almost entirely a grass-eater, while a Grant's sometimes needs grass for less than half its diet, and it chooses the sorts that are little used by Thomson's gazelle, or by wildebeest or by any other creatures that are mainly grazers. In fact, the Grant's gazelle chooses just those plants that proliferate and take over in places that have been overgrazed by cattle. It does not take long for too many cattle to finish off their own preferred grasses, leaving the others with a field day. It might even become a measure of good ranching to keep a few Grant's gazelles in among the steers!

The Grant's gazelle is far less dependent on water than a Thomson's. While a Tommy is rarely seen drinking, it is not often found far from water; a Grant's can go for months, possibly forever, with no surface water at all. Both are cautious creatures, difficult to approach for the rush-around visitor. From a moving car all you see are so many white

Below: A Thomson's gazelle is rarely found in dark spots like this, enclosed and with little grass. But at the end of the dry season the gazelle must find food where it can, and if that means along the watercourses, with their thickets and ambush sites, then that is where it must go. Here it becomes more prone to the leopard, though less vulnerable to the cheetah; more so to the lion only if there is not enough larger prey around.

Near right: A female Grant's gazelle is inclined to stamp her foot at any alarm, particularly when she may be less capable of instant flight. The infant feeding wags its tail in satisfaction, which is about the only time a Grant's gazelle uses its tail for anything except for swatting flies; a Thomson's gazelle, on the other hand, keeps its tail on the go from the time it is born until the time it is a fraction too slow in noticing there are no more wagging—and warning—tails

in sight. The Thomson's is a gazelle of the open grasslands; the Grant's feeds much more off bushes, where an open field of vision is not so common.

Far right: Grant's gazelle bucks find it difficult to do each other much damage with their horns set at such an "impractical" if imposing angle. They spend much time jousting with each other, displaying the muscles of their necks as they twist their heads, until one recognizes the other's dominance and gives ground; no damage done. Thomson's gazelles, by contrast, sport shorter and straighter horns that are more capable of injury, but their method of fighting amounts to a series of head-on clashes, using their horns hardly at all—a style rather more vigorous, and leading to much more direct contact; but again, no damage.

rumps trotting away—the black-striped ones are Thomson's. But a fair photograph of a gazelle is not all that difficult to get. It takes patience, a far more important piece of equipment than the largest telephoto lens. East Africa may be a place for jet-set people, but not for jet-set tactics. Watch gazelles from a distance, then go and wait ahead of their line of advance. Twenty minutes later you will have a close-range shot of your gazelle. If alarmed, they give a warning snort like that of an impala or a waterbuck or many another antelope. But they have other alarm signals peculiar to gazelles, warnings that do not seem to be recognized by other creatures: they twitch their flanks, causing the patterns to move conspicuously. No other plains animals have these horizontal stripes, and they take no notice if a Tommy flicks his. Another warning signal is the stiff-legged bouncing gait: when one sets off the alarm, the others are immediately flat out. This "stotting" means that the gazelle giving the alarm does not immediately reach its top speed of around forty-five miles an hour. It could all be part of a system that helps to preserve the species by sacrificing the individual. But if the gazelles more inclined to start stotting are the ones to be eliminated, one wonders why the reaction has not gradually disappeared altogether; natural selection does not select unnaturally (although it selects through the population as well as through the individual).

There are other social differences between the two gazelles that keep them from getting mixed up—either for the onlooker or the gazelles. The Grant's male, needing much larger patches of ground for its browsing habits, marks out broader stretches of territory for its mating season. Male Grant's post themselves half a mile apart, while three or four Tommy males may stake out territories in the same distance. Again, a Thomson's gazelle is much more enthusiastic about safeguarding its territory and the number of females he can keep within it. While the Grant's male demarcates his territory by the usual piles of droppings at strategic points, the Thomson's reinforces his with another and possibly more emphatic method. He marks grass stems or twigs with a dark sticky substance produced from the preorbital glands on either side of his face. If he keeps at it long enough, the deposit grows half an inch across, plain enough to any interloper, especially when these warnings are only five or ten yards apart and twenty times as frequent as the Grant's droppings.

Gazelles often attract more predators than any other antelope. Lions obviously prefer zebras or wildebeest, and so do hyenas sometimes, but nothing ignores a gazelle if it gets a chance. A Thomson's gazelle is harried by as many as a dozen predators, not only the usual prowlers of the plain but also birds and pythons. Yet the gazelles are highly successful at the game of evolutionary roulette, and they have devised many a formula for staying out of trouble—at any rate, out of too much trouble. If you see one Grant's gazelle you will see a dozen, and if you see one Tommy you may be looking at scores, if not hundreds. Watch them in the early morning: this is not Africa harsh, it is Africa arcadian.

HIPPOS

Early morning is a good time for seeing hippos. They are out on dry land, waddling back to their pool after a night's foraging on the savannah grasslands. They follow well-used tracks, which may help them find their way around in the dark.

Hippos rarely eat aquatic vegetation, even on the River Nile where the plentiful "cabbage" has given rise to stories about hippos keeping river channels open by their remarkable appetites. The outer hippo can do much in the way of engineering, but not the inner hippo. A hippo needs around 150 pounds of food a night to keep it going, and where the grass is in good condition it may eat twice as much. Only four and a half feet high at the shoulder, the hippo is the second largest animal on land. And although its legs seem ludicrously small, they can propel the hippo into a sprint you would hardly think it capable of until you get between the hippo and water. It can outrun any man and give a good race to a rhino or an elephant. In fact, more people are probably killed every year by those fearsome jaws than by any other animal, even though a pugnacious hippo may merely be reacting to the poaching the herds are subjected to.

A hippo at work on the grasslands is one of the finest mowing machines in nature. That enormous head ends in a pair of flat wide jaws that scythe off swatches of grass. A herd can clear five or six tons off a square mile in a single night. Yet in relation to its body weight, a hippo eats only half as much as many herbivores, including domestic stock. It can range over thirty different plants, but generally concentrates on seven or eight types, which is still a wider span than cattle generally manage. It crops short grass shorter, and holds the grass at an early stage of growth when it is most nutritive for hippos and for other grass-eaters, such as warthogs. The hippo takes the grass between its lips and plucks it off; it uses its teeth only for chewing. The continual plucking in areas where hippos are overcrowded leads to grass being uprooted, which serves to accelerate such erosion as has been started; in turn, there is an increase of rainfall run-off, and soon large patches of bare earth appear.

The hippo's head is armed with four tusks, one at the corner of each jaw, with edges like shears. They are the only weapons in a hippo's armory, but they do the job well enough. A tusk can grow to thirty inches, a commercial asset for which the hippo has had to pay a heavy price. Nowadays the hippo is poached more for the tons of meat it supplies to protein-starved locals. When the hair on the head of an African baby is turning red through gross lack of protein, there are more than just tourists eyeing the hippos behind the park boundary. Africans have lived off hippos for centuries—and they have watched European explorers shoot hippos by the thousands as they penetrated into the continent along its natural pathways, the watercourses.

To digest grass efficiently, a hippo is equipped with lengthy intestines, split into seven sections (fourteen by some counts), each with its own function. But this highly selective digestive process is still not selective enough to allow it to be really adept at turning grass into meat. Moreover, much grass is left unused; whole clumps are left strewn around after dropping from those shovel jaws. At dawn, after a nighttime's grazing, the hippo

Modification to the grassland by herds of hippos can be extensive. The grass patches disappear and the bushes spread to take advantage of the extra space—helped by hippos when they spray the thickets with their droppings on their way back to the pools in the early morning. Less grass means in turn fewer fires to help keep the bushes in check.

takes its grass nutrient back to the water hole, where it spends most of the daylight hours snoozing and digesting. This organic matter reaches the riverbed and stays there (except for such fish as are taken out), a system that turns the lakes and rivers into "energy sinks" at the end of a one-way nutrient flow. Often, too, the hippo dies in the water and decomposes there, which means the cycle cannot be maintained by the scavengers and predators as happens on land. Some of the dead hippos in the River Nile are devoured by crocodiles; hyenas help in Queen Elizabeth Park in Uganda; but much good material is lost to the dry-land system. Over the years these energy sinks lead to basically unstable ecological situations, especially where hippos gather in such tremendous concentrations. Of course, the ultimate energy drain is a consequence for the long term, and often difficult to discern; in the short term, the process makes for denuded riverbanks and eroded countrysides such as anyone can pick out.

But the process may also make for marvelously fertile rivers and lakes. The Lake George and Lake Edward area on the Uganda–Congo border contains the largest hippo concentration in the world—25,000 of them—and could rank as one of the most productive freshwater areas anywhere. Ten million fish, mostly one- or two-pound tilapias, are taken out each year on the Uganda side alone. This represents well over a ton of fish *per acre*, and the water of Lake George is only a couple of yards deep—though how much of the lakebed is made up of hippo dung is anybody's guess. It is also apparently anybody's guess how far the hippos really do contribute to flourishing fisheries, despite theories that fewer hippos could mean far fewer fish. Probably only a small fraction of fish food comes from hippo dung; areas with no hippos produce just as many fish.

Whatever their consequences for local fishermen, such concentrations of hippos do not help the surrounding grasslands. In certain areas of Queen Elizabeth Park the vegetation has been destroyed for miles around. The hippos have been not only ruining their own habitat, they have been wrecking it for the other inhabitants of the park, among them 4,000 elephants and 20,000 buffalo, to say nothing of the antelopes. In 1958 the drastic step was taken of cropping the excess hippos. Some people were aghast at the idea of shooting animals in a park. But there was hardly any other way. Eventually the mechanisms of nature would have eliminated the surplus hippos, which might have eliminated a lot of other creatures as well. So the scientists tried a bit of selective adjustment of the system. The forces of ecological equilibrium are delicate indeed, and you tamper with nature as discreetly as you know how. In Queen Elizabeth Park 1,000 hippos

Overleaf: These are not so much supersize tusks as lower-jaw tusks that have lost their corresponding set in the upper jaw to keep them in check. Hippo ivory is close grained and softer than an elephant's, hence easier to carve and more sought after. It is these few pounds of ivory, often a mere half dozen, that have caused the hippo to be persecuted in the past (although now the poacher is more likely to be after the other thousand pounds of animal).

a year were removed until the population eventually reached stability around the 8,000 mark—a long way nearer the optimum of 20 hippos a square mile than the 80 a square mile in several areas before the cropping began. Checks were kept on the ages of the remaining hippos to find out when things were nearing normal. If it can be established how many are under a year old, then it is simple to decide how far the community is nearing stability. If a hippo lives for about forty years, and a female usually starts to breed before the age of ten, producing a calf every three years, one can soon work out what a "normal" number of calves should be.

But during the great concentrations of the 1950s, when grazing became scarce and the tensions of overpopulation built up, the hippos practiced their own form of birth control. They deferred breeding by two years, sometimes more, and lengthened the interval between calves. The proportion of calves dropped to only 5 percent. Hippos, like elephants and other wild creatures, are remarkably capable of adjusting their rates of increase to match changes in their habitat, but there is a built-in time lag to avoid sudden oscillations in the numbers. If left alone, the situation would eventually adjust itself and the hippos would undergo a "depression" until the habitat recovered—if in fact it ever got the chance; as the hippo numbers plunged, so could the environment's capacity to support them—if it didn't decline at an even faster rate. The whole process could take a long time, spread over several generations, since a hippo needs at least ten years before it is ready to produce more hippos, and then it produces calves relatively slowly. Moreover, they are long-lived creatures and do not experience the rapid turnover of, say, wildebeest, with a calf the second year and another every year of what may be a ten-year life span. Meanwhile, the other animals of the park would have had nowhere to migrate, for this park is surrounded by a boundary, and beyond the boundary at Queen Elizabeth Park there is cultivation and settlement. It would never have been appropriate, even at the time of setting up the park, to say, "Let's draw lines on a map and leave nature to get on with things undisturbed" (if that was ever the intention). The mere act of drawing lines on a map is itself a gross intrusion on the environment, and may well require further intrusions to adjust the strains and stresses set up inside.

The hippos themselves soon found they no longer had anywhere to migrate. Only twenty years ago the rivers outside Queen Elizabeth Park harbored numerous hippos—not only hippos staying in one place but hippos markedly going somewhere else. Now

Far left: Hippos like to take their ease in groups at the pools. Bulls stake out certain stretches of shoreline as territories where intruders are not welcome (although when a male gets too old to maintain his standing, he leaves the main wallow to go off to smaller side-areas where he gathers with other past-it patriarchs). The particular encounter shown here amounted to no more than display sufficient to warn off the interloper. Nowadays, when there is much congestion among hippos, there may be more such confrontations provoked than in the spacious times of the past.

Near left: A hippo calf is born under water and suckles under water: the mother pumps in the milk, like whales and other water-dwellers. From time to time a calf climbs onto its mother's back for a rest, but at most times the youngsters are difficult to spot, which makes it harder to assess how far the hippo herds are in equilibrium with their environment (too many calves means trouble ahead, too few means trouble already arrived). Around one calf to every seven adults could be a fair ratio, but in stress areas the hippos practice such severe birth control that there may be only a third as many offspring.

the rivers are empty. Human populations have expanded and are crowding along the riverbanks. The hippos have learned. Not that they have to migrate along Uganda rivers; they can go straight across Lake Edward into Zaire, into what is Albert National Park. It is not clear how much poaching has gone on in the Congo in the last tumultuous years. Some people say remarkably little—and all credit to the Congo if that is so. But the shores on the Congo side of Lake Edward are not the gradual sloping banks that hippos prefer for getting in and out of the water. Hippos, particularly those with calves, look for lightly shelving shallows where they can bask, kneeling down, some way out into the water, where they feel more secure. A few hippos migrated across to the Congo, possibly to escape the cropping, since the migration took place at a time when they would have found more living space on the Uganda side. But most remained.

The hippos on both sides of the lake have given rise to a good deal of controversy, together with contrasting conclusions. The environment is much the same on either side, except that in the Congo there may be more rainfall, hence more grass. Moreover, the grass in the Congo is inclined to be of a hardier sort, better able to withstand severe grazing by hippos. The Albert Park scientists have tended to tackle the problem by saying there is no problem. They have maintained their parks as sacrosanct areas where man may *not* intervene. They have even tried to keep visitors out for long periods to maintain their ultrastrict policies. There may be hippo crowding: is it overcrowding? And if it is, will it not regulate itself in good time? Above all, what helping hand can be given by upstart man? All of which somewhat begs the question of whose problem this is, nature's or man's. The Congo park supports very large numbers of very large animals, just as does Queen Elizabeth Park, perhaps even the highest total in the world. But it may not be as "congested." Conundrums of this kind take a long time to work out, and the scientists at Queen Elizabeth Park found the eroded sections did not look as if they could wait that long.

At the same time, erosion is not invariably a retrograde development: a small degree provides gullies and inlets for a wider range of creatures, as well as denser thickets for small antelopes and cover for predators. It also helps to stop fire from getting too close to the fringes of the waterways and their vital vegetation, such of it as is left by the hippos. Perhaps the Congo park has been spared the widespread erosion because there are fewer lakes and channels than in Queen Elizabeth Park, so hippos cannot rove over such wide areas and spread their "damage." Possibly, too, they can migrate beyond the park deeper into the Congo, where cultivation pressures are not so great as those around the Uganda park. Yet, as Dr. Kai Curry-Lindahl, with Congo experience, points out, the Albert Park hippos are often thicker on the ground than in Queen Elizabeth, with 150 to a mile of shoreline; and the total has been increasing. So if there is a natural limit to their numbers, it has not been reached yet. Along the riverbanks in the Congo there are the same erosion patterns as in Uganda, but they may be due to the trampling of those ponderous feet rather than to overgrazing. These bare patches are concrete-hard, resisting the efforts of colonizing grasses to come in and re-cover them, even in places where hippos are not so dense and might allow the vegetation an opportunity to dig in. But they aren't spreading; they stay just as they have been for the past twenty years—or the past hundreds of years. There are similar patches of "shocking erosion" in other places in Africa, but they cannot be blamed on excess grazing by hippos because in those places there aren't any hippos. These patches, too, stay just as they are, so possibly what counts is not the makeup of the wildlife community above ground as the makeup of the soil layers below ground, with their own wildlife communities.

On the Uganda side, however, there are signs that the denuded areas have been fingering out to grasp at farther parts of the grasslands. Not that these areas have become all that widespread: it is not as if the whole park was being devastated, just particular areas. The resident researcher, Dr. R. M. Laws, decided they were enough,

and he advised carrying on with the cropping, thus confirming the approach of massive intervention as opposed to the absolute nonintervention upheld on the other side of the narrow lake. Eventually, 6,000 of the Uganda hippos were shot. The more pessimistic veterinarians prophesied that diseases like anthrax might make many of them unsuitable for eating, but not one hippo was found infected. Hippo steaks proved very popular on the local market at twelve cents a pound. All appearances to the contrary, a good half of a hippo is sound eating, with little fatty tissue. As much as 70 percent of a carcass may be usable, compared with 55 percent for a high-grade cow and 45 percent for a poorer one. Up to a quarter of every pound of meat is solid protein, around twice as much as in a pound of pork or beef or mutton.

The scheme's proceeds amounted to 6,000,000 pounds of meat and an income to the park of well over $100,000. But the main intention was not moneymaking. An analysis of one particular area, a small peninsula less than two square miles at Mweya close by the park lodge, showed that almost 100 hippos had been causing what looked like critical erosion. After they were reduced to a mere handful, the vegetation quickly recovered. And after a few more years the situation was vastly different again: the elephant population had doubled, the waterbuck population had trebled, and the buffalo had increased sixfold. The biomass—the total amount of living animal life—quickly returned to over 140,000 pounds a square mile, despite the disappearance of those 100 two-ton hippos. Later on, as the grass further recovered, the biomass soared to twice as much at certain seasons. If the hippos had not been shot out, there might soon have been few animals of any sort left. More important still, in terms of "energy flow," the situation improved far beyond what mere numbers show. Buffalo are now the predominant species. They do not live as long as hippos, so they achieve a better turnover of fresh blood. Hippos, like elephants, are large and inclined to live until they are ancient. An elephant can grow to the equivalent of twenty-five medium-sized antelopes in body weight, but it achieves an energy transfer of only a few of those twenty-five.

When researchers looked at the vegetation all around, however, they found it had not revived as rapidly or as dramatically as they had anticipated. But one can only find out what is really going on by getting down to the grass roots, so to speak: they tell just as much as triumphant figures for spectacular animals. As Dr. C. R. Field has described in detail, there are basically two prime sorts of grass in the park, the low-lying, creeping forms that are quick to form matt-patches covering bare ground, and the larger tussock-like grasses in between, standing tall above the surrounding sprawlers. The hippos like the short grass: if any patch gets beyond an early height, they cannot cope with it. But the tussock grasses tend to grow tall and rank, then spread about until, given the chance, they choke the ground-level creepers. Fortunately, there are plenty of buffalo to keep these tougher grasses cropped back to a stage where they do the buffalo some good and nobody any harm. Hippos return the gesture by preventing the matt-forming species from crowding out the tussock grasses. Of course, other factors have a bearing as well. Red soils produce certain kinds of grassland mosaics, black soils produce others: hippos prefer the red. Hippos are likewise influenced by the terrain, since they cannot manage the steeper slopes that present little problem to buffalo. What goes to make up "hippo devastation" depends on more than just hippos.

At first, the areas where the hippos were greatly reduced revealed a regular spate of grass-growing. Slowly, however, the creepers, no longer invigorated by hippo-grazing, began to lose their resilience. But as the tussocks gained ground, they slowly attracted the buffalo, which eventually restored the situation. Annual plants, which are a sign of vegetation that is debilitated and unstable, started to give way to perennials, which make for a more durable vegetation cover. Gradually the unbalanced flourishing of the early days leveled off. Possibly the hippos should have been reduced more slowly to avoid the lopsided recovery of the grasslands; but, as so often in Africa nowadays, there was no time.

The hippos could allow for a perpetual cropping scheme, an advance on reduction cropping to meet a particular crisis. It would entail taking off the natural increase each year, rather than a huge excess in emergency situations. When subjected to such regular "predation," the hippos would produce more offspring—and thus more potential for protein-production—than they would under congested conditions; and unless something of this sort is planned, the hippos could build up their numbers to the danger level once again. Already they have increased from 8,000 at the end of the cropping program to 11,000. A new program of "sustained-yield harvesting" would allow the people living outside Queen Elizabeth Park to benefit from all that meat walking around inside.

Left: This salient of land forms part of the 1¼-square mile Mweya peninsula at Queen Elizabeth Park, where almost a hundred hippos were virtually eliminated by cropping after they had reduced the grassland cover to only one-fifth what it could be. With no more hippos, the grass quickly made a comeback to cover three times as much ground; some of the better quality grasses increased four times, others fifteen times. The elephants doubled their numbers (thus helping to keep the bush patches under control) and the buffaloes shot up from 21 to 130. But by 1970, the hippos had started to return, the cropping was not maintained, and the bare earth was on the spread again.

Right: Hippos occasionally attack crocodiles, but there is little to fear from a buffalo, whatever the gaping mouth might suggest. Hippos also attack other hippos, leaving scars to show where hunks have been torn out. Hippos eat the short grass shorter, which allows tough tussock-grasses to proliferate if there aren't enough buffaloes to keep them cropped down: the two creatures complement each other, as well as maintaining a mosaic of grassland for in-between grazers such as waterbuck.

Africans use the same word for "animal" as for "meat," which tells a story in itself. (Other people refer to wild animals as "game," with just as sinister connotations.) Hippo-cropping could provide an answer to the poaching problem: if people once see that a properly regulated system for "harvesting" a limited number of wild animals does everybody some good, and that the animals are by no means sacrosanct, then the most powerful weapon of all—public opinion—might be mobilized against the poacher. Uninhibited poaching would be disastrous in more ways than one: if all the hippos were to disappear, the lake bays and inlets might become so overgrown with wood and sedge that the whole water ecology could be disrupted, fish breeding grounds and all. There are few more sophisticated ideas for an emergent community than conservation; it has taken a long time for it to catch on in Europe and North America. But when it speaks in terms of hard cash, everybody knows the language. It came as rather a surprise to local Africans when they were told a few years ago that as of a certain day of a certain month there was to be no more hunting of any sort in the area that was to become the park. They were even more bewildered when they subsequently saw those same white wardens who had announced the ban killing the hippos in their own way. But so long as hippo meat is not denied them, the Africans do not mind whether their food is the result of a spear or a bullet.

The biomass over an average square mile in Queen Elizabeth Park amounts to fifteen tons of hippos, ten tons of buffalo, and fifteen or more tons of elephant, plus the antelopes, warthogs, and the rest. This huge total is partly accounted for by the unusual size of some of the creatures: one hippo is equal to a dozen topi and a buffalo matches eight or ten kob antelopes. The Serengeti supports a tremendous total of animals, but it does not match the biomass of Queen Elizabeth Park. A highly diversified array of trees, shrubs, and grasses can often support more animal life than grasslands can, and Queen Elizabeth Park features a remarkable range of plants. It is one of the most efficient places in the world for turning vegetation into protein, at 100,000 pounds or more a square mile, year after year. Beef-producing areas in North America carry a biomass that often does not run to much beyond 15,000 pounds a square mile, while the best range areas rarely reach beyond 30,000 pounds. But Queen Elizabeth Park would be of little use to domestic stock anyway, even if the wild creatures were no longer there. The tsetse fly, which drove the human population out sixty years ago with epidemics of sleeping sickness and nagana cattle disease, is still there. The great scourges of pastoralists and their livestock have little effect on wild animals.

The continuous-cropping idea has considerable potential. The 11,000 hippos could supply at least 5 percent of their numbers each year to allow for natural increase. Moreover, this scheme could be extended to the 20,000 buffalo—much more rapid breeders, so a good 10 percent would be a fair target to start with. There would be greater scope still if the scheme were to include the "buffer zone" surrounding the park at various points, which is made up of game reserves and hunting blocks: more buffalo again. Hippos and buffalo (without counting the kob antelopes or the topi, much less the elephants) could produce nearly $100,000 a year, far beyond the $50,000 that the park needs to run its 800 square miles (which compares favorably with ranching costs anyway). Some people object that this would impugn the basic idea of a park as a place for looking at wild creatures, rather than eating them or exploiting them for money. But Africa has no time yet for standing and staring. It is a continent bent on development, and instant development at instant pace: philosophic ideas will come later, provided there is still wild country to be philosophic about. Of course, the parks should not be turned into straight ranching country. A park is a park is a park, where the goal should be conservation now and forever. If a few hippos have to be removed each year to keep the place maintained in its present form, then one might as well derive as much benefit as possible along the way. As long as one keeps cause and consequence the right way round, there will not only be a park in a flourishing state now, there will be a park in a future time.

A cropping scheme on these self-perpetuating lines has been tried, and it revealed clearly enough that the hippos could keep it going. But another factor appeared that halted the perpetual bit right at the start: "difficulties" in administration. Some people think that even if the scheme were not run as the best of all possible schemes, it would still be better to let it carry on with one or two snags rather than to throw out the baby with the bath water. If the return is only part of what it should be, that is still better than no return at all, and too many hippos as well. Meanwhile, the local people look at the color of their infants' hair and then look at those hippos just over the boundary. The researchers look at the hippos and see them once more building up their numbers now that all restraint has been withdrawn. They watch the overgrazing setting in once more. This is what conservation often amounts to in Africa: a prospect of promise and problems. If funds are needed on a large scale, hope and patience are needed on a larger scale. Without persistence in the face of every setback, the best intentions in the world are of little use, as are the best researchers or the best money. Queen Elizabeth Park is where the first great experiment at wild animal management was tried, a trial that brought remarkable success. Now the park has encountered a trial of a different kind.

HYENAS

Adult hyenas sleep a lot during the day; pups don't. This network of caves and tunnels in the center of Ngorongoro Crater is home for the lakeside clan.

The first hour after sunup is a good time to look for hyenas. They will be returning from a hunting or a scavenging foray. All legends apart, it could as likely be the first as the second. But legends linger. The hyena is reviled everywhere. It is a misshapen wretch, an abortion of creation, as debased in its habits as in its appearance, a mere scavenger, living off others' leftovers, a dealer in carrion and putrefaction. As malformed as it is in character, so it is in body; it can't even get its sexes sorted out, looking like both together and neither, a veritable abomination of the natural world. Well might it slouch along as if it had the crimes of the world to answer for. According to African legend, it acts as a carrier of witches who ride around on moonlit nights, only to dismount and transform themselves into other hyenas. You need only hear its laugh, a cascade of maniacal screechings, to sense it is in league with the devil.

Poor hyena—every man's hand is against it. But the curses attributed to it reflect as much on their originators as on their target. Wild creatures and their behavior are often represented by human standards, as if the world of nature could—or should—conform to the world of man. Even on these terms, a hyena's diet does not stand up too badly compared with some of the tidbits humans seem to enjoy, such as the entrails of domestic stock. The hyena's craving for rotten food is not too different from the human's enjoyment of delicacies that require some degree of "maturing." And what if a hyena smells bad to us? The human odor is equally offensive to many animals.

The one feature about a hyena that should count is that it has its place in the wild-world community. In some places there used to be a price on the hyena's head, or rather on its tail; anyone who brought in a tail stump received a reward. The wretch was looked upon as a pest, a monstrosity to be hunted until, with luck, it might disappear altogether. Such schemes did not last long. The plains degenerated into a stinking place of putrefaction and disease. Those who want to improve on nature by eliminating "mistakes" are tampering with they know not what. People who would drive the hyena off the face of the earth are akin to those who would spray insects into oblivion without too much thought about the consequences. The hyena occupies a slot in the network of savannah relationships that is not confined to simple sweeper-upper. Its role is far more complex.

Just how complex nobody knows, except that it is a good deal more far-reaching than anyone had imagined. The hyena is a creature tangled up with the lives of a whole array of creatures, not just with the deaths of a few.

Things have changed now for the hyena. This creature under reprieve, granted life only on sufferance, is a most interesting being for those prepared to take a second look. Its lumbering gait and tattered appearance are no more than a reflection of its scavenger's life: its long front legs with ungainly paws can hold a carcass to the ground as firmly as a lion can; its fur looks rough and moth-eaten, but does not get matted with gore; its thick neck muscles and ungainly jaws rank among the most powerful tools in Africa, well suited for crushing bones that would otherwise lie around and make the savannah a charnel house. The hyena is now regarded as an animal of superbly adaptive build; some people even say it has a functional beauty all its own. In a chase it would leave a lion behind after 100 yards, a leopard in not much more, and even a cheetah after the first half-mile. It can run at forty miles an hour and keep up the pace from one African plain to another.

Despite the fact that it cannot properly retract its claws, the hyena is not a member of the dog family. It is a throw-off from the cats, 30,000,000 years ago in the Tertiary period—but in Africa's long day an hour and a half ago. Through the ages there have been some huge hyena-like creatures, some of them capable of killing a modern rhino. They disposed of many of the bones of the ancestors of today's animals (including our forebears) and have proved most unpopular with those people who have tried to uncover the fossil facts of Africa's past.

Modern hyenas are astute enough to watch the activities of vultures patrolling the skies. Conversely, the vultures keep an eye on the hyenas. There can be few creatures with a sense of smell as acute as a hyena's, and for all its clumsy manner it is quick enough to catch fish. A pack of hyenas has been known to track down a young hippo or even an infant elephant, which says something for their tactics. They are creatures of unusual determination and savagery, the only animals likely to cause real danger to a man walking at night or to a park visitor asleep in a tent. Elephants, lions, rhinos may come close, but they won't come too close. Only the hyena is likely to penetrate right inside the tent and make off with a pair of safari boots, or more. They show remarkable pertinacity: one pack spent almost an entire day dodging the lunges of a rhino before making off with the calf. When they are scavenging they are very timid, but they can suddenly be driven to extraordinary risks for a scrap of food. A carcass with lions around it is sometimes accompanied by a hyena body or two. In its habits, as in its appearance, there is more to a hyena than it is given credit for. So why talk of "rehabilitating" the hyena? It is rather man who needs to rehabilitate his way of viewing the animal world.

Not only is man now looking at the hyena with a closer view, he is looking with a broader view. He is tracking down the details of the hyena's daily round, and at the same time he is searching out the extent of its yearly round. This means following up what happens to the other animals that occupy the same patch of Africa. Obviously, the hyena has a bearing on them. And, not so obviously, they have a bearing on the hyena. Who would have thought that a plague of flies could have brought new times for the hyenas in Ngorongoro Crater? In 1961 there was a drought. Some of the wildebeest and zebras starved, but the hyenas prospered. They did not have to wait for lions to leave a carcass; the animals just died, or they became so weak it was less trouble for the hyenas to finish the job themselves. What was a land of famine for one group of the wildlife community became a land of plenty for another. In 1962 the drought gave way to floods. Dried out lake beds became swamplands. The muddy shores were pushed farther and farther back, constantly renewing the flies' breeding grounds. Multitudes of flies killed off almost all the lions in the Crater. The hyenas had less scope for feeding off lions' remains, so they took to doing more killing for themselves. And, as a further result, seventy lions fewer meant much more room in the ecological spectrum for a new array of smaller-sized hunters. The hyenas waxed strong, as strong in hunting techniques as in numbers. Ngorongoro now has well over 400 full-grown hyenas for its 100 square miles. Nairobi Park, with half the area, has probably fewer than a quarter as many. The Serengeti eco-unit, well over a hundred times as big as the Crater, has only seven times as many, though there is more to the Serengeti with its migratory herds than figures alone can indicate.

Many questions have arisen about this phenomenon of hunting hyenas. Had the Ngorongoro hyenas taken to hunting so proficiently because they had always known how but had never bothered? Or had they always done a lot of hunting that no one had ever noticed before the drought? Or had they learned the technique during the starvation period, with its hordes of debilitated animals standing around? Or had they perhaps learned to hunt because they had multiplied somewhat during the prosperous drought period, and now had to shift for themselves or starve in turn? Nobody is sure. What is plain is that there is now a tremendous number of hunting hyenas in the Crater. More riddles resolved, more riddles raised. The hyenas continue on their way, not telling—except to those who will look and pause and ponder that when they are looking at a hyena they are seeing not a creature in isolation but a whole world that is a hyena world as much as it is a world of other creatures.

The hyenas of Ngorongoro Crater and the Serengeti have been the subject of lengthy investigations by Dr. Hans Kruuk. Some insights confirm the views of the old explorers whose stories of hyenas as hunters in their own right were conveniently disregarded for a long time. But there is much variation in hyena society. In Ngorongoro they live in clans, each community ranging from ten to a hundred members. A quarter of the animals in each clan are often less than full grown. The Crater contains eight such clans. Each clan has its own hunting area. If a group of hyenas is still feeding on a carcass in the early morning, the chances are three in four they have killed it themselves. Those hyenas living close to a Masai village in the Crater get through a greater proportion of scavenged food than the others, which shows that they do not disregard carrion if they can get it—it's easier than going after a wildebeest.

Running a wildebeest to a standstill is a feat only a pack of wild dogs can equal. A wildebeest in flight makes for water and rushes in up to its neck. This tactic helps it against a lion, but it is little use against hyenas. One wildebeest in three killed by hyenas in the Crater is brought to bay in this manner. Sometimes a wildebeest fleeing from hyenas finds its pursuers suddenly stopping. This means only that it has crossed into another clan's hunting territory, where it will be promptly set upon by a different batch of hyenas. Hunting rights are strictly observed, and when a hyena encroaches on foreign territory it is met with aggressive responses; sometimes it is torn to pieces on the spot. Yet there are odd males who manage to belong to more than one clan at once! Nobody knows how the clan boundaries are fixed. They seem to be determined not so much by natural features, since a boundary might run right across the open plain, as by some mechanism at work in the hyena's psyche. One wonders if the males fix them, as is usual among hunting communities such as lions. Yet male hyenas are occasionally tolerated on a neighboring territory in a way a male lion would rarely be. More likely the females set the boundary limits.

And within each territory, what is the standing there? Is there a hyena hierarchy similar to the social strata that act as an inhibiting factor on breeding in lion society? And do the clan areas serve to limit the hyena population from getting *too* big? How big *is* too big? Lions and their numbers are dependent on the numbers of prey around; but if food is more than plentiful, the lions will not proliferate so fast that they eat their prey out of existence and thereby eliminate themselves as well. They limit their numbers, in part, as a consequence of dividing the country into hunting ranges, which are generally

Overleaf. Left above: Having "tested" the herd to see if a member is ailing or somehow off color, the hyena pack sets off after the singled-out victim.

Middle above: After a three-mile chase, the wildebeest tires; but the whole pack does not attack at once, some seemingly diffident or not sure what to do.

Right above: A more concerted effort brings the wildebeest to bay, though still fighting back hard.

Left below: With several hyenas hanging onto its soft underbelly, and having lost huge patches of hide off its rump, the wildebeest is losing strength.

Middle below: Unable to watch all sides at once, it is soon seized again from behind.

Right below: This time, severely torn and losing blood, it goes down: the rest is extremely rapid.

defended by the senior males. No matter how congested the lions over the hill might be, they will often starve before another pride will allow them to expand their hunting area. Possibly they extend their rights by forcing another lion community into a smaller area. Enough lions are enough. If hyenas are normally scavengers, how much do they need to operate in a territorial network with exclusive rights for each clan? If there is little hunting, is there also little conflict about who scavenges where? Or does scavenging entail the same consequences since it is a search for food? Hyenas, like any other creatures, must be subject to some limitation on their numbers, and it must be an early one or they might become the one carnivore to devour the wildebeest herds before the wildebeest could develop a countermove. One can speculate on how hyenas keep their numbers in check: by conflicts between the boundaries or by conflicts within the boundaries, or both? It is like asking whether a hyena is a hunter by nature or a scavenger by lazy nature, or both.

The clan system is more pronounced in Ngorongoro Crater than on the Serengeti Plains, since the Crater hyenas depend on prey communities that are largely confined to an area of 100 square miles: not many roam outside. In the Serengeti the herds are constantly on a great migratory sweep across the 12,000-square-mile eco-unit, and the hyenas must move with the antelopes and zebras or look for alternative food. Some act as commuters, wandering fifty miles to follow the moving herds and returning a week later. Partly because of this more mobile way of life there are fewer young hyenas in the Serengeti as compared with the Crater. The Serengeti hyenas also number two or three times as many as the lions, making them the number-one predator. A hyena in the Serengeti has been seen to eat up to fifty pounds at a single meal, a third of its body weight. A 400-pound lion could not usually manage much more. In general a hyena can get by on six or eight pounds a day, and at Ngorongoro they make do on far less. A pack eats more of a carcass than do lions, which leave a good third. Hyenas stomach the offal and the bones, even the hide. The 400-odd full-grown hyenas in the Crater require nearly 2,000 wildebeest or zebras a year (if they are getting little from scavenging), which accounts for most of the annual increase among the 20,000 wildebeest and zebras in the Crater.

Dr. Kruuk has described how the effects of these hyena activities vary from place to place. In the Serengeti there are 500 prey animals to each hyena and at Ngorongoro only 40. Thus the "predation pressures" exerted by hyenas overall must be far greater at Ngorongoro. This is primarily why the Crater antelopes and zebras do not grow really old: the hyenas are making for a healthy population. There are around 3,000 gazelles, 5,000 zebras, and 15,000 wildebeest in the Crater. The hyenas kill one gazelle for every three zebras and every five wildebeest, which suggests that the predation pressures are about equal all round. But the hyenas seem to go out of their way to hunt zebras. They will follow a herd across the plains, disregarding wildebeest on the way. A zebra community is often made up of a stallion and a dozen or more females and young; other zebras congregate in bachelor herds and would be difficult for the hyena to tackle, since the males often gallop right toward a pack and drive them away. The hyenas concentrate on the family herds, yet these zebras, too, are well able to defend themselves. The zebra stallion stays behind his group so he can keep one eye on the hyenas and the other on his retreating harem. This makes for a slow and disjointed escape, but it keeps the rear guard covered. The rest of the herd do not respond to the stallion's tactics, and they mill around. If the hyenas once close in on a member, the end is quick. Only a single hunt in six like this may turn out successful. Wildebeest, on the other hand, turn and flee in a mob, which makes it easier for the hyenas to pick off one at the back, even though a cornered wildebeest can defend itself as strongly as a zebra.

During the calving season, a special pressure is brought to bear on the wildebeest, and the hyenas take a massive toll of the newborn calves. The slaughter at first varies from herd to herd. In a massed mob the hyenas may get only one calf in five, while in a smaller herd they can pick off every other calf. Either way, it sounds like a lot, but if the hyenas don't take this number—and many more later—there would be a surplus of wildebeest, with drastic consequences for all the wildebeest, as well as for many other creatures. At Ngorongoro the hyenas sooner or later get most of the calves. But the "right" number survives, about one in ten of those born, whereupon the hyenas direct their attention toward the full-grown wildebeest again—and take around one in ten. One may wonder if the hyenas help in eliminating the sick and lame among their prey, more than, say, lions, which tend to take healthy animals much more than ailing ones. Hyenas launching into a chase in the Serengeti sometimes "test" the herd to see if a less capable creature falls behind, much as wolves do with moose. Yet in the Crater, despite all those hunters on every side, there are still ailing animals that just stand around and die, with no predator coming along to speed things up.

If it sounds as though the hyenas are controlling the total number of prey animals in the Crater, the wildebeest and zebras may equally be controlling the hyenas. The Crater hyenas do not live as long as those in the Serengeti, because there seems to be scarcely enough food for all of them. What most likely happens is that the amount of grass in any one year decides how many wildebeest and zebras there are, which in turn creates greater (or less) competition among the hyenas. These sensitive reactions are especially important when the rains fail and the grazing falls off, since the hyenas are quick to pick off those grass-eaters that suffer first, which means that they speedily stop the grasslands from being ravaged by overuse. The balance is maintained through a refined series of repercussions in both directions. By contrast, the Serengeti hyenas are limited by their food supply in a different manner: since many of them have to travel long distances to find their prey, their offspring starve more often than those in the Crater.

As soon as twenty or thirty hyenas pull down their prey, they start a fight over the carcass. There are screams of cackling laughter shivering up and down the scale. Before long a pride of lions may come racing across the plain, trying to get at the kill before it is finished. If they get there in time, they will drive the hyenas away. Who then is the scavenger and who the honorable hunter? The lions in Ngorongoro sometimes acquire up to two kills out of three in this way. A tape-recording of hyenas on a kill will soon bring the lions into view at top speed—and also bring dozens of excited hyenas from the local clan to join in the feast, as has been demonstrated by Dr. Kruuk.

Nobody is sure how much hunting went on in the past because nobody was there to

A lion gnawed for an hour at this tortoise before giving up. The hyena smashed it with a single crunch.

check on it. Nobody is sure precisely how much is going on now for the same reason. Hunting by hyenas may not be a permanent phenomenon. Already it seems to be shifting toward a seasonal affair, much like the scavenging by lions. Some lions in the Crater eat a fair number of buffalo at certain times of the year, a killing feat surely beyond hyenas. Meanwhile, following the end of the fly plague, the number of lions in the Crater has increased. What will happen when the lions reach their former numbers, which they are fast approaching? Or have the hyenas expanded until they have reached sufficient numbers to "stop" them? Or will they tend to scavenge more off the extra kills of the extra lions? The safarist can ponder what would happen in the Crater if half the hyenas were killed off. Which would be first to take advantage of the gap—the lions or the remaining hyenas? Insofar as visitors to the Crater are keen to see lions and more lions, and are much less interested in hyenas, it has been suggested that the two populations be adjusted, especially when the few visitors who now descend into the Crater each day become hundreds if not thousands, and more lions are "needed."

Perhaps some hyenas in certain areas live out their lives without ever knowing what it is to go hunting. Pack hunting could be a reflection of high numbers in small areas; not only because of the food shortages that develop under crowded conditions, but because a lot of hyenas seem to stimulate each other. When they are all crowded together they become easily aroused. They run around with their tails arched over their backs in general excitement, a frequent prelude to a hunt. Sometimes, however, it is only a pair of hyenas that will make the first strike. So one cannot generalize—the situation changes even within the same locale according to the dynamic fluctuations of the total environment: better rains, more grass, more wildebeest, more ———. Whatever happens, things do not stay the same. Another time, another place, another season.

Yet whatever the hyena's capacity as a killer, there are signs it is not the compleat competent one might think. Dr. Richard Estes spent some time at Ngorongoro and learned something too about what makes the hyena community tick. He found that hyenas are less adept than wild dogs. Hyenas are far from having the dogs' "packing instinct" or their highly integrated social systems. In fact, a hyena is something of a sociable creature and an individualist as well. When it goes scavenging it goes alone. When it goes hunting it starts off singly or in pairs and does not join in big packs until the action is under way. Then hyenas come dashing in from all sides. Often they wait until the prey is on the ground. The first of these late arrivals fall out over the carcass with the original killers. Their fearful din brings other hyenas from all sides—lions too. The hyenas do not seem to sense what a doubtful tactic this is. Instead of cooperating among its members in the well-developed manner of wild dogs, the pack works in con-

A mother hyena is very protective toward her offspring: she must be, since the pup is constantly probing into territory a fair way from the den, and must be brought back forcibly if gently. She also must be on guard against cannibalism among others of the clan, which may be why female hyenas are larger than males.

flict and confusion. When a hyena is attacked by a wild dog pack, the others sit and watch. No doubt if they were to show the strong "mobbing" urge of wild dogs, they could plunder many more kills than they do and could regularly drive off lions. Yet hyenas have a fair degree of gregarious instinct. The striped hyena is not as big and bold as the spotted variety, nor as sociable; which may be why it is much less common.

Taken all round, a hyena is not built to be a hunter, despite its superb stamina. It has neither the powerful claws nor the muscled forelimbs that are needed for dragging down a victim. It cannot spring on an animal's back like a leopard, a predator of about the same weight. It has the sharp sense of smell that is characteristic of dogs, but it lacks the other traits that make wild dogs (and wolves) such efficient hunters. It has the bodily structure and the tough digestive system that mark the scavenger. Where then does it fit in? It does not match any neat theory. It is not properly a cat or a dog in build or behavior. A hyena is a hyena. It meets each situation as it comes along. It can be a scavenger and a scavenger-predator and a predator-scavenger according to circumstances: is it ever a predator pure and simple? Dr. George Schaller doubts if any animal could be a scavenger pure and simple, since there is rarely enough food left over from other carnivores, season after season, region after region; and if there is little ecological living space for a straight scavenger, the hyena is not built for the scavenger's life exclusively, nor is any other creature. Rather, the hyena occupies a niche in the ecological scene where it does not conflict or overlap too much with other creatures. Its life-style is a ramifying affair, shading off into the other compartments of the total environment: it is full of checks and balances, just the sort of arrangement to make a whole system work through good times and bad. There is plenty of mystery to this creature that ostensibly makes no bones about its way of life. With the hyena one can indulge in a bit of speculation, rubbing a few thoughts together on any clues one can pick up.

The savannah would be a different world without the hyena; you could smell the difference before you noticed the hyena was no longer there. It may once have set an illustrious example. At some stage in remote times one of the less sturdy apes of the Pliocene may have sniffed the wind and wondered whether it shouldn't try a bit of decaying carcass as a change from wild fruit. Perhaps from here it evolved through a lengthy apprenticeship as a scavenger, a scavenger-predator, then a predator-scavenger, and emerged as a part-predator; all of which helped to develop its singularly precocious set of senses and reasoning processes. It could even have been a rival to the hyena for some time. But a trial project by George Schaller and Gordon Lowther in the Serengeti, where they tried to exist for a while in the manner of such meat-seeking beings, suggested they would have had a thin time indeed as complete carnivores, living by picking off others' leavings and killing an occasional young or sickly creature. More likely such an animal would have had to live off fruits, roots, and similar plant foods, with meat as an incidental. Either way, the pristine ape has now passed on to higher things. But the hyena is still an integral part of its own world: the visitor has only to lie in his safari tent and hear the "whoop-whoop" of the hyena going its rounds to know where he is.

IMPALA

Impala are easy to spot before the dew disappears. They snuffle around on the edges of shadows, licking at the moisture. As the shadows retreat, the impala follow them, and later on they wander off into the thicker brush vegetation.

An impala is all that an antelope is supposed to be. It steps across the ground as if it would not harm the grasses; but that is not for want of strength. When a herd of impala is disturbed, they start leaping around, a sight as astonishing as it is splendid. Yet these are not powered leaps like an eland's, with a good thump at takeoff. The impala suddenly switches to a world where there is no gravity. Nor are these leaps of desperate escape; the herd springs in several directions at once, even after they know where an intruder has come from. Nor do impala leap up to see over the tops of bushes; they leap about in the same manner when they are disturbed in the open. The aim may be to distract an attacker, since fleeting bodies may have a better chance of becoming fleeing bodies. As they soar aloft the dark patches on their feet and bodies become more prominent—a warning to those not already alerted. A lion's vision is not as coordinated as a human's, and may be disrupted by such antics. Only a lion—or evolution—knows the answer to that one. But such a phenomenon stems from recent evolution, since impala have not been gracing the scene for more than the final few moments of the African day —possibly little longer than man.

If they have used their short time to decorate the environment more than dominate it, they are no less successful for that. If success is measured in terms of survival and readiness to live in a variety of places, then impala have an edge over many creatures. The wildebeest flourish by the hundreds of thousands in the Serengeti, yet in most parts of East Africa, as in most parts of Africa, there is not a single one. The same is true for gazelles and buffalo and zebras. Impala, on the other hand, are to be found from the northern Kenya deserts to Nairobi Park and the Serengeti, even as far as southern Tanzania. And this is only part of their range. In Rhodesia they teem more than any other antelope. In parts of South Africa they outnumber all other creatures put together; in Kruger Park there are well over 100,000 of them. Not that impala are often seen in great numbers together; indeed, they are often not seen at all. During the sweltering hours they wander into the thickets, which suits these grazer-browsers (or browser-grazers).

In the Serengeti, where Dr. Peter Jarman has counted 70,000 or more impala, a male with his harem and their offspring might amount to 100 animals. In South Africa there may be ten times as many to a square mile—up to 400—but the herds do not go much above 50. Perhaps a smaller herd needs a much smaller area. Or perhaps it can make more efficient use of its immediate environment. Or, to take it the other way round, a male may be better able to build up a big herd when there are fewer impalas, particularly competing males, in the vicinity, for whatever reason. Or perhaps it is just that the country of the Serengeti makes for big herds anyway, regardless of how many impala there are.

Of course there are bound to be big differences between East Africa and areas so far south that they are outside the tropics. For one thing, the day-length varies as you move away from the equator. In East Africa there is hardly any difference all the year round. There are rainy seasons and dry seasons, but there is no spring when days lengthen. In South Africa this may be what influences the birthing season, which in turn affects the breeding patterns, which influence the herd formations—in fact, much of what makes an impala. In Rhodesia the births seem to be tied in with the rains and the fresh vegetation. In two recent years the births were a couple of months later than usual, at a time when the rains were delayed too. Perhaps the previous breeding season had been a couple of months off standard as well, or perhaps the impala can exercise some kind of hormonal control over the time for giving birth; the latter seems more likely, except that two months is an enormous delay.

As many male impala are born as females, but by the time they are grown up there are sometimes only half as many males left. It is hardly likely that they kill each other off by fighting, since the impala is not built for vigorous battle, even though an occasional horn is broken off. Moreover, this sex discrepancy seems to operate wherever impala are found, both in areas where they are thick on the ground, hence more prone to fighting, and in areas where they are fairly scarce. Perhaps when the males set up their harems they become so preoccupied in looking after them that they have little time to look after themselves and so become more vulnerable to predators. But males seem to have a hard

Impala are often to be found in exceedingly dry country, but where water is available they drink fairly frequently. The male's horns are among the finest-looking in Africa, though they are too long and angled to be much use for fighting, and they snap off easily.

time of it even on Rhodesian ranches, where the main predators have been eliminated. What is certain is that impala males defend their females with much dashing around, threatening, and clashing of horns. This could mean the males are defending their territories; and if the females were to wander off, the male would try to keep them within the boundary of his own domain and only let them go when they encroached on a rival's territory. Or would he defend them wherever they wandered?

Males deposit their droppings in the same spot, like the dik-dik and gazelle, presumably as a way of marking certain patches of ground. A male has been seen to urinate three times in ten minutes, a further sign of special intentions. They rub their faces against grass stems, as do those antelopes that build up layers of gland secretion on the grass stalk until it forms a blob. But impala have no preorbital glands on their faces; only a spot between the horns for producing oily secretions. Possibly their sideways rubbing is a hangover from processes that played a part in the evolution of antelopes to equip them for survival, and have since died out in the impala, leaving a vestige of the eons-old habit somewhere in the impala psyche. Preorbital glands of this kind are used by gazelles and gerenuks. On the other hand, waterbuck and Uganda kob, antelopes with very strong territorial instincts, have no such face glands.

When there are a lot of male impala in one area, there is intense competition, and the territorial instinct, often a shadowy impulse elsewhere, is intensified until it amounts to a pattern. In the forty-four square miles of Nairobi Park there are several hundred impala, though limited by their feeding needs to two small areas. Dr. W. Leuthold has described how the basic pattern is a male dominating a group of females. There are also a few bachelor groups, an occasional solitary male, and a group or two of females with no male in apparent command. This suggests that the male gathers together his does after they have come into his territory; he does not go out seeking them. Supporting the same idea is the fact that males have been seen fighting when there are no females around. Moreover, the males of Nairobi Park seem to extend their territories into "home ranges," which are areas where they wander at different times of the day to satisfy their various needs. These ranges may be half a dozen times greater than the territory, which often amounts to only a third of a square mile, suggesting a further weakening of strict territorial behavior. However small these territories seem, they are relatively large, as big as a Grant's gazelle's. The Grant's is another antelope rather thin on the ground as compared with wildebeest or Uganda kob, which, being grass-eaters, are not nearly so limited in their needs, can spread far and wide across the plains, and tend to be much thicker on the ground wherever they are found. This means that their territories have to be smaller and closer together and have to be more strongly defended, since there is likely to be more conflict: the owner of the territory has to be more "territorial."

So, what is an impala? Impala in the Serengeti do one thing, those in Rhodesia do something else, and those in Nairobi Park do as impala in Nairobi Park do. They have their own conditions: any area constitutes a dynamic entity of its own. These characteristics shift and fluctuate. In a few years Nairobi Park may have changed so much that the impala may be able, or obliged, to adapt their behavior, either making their territories more definite or allowing them to disappear altogether. It would be interesting to take a Nairobi Park impala male, with its habitual ways of going about things, and haul it off to the Serengeti with all the different traditions there. Would it be so disorientated by its new environment that it could not cope? This is a factor hardly ever considered when animals are shifted from one place to another. If the vegetation looks suitable, then it is taken for granted that all else will be well. The same applies when bringing animals back to an area from which they have been eliminated at some point in the past. What has happened in the meantime? Perhaps excessive grass-burning has brought on an increase of bush cover, which would help a creature like an impala. But the increased undergrowth could also benefit leopards, until they are more than equal to a few newly returned impala. Generally situations of this kind sort themselves out into a new equilibrium, although the initial upheavals can be fierce indeed. Whole herds have sometimes failed to survive in the most "perfect" conditions. A wild creature needs its niche. As long as it stays in one place, it tends to perpetuate its niche, just as a niche perpetuates the animal. If the animal disappears, the niche may be taken over by another, or squeezed by the occupants of surrounding niches until it virtually disappears; or it may be modified until it is half unrecognizable. One can talk about environment in terms of basic geography, but habitat is another thing again. It is a dynamic affair and nothing less.

The dynamic habitat concept applies particularly to impala. An impala is a "successional" animal, favored by a transitional stage in the vegetation from thick woodlands to open grasslands (or vice versa). A vegetation zone is often on its way from one state to another, especially in this modern day when change after change is triggered off in rapid succession by man and his doings. Fires sweep across the countryside. The flames leap into the edges of the forests and open up new pathways where grass can intrude. This stimulates a zone of undergrowth—a line of thicket material where the forest attempts to protect itself against encroachment—which is the kind of environment an impala enjoys. Such conditions may have followed the spread of modern man across Africa and fostered the tremendous numbers of impala that are now found in southern Africa. Because impala belong to a zone that is neither woodland nor grassland, they thrive in what would generally be regarded as poor country for livestock, since cattle need out-and-out grassland. Overgrazing and overburning lead to regrowth of brushwood; during the stages before it actually reaches into taller, treelike growths, impala thrive. In fact, the number of impala on a stretch of savannah might indicate how successfully the local pastoralists are protecting their country. Impala almost always reflect which direction the vegetation is going in—and it will be going in one direction or another, hardly ever standing still unless it has reached a stable state like final rainforest or desert. This means the impala are either coming or going; that is, either coming in or going out.

MASAI

The Masai are one of the most interesting and colorful tribes of East Africa. They are also one of the most conservative, according to tradition: unchanging and unchangeable. Their way of life is cattle—first, last, and all the way. Certainly, they own as many domestic stock per person as any community in Africa. The land they occupy is also some of Africa's finest wildlife country. Not only does their territory include Ngorongoro, Amboseli, and the Mara, but it provides the main "overflow area" for Nairobi Park, Tarangire, and the Serengeti. Moreover, Masailand features much of the best wildlife country that is not yet conserved in parks or other protected areas. For a long time the Masai and the wildlife have shown a degree of coexistence. It has not been that they have tolerated each other; rather, they have ignored each other. Now a clash is brewing.

The Masai style of living is as complex as it is colorful and long standing. It is precisely the simplistic account foisted off on them from outside that the Masai object to, as do most of their East African neighbors. One way of penetrating beyond the popular image is to see one of their *Eunoto* ceremonies, when there may be several thousand Masai, many of them warriors, gathered at a single mammoth-sized *manyatta* village. The overall timing of the ceremony depends upon the moon, which is why a recent occasion found a group of Masai watching for portents from the skies while a community overseas was watching the same moon for signals of significance to *their* tribal affairs.

Every few years the Masai tribal structure shifts along a notch. The current warriors become junior elders, and a new set of young men take their place. Early in the morning on the ceremony days the warriors take off to celebrate certain of their rites outside the *manyatta*. They are as easy to watch as they are impressive—unlike the occasion late on the final day when these *moran* lose their long hair, the last mark of their warrior status. They enter a specially constructed hut and emerge shorn of their locks and their youthful prestige. A young man nowadays becomes an elder at twenty: it used to be much later, but the limit has been constantly pushed back to reduce the warrior span. Gone are the days when the warriors made up a fifth of the whole community.

When the Europeans first arrived in East Africa they found an area the size of Britain sparsely inhabited by a few million agriculturalists or semipastoralists, and dominated, if not terrorized, by fewer than 50,000 Masai. But if one looks closely at the basis for the Masai reputation of unmitigated aggressiveness, one is not likely to find much evidence beyond hearsay. If the Masai way of looking at the outside world is changing, so is the outside world's view of the Masai—and it is difficult to say which has been the more resistant to "things as they really are." It is even more difficult to say where these people came from. In the 1500s they probably occupied lowlands near Lake Rudolf in what is now Kenya's desert country, where the Turkana people live (the local folklore still tells of greenery and wild animals in the area somewhere back in the misty past; did the Masai set off the devastation that brought on the semidesert of today?).

A while later the Masai shifted to Kieru, a region in the direction of the more fertile highland country 200 miles to the south; from there they penetrated in the 1600s toward Ngong, a few miles south of present-day Nairobi. For another 150 years they pressed steadily southward until the first European explorers found them occupying a territory

During the warriors' *Eunoto* ceremony, the *moran* file back and forth across the plain, returning periodically to the *manyatta*, where many of the main ceremonies are held.

All legends to the contrary, the Masai rarely bleed their cattle. An animal is left for another month or so before it is bled again, the Masai generally needing blood only during the dry season when other sources of liquid are thinning out. The cow suffers no more than any other donor of a pint or two of blood.

500 miles north–south by 150 miles east–west. That was their greatest era. Then, around 1890, disaster struck: a smallpox epidemic among their people and a rinderpest plague among their cattle, followed by famine and civil war, left half the Masai and almost all their livestock dead. The turn of the century and the start of British rule found the tribe at their lowest ebb.

The early colonial period was deeply influenced by the reputation the Masai had built up for themselves, or rather the tradition other people found convenient to attribute to them. The Arab slave-traders, anxious to keep the European explorers out of Masai country since it lay directly across their routes to the Indian Ocean ports, told a tale of savagery and slaughter. The European colonizer, in turn, represented the Masai as fearsome people requiring a firm grip, so as to justify pressures on the tribe to part with slices of their territory needed for white settlers: if the word went out that the Masai were fierce and not to be trifled with by outsiders, there was less chance of anyone's asking what was going on. Anyway, had not the first European immigrants in the 1890s come across a people warring and pillaging?

Thus the great Masai myth was fostered on all sides. But their reputation for insensate bravery is as assured as their reputation for incessant aggression is suspect. To suggest that they rampaged across East Africa in the old days spreading rapine and worse is to impute a record to them where tradition is less than truth. It makes splendid pop history. It supports the aura these people are wrapped in like their cloaks, suggesting they are independent, upright, and determined to follow their own path—let no one stand across it. But it is a fake image that has left the Masai with a burdensome past. It has obscured the vision of many a person trying to deal straight with straight people. An outsider already convinced that the Masai are given to aggressive self-aggrandizement is inclined to exhort them to recognize that this is the modern age, and they had better abandon their delusions of grandeur.

They never had many. The Masai people have scarcely ever existed as a people, according to Dr. Alan Jacobs, who has done as much as anybody to restore a realistic reputation to the Masai, a fair one that reflects no less on these hardy people than the inflated fables. Far from having banded themselves into a powerful nation bent on military conquest, they amount to sixteen or more separate tribes who speak the common language Maa, or, at least, a loose confederation of subtribes. Other people spoke Maa, but they broke away from the Masai way back in the days of the departure from Kieru. There are the Wa-Arusha and the Njemps and others, who dig in the soil or engage in other un-Masai activities, and the Samburu, who have a clan system more akin to the Bantu arrangement. These *Iloikop*, or "fierce ones," people who "acquired their cattle by violence," lived up to their name, and gave rise to terrible tales of Maa-speaking people who roamed East Africa scourging the countryside. From time to time these pseudo-Masai tackled the Masai themselves. In self-defense the Masai set up their warrior grades. After a couple of centuries of indecisive skirmishing the Masai were gaining the upper hand, until they embarked on their disastrous internecine forays; to recoup their stock losses they temporarily took to cattle-rustling themselves. Onto this scene of battling Masai and raiding bands stepped the first large-scale European arrivals. They had been forewarned by the Arabs about the Maa-speaking people. It was all plain enough.

The tradition persists. Yet the records today show that the Masai are no longer responsible for nearly so much stock-rustling as many of the tribes around them, nor have they been for a long time. Yet the Masai get the blame—who else? It has not been an easy period for them. So much did they retire into their own affairs that, compared with other East African tribes, they were distinctly unadvanced, though nobody dared tell them so. Their nomadic way of life had no place for European goods and chattels such as clothes and radios and other impedimenta of the good life. Children were sent to the savannah for stock-herding rather than to school for alien indoctrination. By 1925 the Masai had built up their previous numbers; another generation, and they had doubled again.

They achieved their advance by keeping to themselves and biding their counsel, and by accepting the white man's medicines for cattle and cattle-owners alike. They maintained their own traditions, together with their own priorities, in which a cow headed the list. A cow was value indeed. It still is. The Masai never counts his stock (that would bring bad luck), but he can tell at a glance if one is missing from a herd of a hundred. No matter how skinny, a beast is a treasured possession. The Masai build up hordes of pitifully thin animals that are not primarily for disposal or sale; what white man would part with a dollar bill merely because it has become a bit tattered?

However much this passion for cattle seems to fly in the face of common sense, it makes sound ecological sense. The Masai follow a pattern shared by other cattle-keepers in East Africa, such as the Karamojong in northeastern Uganda, who live in similarly harsh country. These arid environments place a premium on rainfall to keep alive the supply of food on the hoof, and if actual rainfall in temperate lands is generally the same as effective rainfall, in savannah Africa it generally isn't: warm winds across the grasslands dry out what little moisture there is, and make for an evaporation rate potentially twice the precipitation rate. Moreover, rainfall averaging ten inches or thirty does not mean much when one year in four it is a fraction as much. In these areas it is absurd to try growing grain, even though having the vegetation converted into your supper via an animal means that only one-tenth as much material appears on your plate. (An equally inefficient system is followed by those of more advanced communities who feed grain to livestock on the grounds that they prefer steak to bread.) The policy of subsisting off the one product from a cow that a modern rancher would think least likely in such unhelpful habitats means that you need many many animals, plenty in reserve, too, to guard against sudden disease or sudden marauders from over the horizon. When the milk starts to run low in the dry season, you can supplement it with a little blood, though a pint or two from an animal each month is as much as it can stand in such straitened circumstances (the image of the Masai as inveterate blood-drinkers belongs to a Masai image as mythical as mystical). Eating a cow now and again would be eating into your capital, and who would come to your help on a far-from-rainy day?

All of which goes some way to explain why the Masai feel they can never have too many cattle, just as one can't have too much money in the bank. If plenty of cattle are their main insurance against disaster, they will naturally be reluctant to dispose of the "surplus" through modern markets (whatever way they reacted during the 1961 famine when they found that relief food fell manna-like from the skies). Not that the Masai have turned their faces flatly against selling any of their excess at all; it is rather the Kenya colonialists who did that. The beef barons of settler days wanted the markets confined pretty much to their own stock, and the Masai were subject to severe quotas or were obliged to send their cattle to abattoirs for dismal rates. Tanzania had no settlers, and the Masai there achieved far greater sales.

If a Masai is to live off milk he needs a lot of it. An elder likes six pints a day, a warrior eight, a woman or a child up to three, right through the year, good times and bad. In the wet season they may get two or three pints from a cow, but as the dry season advances it falls to a single pint or none. There have to be enough cattle to cover the worst times of the year, including such droughts as come along. Around these short critical times the whole of Masai life revolves; during the rest of the year there is milk enough and more than enough. If the tribe could be persuaded to expand grain foods from one-seventh of their diet to a half (provided such supplies were readily available in that wilderness), the Masai could buy a year's supply from the sale of only two or three steers. But they are no more prepared to change their eating habits than any other people—rather less, given their distinctive regimen. They chose to live off cattle a long time back, and cattle have determined many of the sanctions as well as the supports of their system. Telling the Masai to change their food customs is like telling them to change their history and all that has made them Masai—and still makes them Masai.

This situation puts a special emphasis not just on cattle but on milk-producing cows. Cows make up well over half the Masai herds, instead of one-fifth as they would under modern ranching methods. Bulls and bullocks make up only 20 percent of the herds and are kept for ceremonial purposes; the rest are calves. A lot of cows means a lot of calves, which further delights the Masai. The herd may undergo an increase of up to one-third each year, a staggering rate of buildup—precipitating the spasms of destructive over-grazing that gather with the force of a hurricane, not to mention the devastation. Calves are frequently born at the end of the dry season, just before the rains bring the fresh grass; this is a common pattern among savannah animals, but it means the calves want milk from the cows just when the Masai need every drop themselves. Not only does the Masai see the need for still more cows, but the calf is deprived of the sustenance it requires if it is to produce better-grade offspring in due time: the circle spirals further downward.

A family owning eighty cattle, of which fifty are cows in milk, owns no more than will see them through normal times, let alone hard times. What actually aggravates the situation is a year of unusual rainfall that triggers off an unusually fine crop of calves; the sudden outburst in numbers exerts its full impact on the environment a season or two later when conditions may have become rather different—and if they haven't, the progressive boom soon makes them so. The herds have undergone an eruption in numbers until they far exceed the capacity of the habitat to support them: having erupted, they are ready for a crash. The 1961 drought left three-quarters of the cattle dead in some regions of Kenya Masailand, and insofar as those 600,000 would have brought about $8,000,000 if the markets and the social system alike had allowed them, it could well be termed a dead loss. Yet it took only half a dozen years for the numbers to build up again;

by 1970 there were once again at least twice as many as the country could fairly support. Another drought, in 1971, and as many as 60 percent died in some parts of Kenya.

Over the long term the herds follow a series of such eruptive oscillations, leaving the environment at each stage that much more impoverished, that much less able to stand the next strain. What to do with a situation that is as self-perpetuating as it is self-impoverishing? Conditions are not likely to change until the senior scions of the tribe have disappeared, those eldest of elders who cannot forget the dark days when the Masai found themselves in danger of dying out altogether after their cattle had been decimated by the 1890 plague. As long as these prophets of doom continue to preach that there can never be enough cattle, it is hard to bring about changes in four or five years that would alter the face of a tribe left unchanged for four or five centuries. Some people ask if the fresh approach will leave the Masai still Masai. Others ask if any other approach will leave any Masai. But change is coming, as it must come; to a Masai with difficulties enough in a constrictive world, the best change sometimes seems the least change.

All of which helps to explain why Masailand has such vast numbers of cattle, which yet are scarcely sufficient. The Kajiado area of Kenya supports 60,000 Masai in its 8,000 square miles, who live off cattle that soar to well over 700,000 at peak periods. The region is not so much overstocked with cattle as overpopulated with people, even at eight to a square mile. And the population is rising more rapidly in the wake of modern medicine, just as it has been rising for decades. The increase in livestock to keep pace with their owners is no new phenomenon, nor is it confined to African pastoralists. In Rhodesia the 500,000 cattle of about eighty years ago slumped to 25,000 after the 1896 outbreak of rinderpest; but in only a quarter of a century, following the arrival of the white man with his laws and vaccines, there were around 500,000 African cattle together with as many white-owned stock. Another fifty years, and the African herds had expanded to well over 2,000,000, while the European ranches accounted for 1,750,000 (for a fraction as many people). Degraded environments in Rhodesia are now to be found in European and African areas alike.

The Masai cattle represent not so much a way of life as a means of staying alive, valued no more and no less. They are not used for social transactions such as bride-wealth or blood money nearly so much as among the stock-raising people to the north, the Turkana and the Nuer—yet among the Turkana there may be only three or four head of stock for every person and in Nuerland only one, compared with the twelve or fifteen among the Masai people. The Masai discharge their social dues with only a tenth as many cattle offered in exchange, or they make up the difference with sheep and goats, which often outnumber their holdings of cattle (these are kept also for the meat that makes up one-quarter of their diet). The hazards of environment are reflected by the constraints of tradition, the one reinforcing the other. Until a Masai can be assured, and reassured, that by selling off part of his huge herds he will not find himself in starvation circumstances such as his history and environment threaten him with, he sees persuasive attempts to change his way of life as perfidious inducements to end all he stands for and survives through. The most modern world and its finest techniques are urgently needed to clear the mess left by a recently retired world and its "modern methods," when a situation delicate but balanced was suddenly needled by the foreigner's syringes. The social and medical imbalance of the colonialist approach has proved more disruptive than any ecological imbalance of the Masai, and it has left a situation where what was barely tolerable has become critical, if not catastrophic. It is not that the Masai shouldn't enjoy all the benefits of the modern world, but they should enjoy them *all* in order to keep their affairs in harmony, rather than have stock vaccines inflicted on them without stock markets imposed on the grounds that "forcing change on the Masai would be unfair." And, as is usual in Africa, it is not the rising birthrate that has brought on the present state of affairs, but the decreasing deathrate. No Masai can fairly be expected to trade an advantage of that sort for better livestock proposals that so far appear speculative at best.

In the midst of this crucible situation the Masai are exhorted by conservationists from outside with cries about the wildlife and their heritage. The Masai know well enough what is their number-one heritage: their way of life. But when they try to explain a few aspects to the conservationist, they often find him too impassioned to listen. The Masai don't actually launch a direct assault on the wild creatures, as some East African peoples do. They engage in a contest of attrition, which in the long run can be worse. There is no sudden slaughter by poachers, only a steady undramatic destruction of the habitat which does not lend itself to short-term blitz campaigns of "conservationists versus slayers," with jail sentences at the end for the malefactors. What has to be mounted is a long, steady program of persuasion, which hits the headlines at first, but rarely during the years of effort afterward. You can enlist energy and funds for a sudden-death battle against snares and traps, but you cannot publicize a scheme with no battle statistics every few months. "The Masai are to be educated," cry the conservationists, but the real education might begin elsewhere.

If the Masai have disregarded the modern world, it is not because they are incapable of dealing with it. The first African doctor in Kenya was a Masai, and several Masai are now at Harvard and Oxford. The latter-day Masai is a company executive, a university lecturer, a leading civil servant, a prominent politician. Not that there is a rush to the nine-to-five way of life and the blessings it brings. For many a Masai, life is still an affair of little frenzy. He toils not, neither does he spin; he doesn't make many concessions to the modern world beyond accepting spears fabricated not by a neighboring tribe but by a community overseas.

Now the world is closing in on the Masai. They may not want it, but it wants them. Or rather it wants their lands, if they will not develop them beyond rudimentary cattle-raising. Some of their neighbors look upon these areas with envy and more than envy.

Many people in East Africa do not have enough land, the Masai have a great deal—the solution is obvious. The Masai are less than enthusiastic. In Tanzania the authorities are trying to ease them out of tradition and into trousers (and if they come to town, they had better bring their deodorant). Well-intentioned administrators have tried to show the Masai the benefits of cash systems: perhaps the day is coming of blood kept in refrigerators and television aerials sprouting from mud huts. The Masai reaction has been to turn a blind eye. It is not that they are against the twentieth century; they are against any century. They listen attentively while you hold up the allurements of prosperity before them, then they wrap their blankets around themselves and inquire about the state of your cattle and your wife—in that order.

But the day cannot be far off when the Masai become good citizens of the twentieth century, acquisitive instincts and all. Or they will disappear. It is a pity they cannot be left alone until they are ready to make the shift of their own accord. While one part of the world, the more strident part, is insistent that all people shall be one and look like one even if it is little more likely to make them act as one, there is another part of the world with a less powerful voice but an expanding appeal that asks whether people like the Masai cannot be allowed to look after themselves, at least until they show positively they do not want to be left alone and have sufficiently safeguarded their culture, their ideals, their differentness, to risk the move. People from outside do not regard the Masai as museum pieces, however much the occasional insensitive intruder may suggest it. They look on the Masai as people with secrets they do not share themselves, and often wish they did. There may even come the day when the outside world wants to look more closely at communities like the Masai, not just for the serenity (or the stagnancy) of the present-day scene but for the workings of the whole social system, where wants are met by supplying the necessary items (sometimes) or by doing without (more often).

Regrettably, this is probably not a prospect for this world. The Masai are not only too many, they can no longer look around for new pastures. If their fundamental system has

The cattle may not have started the gulley, but they have certainly deepened it, as is apparent from the clouds of dust kicked up by just a few hooves.

been slowly undermined by alien interference, their life-style is being assaulted far more swiftly by the world of the cash economy. A sight not uncommon in Nairobi is a Masai with spear in one hand, briefcase in the other, heading for the bank (perhaps bank robberies are less frequent on such occasions). The Masai have been shown the tree of consumerdom, and there are plenty of bystanders waiting to show them how the satisfaction of the sophisticate lies in never having enough. The Masai athlete returning from the Olympic Games stands in the middle of his savannah plains and foresees the day when there will be highways here, jetports there, development everywhere. He does not yet anticipate the smog shroud that denotes an accomplishment nobody can doubt.

Yet the Masai are one people who could be fortunate. They could have development and prosperity while retaining many of their traditional ways. They could come to terms with the monied contentment that is being sold to them by exploiting the finest natural resource the East African countries hold within their borders. There would be less need to busy themselves with the techniques of advanced ranching (well, just a few); they could keep their cattle (well, more than just a few). They could grow prosperous off the one resource that would never give out, would never end up in degrading the environment. They could produce protein from their land by the ton. It is there, waiting, by the thousands of wildlife tons. The Masai live in an area of "low potential," of little use for arable farming. This is what makes it land of such unusual potential: it has never been dug up, it has never been heavily settled, it has never been deprived of the forms of natural life which have learned to exploit its meager advantages—it took millions of years for that lesson to be learned, and it has been learned well.

These are the wildlands of East Africa—but by no means the wastelands. Similar tracts of country make up three-quarters of Kenya alone, an area larger than California and Oregon. They include other tribal areas besides Masailand, supporting well over 1,000,000 people, or a little over one-tenth of Kenya's population. The wild creatures have not trampled the maize fields, since there weren't any maize fields. It is not strictly accurate to say these nomads "raise" stock, since the animals rarely rise above a miserable level of subsistence. There are at least 6,500,000 cattle in these areas, the vast majority of Kenya's cattle population. As a U.N. biologist, Robert Casebeer, has pointed out, the commercial ranches in the country account for only one cow in fourteen, but they do it on only one acre in fifty, while producing three-quarters of the country's market meat. The annual take-off amounts to a quarter of their herds, while the pastoral people hardly average even 1 percent of their totals. An average animal from a pastoral area works out at 270 pounds of meat, while one from a commerical ranch at well over half as much more. One of the more advanced pastoralist groups recently reached the exceptional off-take of around one beast in eleven, including stock slaughtered for local consumption. Their area averages thirteen and a half acres per head of stock, so the 270 pounds required 150 acres to produce it, many times more than for a commercial ranching area, and a woefully low rate of production by any standards.

But these rangelands are to be developed if only because they comprise such wide areas in East Africa, at least two-thirds of the total region. In common with rangelands all around the world, they are coming under pressure from expanding populations that feel they cannot limit themselves much longer to the far smaller arable areas. They are to take their place in the modern world, even if they lurch a bit getting there. An East African ecologist, Leslie Brown, estimates that Kenyans eat only half a pound of meat a week, less than the British ration during the war—but about what most people eat in the 6,000,000 square miles of rangeland Africa, half the total continent and almost twice the size of the United States. Forty million stock-raisers are producing little extra for the rest of the 350,000,000 people, and it is in these tracts that radical changes must come in the years ahead, more even perhaps than in the moister lands with their green revolutions. At present these rangelands are mostly deteriorating, from Somalia in the north to Botswana in the south and Mauretania in the west. That is why so many eyes are on Masailand and its attempts to work out its problems.

At present the savannah expanse in Kenya produces $35,000,000 a year from livestock (almost all of it from commercial ranches) to go with $40,000,000 from tourists. The stock side costs about thirty cents per animal to maintain, producing an average of three dollars a year (seventy cents in that form of prime value to a developing nation, foreign exchange); a wild creature costs roughly the same thirty cents' upkeep in government funds, but produces six times as much revenue—and thirty times as much foreign exchange. Out of an area two and a half times the size of New England, the main commercial livestock country is limited to a patch the size of Connecticut and the main tourist territory to little more than Vermont. The first earns two dollars an acre, the second four, while the remainder does well if it reaches fifty cents an acre, usually more like a dime—yet this is where Kenya recently paid out $12,000,000 in famine relief.

The Masai now see looming before them a Promised Land of progress and problems. They are realizing they must learn to talk of "all that part and parcel of land" which is mine, and here is my piece of paper to prove it. They must learn fast, and then they must talk fast. If they don't, there may be other people coming along to file forms for the same patch of savannah. The pastoral system in East Africa has never bothered much with land rights for the individual: land belonged to the tribe, for anybody to go and graze where he wished within the local realm. Diggers in the ground, on the other hand, have generally observed rights of custom, making it far easier for a Kikuyu to go and apply for his title deeds. The Masai have suddenly become hag-ridden with fear, these fearless people, that the subtleties of modern bureaucracy may rob them of what they have defended so long by spear and sword. A sheet of paper can apparently give security against the modern *Iloikop*, the newly risen fierce ones who eye their homelands. Well then, they must go and get that sheet of paper. The Masai are drafting a fresh army to protect themselves, an army of lawyers and lobbyists. It is not so much individual tenure they are after, since that would result in patches of a mere 500 acres for each family, not nearly sufficient in this arid country for year-round grazing. Given their background, social as much as savannah, the Masai are going in for group ranches based on "Elatia," social units within their tribal framework. Four years ago, only one-seventh of Kenya Masailand was under private possession; two years from now, the whole region should be divided up and registered through individual title.

Having got himself assured in the midst of modern tribulations, the Masai finds himself assailed by people who come along with pleas to protect the wild animals within his borders. Hitherto he has not given them much thought. If he is now to be told he should not ring his domain with wire, or that his piece of paper might even be withheld at the last moment because of some talk about game reserves and foreigners, he starts to think again about those wild animals. Hitherto again, wildlife on "nobody's land" has belonged to the nation, whereas wildlife on an individual's land has belonged to the individual. Yet the wild animals living in areas that the safari people most want to visit are supposed to remain an asset of the country at large. They are not to be touched if they damage pipelines or fences, and you are to look the other way if a herd of elephants comes along and wrecks your drinking trough—or merely drinks it dry, which can be just as bad at the height of a hard season. The Masai responds that if the wildlife is to be an asset of the whole country, then let the whole country do something about it: why should he be saddled with problems of maintaining wild animals at his own expense? It is all very fine to listen to talk about the benefits of tourism, but he is more impressed with a dollar in his pocket than fifty dollars in some local council's not-so-local accounts. The only profit he gets out of tourists is when one wants to take his photograph (all right, let him pay high for it).

If the current livestock industry is far from leaving its customers well fed (more likely fed up?), the rangelands of Kenya are capable of producing at least 11,000,000 pounds of wild meat a year by the most conservative estimates, and most of it from Masailand. A team of Food and Agriculture Organization experts is at present working on a project to bring this meat to market, utilizing wildebeest, buffalo, elephant, and whatever else presents itself. The initial off-take aims at a mere 10 percent across the board, all species equally, though in subsequent seasons the gazelle can probably be raised three or four times as high, and other fast-breeders too. When a Masai builds his first fences, he looks at a zebra that breaks them down in a way he has never looked at it before. If he finds that the zebra's skin sells in Manhattan for $200, and the zebra does not need to be protected against diseases and droughts and lions, and that visitors will pay to come and look at this zebra rug in the making, then again the Masai might look at the zebra in a new way.

One of the most experienced ecologists in East Africa, Dr. Murray Watson, puts the potential income for Masailand at almost $3,000,000: income indeed for 140,000 Masai. Possibly still more wild creatures would be available if there were a better balance between wildlife and domestic stock in Masailand, a more equable biomass split than the present one-fifth wildlife and four-fifths livestock. Those who propose adjusting the scene to straight livestock by clearing off all the wildlife (since you "cannot ranch in a zoo") would, according to a survey by Dr. Robert Davis, gain a mere $1\frac{1}{2}$ cents an acre (supposing that removing ten pounds of wildlife allows for five extra pounds of cattle); with predators removed as well (a prospect with problems—how do you stop more lions coming in from that wide outside?), the return could go up another one cent. Meanwhile, a pilot scheme has shown that wildlife—without pushing out the cattle—can produce four times as much return. To all this is added the returns from sport hunting. Whatever one thinks of hardy hunters displaying not the merest fraction of the skill, not to mention the courage, of their primitive forebears who went after even larger beasts with sticks and stones instead of high-caliber rifles "to even up the odds," the 1,400 stalwarts who have been disposing of 9,000 animals a year in Kenya for a return of up to thirty cents an acre could be thinking of an economic bag of 200 gazelles a year each instead of two.

The agricultural expert has his plans. The economist has his. The wildlife man has his. The Masai also has his. Unless his views are taken into account every inch of the way, a hundred ecological surveys and a thousand save-the-wildlife schemes will achieve nothing beyond hardening him further against zebras and lions. One prospective approach in Kenya suggests, in the words of David Pratt's proposal, "that the range areas should be developed, conserved and managed in accordance with ecological principles of proper land-use; that, so far as other principles allow, the range areas should be developed to yield the maximum benefit for the national economy; and that the people of the range areas must be allowed the opportunity for social development in terms of the modern world and in accordance with the principles of human rights." Some people think this is a statement sufficiently obvious to be worth omitting. But these apparently innocuous words center on issues important and impassioned. Little is helped when livestock experts on the one hand and wildlife experts on the other say the solution is simple: eliminate the opposition. Exploiting the wildlife might allow the Masai to find a niche in the twentieth-century environment more in accord with their proclivities, and it would not impose on them advancement in the form of trivia like trousers. It would not change their countryside beyond recognition with cattle-dips here, drinking troughs there, stockades and fences all around—and wildlife nowhere. The Masai could have these facilities in whatever measure they wish. Taking these people of all the ages and of no age, and jerking them into the jet-age with techniques as exotic as the strains of livestock that have sometimes been foisted off on them, would be about as discerning as inflicting modern dress on them just because everybody else wears it.

Several other major pastoral tribes in East Africa inhabit parched country similar to much of Masailand. Overgrazing by the Suk in northern Kenya aggravates the effects of an arid environment, until their herds have to radiate for miles across the desert-like countryside to find grazing. Each rainy season the water runs off with renewed force, taking another few weakened trees with it.

But then advisors with experience of cattle in temperate regions sometimes set out to develop other lands in their own image, even though a ranching economy would represent a near revolution in the outlook of the pastoralists. A wildlife economy, on the other hand, might not amount to such an upheaval. The Masai might even not have to do much about it themselves except collect the cash. In Tanzania an outside organization has been taking an initial harvest of Masailand wildlife. They crop antelopes by the thousand and pay fees by the tens of thousands of dollars into the local exchequer. The same organization has taken 300 elephants in Tanzania, at fifty dollars each. They not only produce streams of cash but streams of information, showing (via volumes of figures where others have produced hardly a sheet) how elephants might produce the best form of "livestock" in some places, cattle in others, elephant and cattle together in still others. Wildlife Services are expert not just at pointing a rifle at an antelope, but at finding out what brought the antelope to that station in life; at discovering not only whether they could bring other antelopes to better stations another year through selective cropping, but how to bring the human owners of the wildlife country to a better standard of living. And there are few organizations that have produced as much for the scientific community as for the local community. They scarcely belong to the wildlife world as it has been for decades, so conservationist are they in a world that is often merely conservative; how far they belong to a wider African world, as it is now and as it is becoming every day, is another story. It is a tale the Masai could tell as well as any.

The Masai could be more modern than the next, while still continuing much of their age-old style of life where the cow is king. They have many enviable characteristics that are still perpetuated by their mode of life. A boy herder in Tanzania recently killed a lion that attacked his cattle (he certainly wouldn't go out and look for it). Some people in Tanzania thought this nothing to be proud of, even if not many people around the world would agree. More important, the Masai have other capabilities that could enable them to withstand features of the modern world as debilitating as any lion. They have an inner security that has not yet been too eroded by the new pressures around them. Nevertheless, they are to be taught to want, and then to want to want. One wonders how the fabric of Masai life will stand up under the onslaught of cash and more cash. Better than many, one suspects. Better than most, if they can get their cash without selling off their living patterns in exchange. The Masai way of life places great value on genial ways of dealing, on living with each other rather than off each other. If these people, who have enjoyed more health and wealth than many in Africa, are suddenly brought the benefits of a greater world, it would be a pity if their social equilibrium were to be upset to match the ecological upheavals inflicted on them from outside. In particular it would be regrettable when, after developing hankerings for more and more and more, their new life-style will, within the lifetime of the same boy herder, have to be brought into balance again with what is available (as will the yearnings of everybody everywhere, when the limitless ambitions of limitless people run up against a limited globe). Indeed, there may well come a time—and soon—when people from that same outside world will come looking for lessons from a community that could live with an equitable amount of affluence and without the knowledge that enough is never sufficient. The return to living in equilibrium with the environment will be most crushing for those who have "advanced" furthest away from it. The Masai are now much closer to the spirit that must soon be shared by everybody, forever. Perhaps they will be able to hang on to a good part of it, until the mysteries of their life-style are sought out not just because they are impressive.

Before that stage, there may be a time when the great ceremonies of the Masai are no longer available for the spectator, ceremonies that have lasted for centuries. They would become another casualty of this flickering moment in Africa's long day. Or they might not. Either way, there could still be a spectacle around as wild and colorful in its own separate way. Or there might not.

DEATH OF A GIRAFFE

The giraffe's height is an obvious advantage to the giraffe. It is also an advantage to any other early-morning lion-spotter. If the giraffes are not gazing intently in one direction, the safarist can probably look for his lions elsewhere. Not that a lion will bother a giraffe unless it is hard pressed for food; the giraffe presents quite a problem to a hunter whose usual means of finishing off prey is a stranglehold on the throat. How to manage with a giraffe? By going after a wildebeest or a zebra instead.

But if prey is scarce and he is hungry, the lion may find it necessary to try final conclusions with a giraffe, though the odds are against him. One kick from a dinner-plate-

size hoof, and the lion's killing days are over; an occasional lion has been found decapitated. A pride has a better chance, but even then there are problems. One or two may distract the giraffe from the front while the others close in behind so that one can leap on its back. The hamstrung giraffe cannot try its ploy of running through thick bush to dislodge the attacker; it is completely immobilized once a single leg is out of action. It may try falling on the lion to crush it, and that ton weight is enough, if it can catch its assailant just once. But if it misses, then its time is short. When the tallest animal alive measures its length horizontally, that is largely that. The creature that is a wonder of balance and fluidity, an intricately efficient piece of construction, fails to meet the needs of another of nature's marvels, the African lion.

The carnage attracts a crowd of spectators. While the giraffe is in its death throes, it might be spotted by a vulture circling the sky. As the bird plunges to earth, another

The results of coordination: only several lions together could pull down a giraffe. The male stands guard temporarily while the others rest in the nearby shade.

vulture patrolling nearby will have noticed. Soon a spiraling column of birds marks the spot. Sitting in a circle fifty yards away are hyenas and jackals. They all have a long wait. In between times they try to catch the lion sufficiently off guard to snatch a piece of meat. But the lions object. All through the heat of the day, while most of the lions lie up in a nearby thicket, one stays on guard. Woe to a vulture that tempts a lion too far. By the third day there is often a vulture carcass or two to join the giraffe's.

The lions keep feeding at the flesh even after it is green and moving. Eventually they have had enough. Before they are a score of yards away the hyenas are fighting with the jackals and vultures over the remains. But generally it does not take the vultures long to win by sheer weight of numbers. They flock over the carcass in a sprawling heap of hissing, clawing carrion-chewers, all anxious to get the last bit before a neighbor grabs it. The other scavengers, the marabou storks, straggle around the edges and pick up what oddments they can find. The giraffe disappears under a fighting mob.

A few hours later all that marks the spot are one or two hooves, the skull, and a few splintered bones. The bloodstains have long since disappeared under the dust kicked up by successive gorgers. All is cleared and clean again as the same herd of giraffe passes by, one less, unaware of what has happened.

VULTURES

Most people look at vultures around a carcass and see just vultures. But there are vultures and vultures. These birds are another example of the concentrated diversity of East Africa. Hardly elsewhere can one find all six vulture species that range across parts of the continent. Four or five species—sometimes all six—may show up at one kill. Old-time safari people say the average onlooker sees only about a third of what there is to see and then misses much of what he is looking at. A less-than-casual observer of a crowd of vultures piled on top of a carcass might notice that they are not all the same size or sort. But it would take an unusual observer to speculate on an extraordinary phenomenon: since all those vultures are scavengers, and all are feeding at the same type of carrion, how do they avoid overlapping until competition becomes conflict, and conflict becomes catastrophe—for some? There is no share and share alike among these creatures.

The six species of vultures do not really compete for the same food. They go for different parts of the same carcass: some for the tougher outside parts; some for the softer innards; some for the bits dropped by others. Moreover, these six vultures seem to divide themselves into three classes, two in each. In Africa as a whole, it is rare for one of a particular class to appear where the other is also common. East Africa is extraordinary in that it features not just both vultures of any one class but both vultures of all three classes. The white-backed and the Ruppell's vulture can pull out the fleshy parts from inside a carcass since both have much longer necks, and necks that are bare of feathers that would get covered with gore. They have large gutter-shaped tongues, with rows of long horny "teeth" pointing inward and backward, presumably to help in shoveling lumps of meat down the gullet. They arrive at a carcass roughly together, though they are not likely to be the first on the scene. The front-runner as often as not is the white-headed vulture, followed by the lappet-faced; both of them tear at the tough skin. If the carcass has already been partly devoured by lions or hyenas, their work may not be needed, but if the creature is still fresh (as with an animal that has just died), then these two vultures must perform their task before the others can get at what is more than skin-deep. As the carcass opens up, the hordes descend on it, clawing it apart, crawling into the body cavity, devouring it from inside and out. The heap gradually declines, until eventually the last scrabblers are left, generally the hooded vultures. Possibly the Egyptian vultures also stay on till the end: judging from their function as well as their build (like the hooded vulture, they are distinctly smaller than the rest), one might expect them to wait until they can get at the final scraps. The hooded vulture seems somewhat braver, at any rate when it is hovering around a carcass that the lions have not yet abandoned. Since it is lighter than most of the other vultures, it does not need as great a take-off distance.

There is a follow-on order among the feeders, as has been described, among many other details, by Dr. Hans Kruuk. If the white-backed vulture arrives at an untouched carcass, it may not be able to do much about the mound of food until the white-headed and the lappet-faced vultures open it up. The Ruppell's, the hooded, and the Egyptian vultures have their places too. The patient observer can soon work out this ravenous pecking order. Not that any of them is really a "pecker"; the curved beak of a vulture serves basically for tearing. But the lappet-faced and the white-headed vultures do much continuous tearing; they have a heavy wide skull with a broad bill that is well suited for the job. The white-backed and the Ruppell's have similar equipment but not as powerful. They cannot tear at the hide and the sinewy strips, and are more inclined to rip out the softer sections from inside the carcass. The hooded vulture and the Egyptian vulture do not attack the carcass itself: they act as sweeper-uppers to the sweeper-uppers. Their beaks are curved but do not end in the heavy hook of the other vultures. They do more pecking around for what the large vultures have dropped, feeding less off the carcass than around it. Even these two are

The giraffe carcass disappears under a horde of white-backed vultures and others, with a marabou stork on the edges. The five lions that fed on this giraffe did not seem to get through as much flesh in an hour as this mob of vultures.

distinct: the hooded vulture picks up oddments from the ground, while the Egyptian vulture snatches scraps from the bones after they have been half torn away by the others. Everyone in its place, and a place for everyone. In fact, there is a good deal of order about the whole process, if not much orderliness.

And there are more distinctions yet. The white-headed vulture and even more the lappet-faced possess not only the strongest bills, but the strongest bodies all round. They both use their feet to hold down the carrion while they tear at it and to snatch up prey of their own, such as a bat-eared fox or a gazelle fawn. While the white-backed and the Ruppell's are hardly large enough to do anything but scavenge, the hooded and Egyptian vultures are hardly large enough to get by on scavenging alone; they eat an occasional lizard or rat, and even insects. They are the only vultures that frequently loiter around human habitations.

A survey by Dr. Kruuk suggests that judging by what one sees at kills, almost two-thirds of the Serengeti vultures are white-backed, a quarter are Ruppell's and lappet-faced together, a twelfth or less are hooded vultures, and Egyptian vultures make up less than a hundredth of the total. But that is the situation in the Serengeti, where there is a far lower proportion of predators to prey creatures than there is in Nairobi Park or Ngorongoro Crater. Many of the Serengeti wildebeest just drop down and die each year; or they drown; or they break a leg. This is how the Serengeti vultures get the great bulk of their food, and that is why, despite the smaller amount of carcass scraps left by predators, there is a greater proportion of vultures than one might find elsewhere and vultures, being birds, have a higher metabolic rate than mammals. A recent researcher, David Houston, has found, however, that the situation changes with the seasons, as does the makeup of the total vulture community as well. Ruppell's vultures are perhaps limited by the number of larger vultures that can open up a dead wildebeest, and by their long eight-month

This young hippo, a mere 2,000 pounds, was fed upon by eight lions until they yielded to forty hyenas. The hyenas spent an hour taking what they wanted, then abandoned the remains to around 120 vultures. The vultures needed only half an hour to leave a pile of bones and hide. From start to finish, it all took less than one whole morning.

breeding season, during which they need plenty of food. (In this tight food situation only the more aggressive ones survive, to produce offspring that display a concentrated amount of aggressiveness—as is apparent to anyone watching them fight over a carcass.)

One can speculate about what else might affect the number of vultures in any particular place. Does the proximity of the city of Nairobi make for more hooded vultures in Nairobi Park? In the Serengeti there are no major centers of human population; hence few hooded vultures. But there are pastoralists on several sides of the Serengeti; perhaps they and their herds do not generate as much edible rubbish as people who till the ground. The Ruppell's and Egyptian vultures like to nest in cliffs, and there are few cliffs in the Serengeti Plains; this could equally account for Egyptian vultures in the Ngorongoro Crater with its rocky walls. What about vultures in an elephant area like Tsavo or a hippo area like Murchison Falls? In these places no predators take a constant toll of elephants or hippos. This may mean that vultures must rely more on scavenging off carcasses that have not died violent deaths; or it may mean fewer vultures, since elephants and hippos, while providing a tremendous pile of meat when they die, have a far slower population turnover than, say, wildebeest.

Since vultures cannot see at night, they must wait for the first light of morning before taking off and circling the plains. They make use of thermals, rising currents of hot air. This puts the heavier vultures at a disadvantage, since they cannot operate until the day has warmed up. Lighter vultures have been encountered as high as 10,000 feet. But exactly how a vulture becomes aware of a carcass is not really clear. An animal flat on the ground is not easy to glimpse from the sky; perhaps they spot it in its last throes. More likely, they follow the hunter—and each other. When one vulture sees other vultures descending onto a kill, it follows the crowd: this is why vultures are often seen flying directly onto a kill, even though they have come from behind a hill, which would have obscured the kill but not the other vultures arriving. If one vulture flies to the ground just to rest, it will soon be joined by others, though they probably will not stay. The vultures that are most often seen on low-flying reconnaissance flights, the white-headed and the lappet-faced, are the strongest, the ones most able to reach a carcass first. They are also the ones most ready to hunt their own prey in the form of small creatures scuttling around on the ground.

A tape recording of hyenas cackling brings vultures in flocks. Hyenas, in turn, watch vultures. So do jackals. So even do lions. Different vultures, different carnivores: they fight each other and they support each other. The interlocking dependence of wild beings is rarely so graphically revealed as when the lions are ready to leave their kill to the more "lowly" creatures. It looks like rampant competition and disorder, but things are not all that frantic and frenzied, however fierce they may seem. There is something even for the hindmost, even for the "vile vulture."

MARABOU STORKS

Circling around on the edge of the fray over a carcass may be a few marabou storks. They are much bigger than the largest of the vultures, yet they are not nearly so aggressive. There would be little point in their staking out urgent claims of their own. Since they have no hooked beak or talons, they cannot rip and tear a carcass. Instead, they stick to scraps. This is why marabous are so plentiful around slaughterhouses, and why they frequent villages. Marabous are one of the species least likely to fall on hard times as the human population soars; rather the reverse. Hundreds of them concentrate around the fishing camps of Queen Elizabeth Park. Vultures need meat to live on—meat straight and raw— so while they may share some segments of the ecological spectrum with marabou

Although it is by far the biggest of the bird scavengers, the marabou stork must wait until the vultures let it approach; even then it can only manage bits of carrion that drop on the ground or that can be easily torn from the carcass by that storklike, unvulturine beak.

storks, they are far from claiming an identical slot. Marabous stalk along the edges of wilderness fires looking for mice and lizards. Such fried prey would have no appeal for vultures but could attract secretary birds, eagles, and kites. Yet none of these birds would show any liking for other oddments that may find their way down a marabou's gullet, such as bits of paper, shreds of clothing, or even metal instruments.

For all their wide-ranging tastes, marabous do not fill their stomachs every day. They spend long periods on the ground or perching in trees, an easygoing life that makes no great demands on their energy, so they have no great need for large and regular meals. A captive marabou can keep going for months on only two pounds of meat a day. If a marabou in the wild, with its greater energy demands, gets through twice as much food, that is still not much for a twenty-pound bird; a pelican can eat a third of its body weight a day.

A fully-grown marabou has little trouble finding food. There are many possibilities. A nestling, however, has to be more selective. Dr. M. P. Kahl has seen how during its early days, especially the first four weeks, the marabou needs nearly a third of its food in the form of vertebrates. Frogs will do; so will tadpoles or mice, or even termites. If it doesn't get this diet it begins to throw up the rest of its food. It must have this bony material, or its own bones will not form and when it starts exercising its wings they will fracture against branches. That may be why the parents breed during the dry season, when water vertebrates are concentrated in small pools. They also choose sites near fresh water, because they have to bring moisture to their young ones, a pint at a time, during the four months in the nest. This water-carrying is unusual among birds. Perhaps marabou chicks need more because of their habit of relieving themselves down their legs to cool off when they get hot. This may seem a disreputable practice, but it is not unlike a man's sweating (birds have no sweat glands). Any large bird in Africa faces an overheating problem. For a bird in temperate areas the problem is the other way round: it spends its time trying to keep warm, and it can always burn fuel, body fat, to generate heat.

A bird in the tropics cannot use metabolic mechanisms to cool down, though it can stand in water, which is what a marabou stork often does—and not on one leg, either; that is a device for staying warm. Some African birds have no feathers on parts of their bodies not used for flying, such as the head, the neck, or the legs, which means they can dissipate heat better. An ostrich has long bare legs; but it cannot fly anyway. Some vultures have long scrawny bare necks, possibly so that they can feed off foul carrion without getting caked with gore. But one rarely sees a vulture so very dirty. And not all vultures are clad, or unclad, in this manner: it could be an adaptation to allow them to reach down into a putrefying carcass, or it could be an adaptation allowing their naked necks to keep cool. Which came first, the large vulture and the large appetite or the long bare neck? Some tropical birds get around the heat problem by panting, as dogs do. A marabou may derive relief from the sac hanging down below its neck: when the sac inflates, it provides a larger surface area for dissipating heat. To each its own device.

Both marabou parents share in bringing up the young, as well as in the preparations that go before. For the nest they choose a flat-crowned tree about thirty feet high, often a spreading acacia or a mvule. If there is no tree, a cliff ledge will do. During mating the male expands his throat sac into a long brilliant-colored appendage as a sexual attraction. He indulges in enough bill-clattering to intimidate any but a bold opponent. He even attacks his mate-to-be. She meets his advances with submissive gestures, pointing her bill downward. After a few days he responds by moving his bill up and down vigorously. She reciprocates in like manner. Away he goes to fetch a stick for the nest. On his return, another up-and-down exchange; more sticks. In this way the male finds himself fetching most of the nest material. A week's work produces a pile three feet across with a slight hollow in the middle. The female lays from two to five eggs, according to food supplies; whereupon she takes over most of the work of finishing the nest. Both parents share in the incubating. After a month the chick struggles out—a day-long task—to present its sparsely feathered self to blazing sun or beating rain. The parents do what they can to protect the nestling by spreading their wings over it. At two months the chick is full grown, but it cannot fly for another two months. Eventually it is ready for life in the marabou world. If it can learn how to find food for itself, it will get along, since a bird with such wide-ranging tastes is not likely to starve and since few creatures prey on a marabou. But only a quarter of the eggs result in full-grown storks. Some fail to hatch; some fledglings meet accidents. Only a few of the marabou throngs take to breeding each year; sometimes only a fifth; sometimes half that. This suggests that behind the glassy stare of a marabou may be the wisdom and experience of a good twenty years.

LIONS AND OTHER PREDATORS

The early-morning watcher may speculate about the effect lions have on the animals they prey on. For the particular victim on a particular occasion the outcome is clear enough. But what about the others? What effects do lions have on overall numbers? And is the effect the same throughout the year? This is what counts—the total comings and goings over an entire period.

The first reaction of the onlooker may be to shudder and think of all those poor antelopes doomed to die. But with greater understanding of the workings of the wildlife world in its entirety, it is becoming clear that more is involved than a lion here and an antelope there—and aren't they both fine in their separate ways, as long as they stay separate? Violence is only a very small part of the daily routine, but a vital part—for hunter and hunted alike. While the lions cause acute ill health for the occasional individual, they cause better health for the many by removing the diseased and incapable, or by removing a few of the excess. They may affect more than just unfortunate species like the wildebeest or whatever animal is the most frequent item in their diet; they may have an effect even on creatures that they do not normally bother with, such as guinea fowl. If the lions turn from wildebeest for a period, as they often must during a migration season, they may concentrate instead on gazelles or reedbuck, the favorite food of leopards. The leopard, in turn, will direct more of its attention to creatures it would not usually consider when larger prey is plentiful: guinea fowl, for example. While the wildebeest are away, the guinea fowl fall on harder times.

If the many different creatures—plants as well as animals—constantly make for greater variety and interest, it is only thus as long as the whole system is not disrupted by a creature that is able to take the environment by the throat and bend it to his will. The system's diversity is also its strength, especially in an African ecosystem, which is more complex than most. The greater the number of permutations and combinations, the more potential there is for flexing with a blow when it comes. The system shifts an emphasis here or a pressure there; among the myriad at work, life continues. In a world of such inordinate variety, it is a pity to take the wild creatures one at a time and look at each in isolation. It is also wrong. The wildlife-watcher who wants to focus on a single specimen is akin to the man who can't look at a butterfly without wanting to stick it on a pin. He thinks he can examine it better that way, that he can at last find out what makes it a butterfly. He does not want to be cluttered up with considerations of the environment: he wants a straightforward approach—he may even call it a scientific one—while avoiding a butterfly technique of flitting from one aspect to another for whatever information he can derive from a dozen points.

The wildlife-watcher on safari may object that he can't watch too many things at once. He can't; but he can give them space within the horizons of his imagination, if not his intellect. He also can't learn about more than a few things at once, but he can watch and wonder. He can be aware of how much there is to know even if he doesn't know much of it yet; and by knowing that, he knows a great deal. He can't really say he knows much about an elephant until he knows where it lives and how. For an elephant, that means how much it lives with others: the rhino and the gerenuk, which are both browsers too; the zebra and the wildebeest, which are not browsers but benefit from the grasslands that the elephant opens up with its vigorous eating habits; and those animals that benefit from the zebras and wildebeest by being there and being fat. When you look at a wild animal, you are not looking at a single creature, you are looking at a wild world and a single member within it. No creature lives alone; none deserves an exclusive position in the community; none enjoys splendid isolation. They live only by living together.

Lions are sociable creatures and often like to do things together, which allows them to survive better, since a lion on its own has a much harder time—despite all those muscles. In the Serengeti a single lion has only about three chances in ten of catching a gazelle, whereas two or more lions have a better than even chance. Yet this tendency to cooperate is only partly developed: a lioness on the hunt (and the lioness does most of the hunting) generally hunts alone.

Top: The lioness drags the two-day-old buffalo remains to a shady spot where she will be less harassed by hyenas or vultures. Her distended belly shows that there must be at least forty pounds of meat inside her, which is not unusual when a group of lions feed off a large carcass, the competition inducing each one to eat more than if it were feeding alone.

Bottom: The lioness on the right killed the wildebeest and shared it with the lioness showing a canine tooth projecting from her outer jaw (she had had her lower jaw smashed by a fleeing zebra). Although lions often strain the prey's intestines for special nutrients, this lioness can no longer tear off lumps of meat, so she has to content herself with the softer parts. She survives well enough, however, having brought up two litters of cubs since her injury, and getting much of her food through scavenging from hyenas. The lion on the left arrived when the wildebeest was already partly eaten; nevertheless he seized the prey's throat and hung on for five minutes with a strangle-grip before starting to feed.

So what is a lion? It is a lion-that-lives-with-lots-of-other-creatures. Since its hunting is only a part of being a lion—they do not kill every day—do lions by the dozens have much effect? Since there are not too many lions—there are only twenty-five full-grown lions or so in Nairobi Park and 4,000 creatures for them to prey on—does so small a number have all that much influence? This is something the researchers do not know much about, and there is a great need to know much more about it. It would require too many trackers to trail even twenty-five lions and record all they do. Moreover, a lion is more active at night, when a tracker would soon lose touch with it. Various mechanical methods have been tried, such as attaching a radio device to the lion by a collar around its neck and getting transmissions during the hours of darkness. But not much is gained this way, only what one lion does at one period; little good for saying what many lions do most of the time.

What is clear is that lions do not march about ceaselessly seeking what they may destroy. And however many animals they manage to destroy, the number is not likely to be harmful to the prey community altogether. There used to be a theory that lions were merely destructive and that it would help the wild world at large to shoot them wherever they were found. This approach, which was tried in Kruger Park in South Africa for many years, was supposed to protect the antelope and the zebra and whatever else could not look after itself. These poor, defenseless creatures promptly multiplied until they began to ruin their habitat; now it is the antelope and the zebra that must be shot in Kruger Park. Of course, there are all manner of other factors involved besides predators and prey. The park has been fenced on several sides to keep the wild creatures from getting out where they would "contaminate" the domestic stock. Cutting off migration routes deprives the grazing grounds of their seasonal rest. At the same time, more animals flock in from outside to escape the harassment beyond the borders. Creating a sanctuary has also eliminated a predator that may have acted for long periods as a limiting factor to match all other predators put together: human hunters were at work while the animals were adapting themselves to their environment. Regrettably, human predation is now either prohibited altogether or inflated through commercial poaching. Whatever the factors, the plant-eaters in Kruger have recently been outstripping the eaters of plant-eaters. Man has set up the trouble inside the park and outside it; now he must settle it.

In a "normal" environment, such as will hardly be seen again in Africa in its full pristine form, it is necessary to find out how many lions are eating how many animals of what species. Lions eat only rarely, but when they do, they eat enormously. A lion has been seen to eat over seventy pounds at a single session, though fifty would be nearer average. These periodic orgies are a result of the lion's position in the food chain. Food is initially produced in the environment when plants synthesize energy from the sun in combination with nutrients from the ground and the air. Plants are then eaten by antelopes and other herbivores, which absorb their share of the sun's energy. They concentrate the energy in a more compact form in the tissue of their bodies, with a loss in bulk and energy on the way that may amount to 90 percent. If this tissue then finds its way into the lion's tissue, there is again a loss that may amount to 90 percent. Thus the lion is receiving its food in a highly concentrated form, which is why the lion needs to eat for only a few hours every few days, while the antelope must eat for many hours of every day.

The lion, along with the other carnivores, thus stands at the top of a food pyramid. It does not occupy a dominating position by virtue of its elevated role; it is only a single stage in the energy-transfer system, even if a singularly imposing stage. One might say it is near the end of the chain as at the top of the pile. It is no more in control of the system than is the antelope. Plants, antelopes, lions, all assist in exploiting Africa's number-one

A full-grown zebra weighs a good hundred pounds more than a full-grown lioness, which makes it a difficult prey at best. But the two have evolved together, which leaves them both occupying a slot in the predator-prey spectrum where the lioness finds she both can and can't . . . and where the zebra tries to keep one step ahead, both as an individual and as a species.

The lions that the wildebeest have to fear are those they cannot see. This herd watched the lions go into ambush by the water hole—then two hours later visited the same water hole and lost one of their number there even though there were other watering spots they could have used.

resource: sunlight. All the environment supports all the environment. It is hard to say when a piece of grass ceases to be part of one environment and becomes part of a zebra—when it is in its mouth, or in its gut, or in its tissue? And when does the zebra cease being part of one environment and become part of a lion? And how long is that package of energy held inside the lion before it is passed on through droppings or ticks, or is dissipated through the lion's exertions as it runs after another zebra? Perhaps not until the lion's carcass becomes nutriment for hyenas and vultures and ants. How long before it all comes around to being a piece of grass again?

Lions are remarkably unfussy in their tastes; zebras and most antelopes of medium or large size will do; so will warthogs, ostriches, baboons, antbears, jackals, and up to thirty items or more. In Albert Park in Zaire certain prides are reputed to live off full-grown hippos as much as any other creature in areas where the smaller prey is scarce. Anything is fair game for a lion, though a porcupine can hold off a lion for an hour or more, and a ratel can drive young lions off their kill. A tortoise is as much of a problem to

a lion as a prey. During their 175,000,000 years of development, tortoises have had plenty of time to refine their external defenses, about 170,000,000 years longer than lions have had to develop counterweapons. Lions will even feed on locusts in desperate times, and they are not averse to another lion that has been killed in a fight, provided the African sun has made it smell a bit less like a lion.

Some people suggest that a predator will go for creatures roughly its own size. A 400-pound lion seems to prefer zebras and antelopes, which are about the same weight or slightly more. So does a lioness at a hundred pounds lighter, though she can have trouble: a wildebeest bull may still be fighting back ten minutes after it has been seized by the lioness, whereas it would be overwhelmed by the greater weight and power of a lion. Occasionally a lioness dies from wildebeest wounds. In Kruger Park the lions make plain how loath they are to pick on creatures much less than their own size. By far the most plentiful prey, outnumbering all the other prey animals put together, is the impala. Yet, according to Dr. Van Pienaar's findings, lions go after impala on only one out of every five hunts (though smaller animals like impala or gazelles tend to be "underrepresented" in findings because they are consumed much more quickly, before an observer has time to spot them).

The equal-weight rule is useful as long as it is followed no more slavishly by the ecologist than by the wild animals themselves. Several lions together can tackle creatures far beyond their own size, such as giraffes or buffalo. On the other hand, when the larger creatures have moved out of a hunting area, there may be nothing better available for lions than small creatures such as warthogs. In Lake Manyara Park, east of the Serengeti, there is little choice. The wildebeest and zebras have almost come to an end, more because their grasslands have been flooded and their migration routes sealed off than because the lions have given them undue attention. The lions now have to live primarily off buffalo. Not many lions elsewhere make a regular practice of taking buffalo, since a buffalo is quite a pawful and more. A buffalo has been known to hold off a lion and a lioness until all three were dead. In the western Serengeti there are lions that prey fairly regularly on buffalo, hardly more than to be expected when there are 40,000 buffalo to work on. But when a lion pride manages to seize a buffalo, the rest of the herd may take off to the other end of the herd range, a dozen miles or more away and well beyond the pride's hunting territory. Buffalo meals have suddenly vanished beyond reach.

Lion and cub drink together: these two enjoyed an agreeable relationship, unlike the occasions when a cub is brought to a sudden end by a male of the pride: much depends on how "crowded" things are. Eventually this cub grew up, along with two brothers; they then turned on the aged male and drove him from the area, leaving him virtually unable to establish another territory with enough prey in it.

The overall outcome is similarly affected by the lie of the land. In Nairobi Park four out of five antelopes prefer the red lateritic areas to the "black cotton soil" areas, possibly because the red soils are more fertile and possibly because they do not get so sticky in the wet season as the glutinous black areas. Lions that have to include black soil areas in their hunting territories may be harder put to find food than others; hence, they cannot be so choosy. In either area, the grass is longer at certain seasons. In the Serengeti, Dr. George Schaller has found that a lion in long grass can catch a gazelle in one attempt out of three, but in short grass only half as often, or less. This is a factor to be borne in mind when grass-burning is carried out in the park; enough cover must be left for the lions. On the other hand, if grass-burning is stopped altogether, as has been done in various parks, the grass may get so rank that many of the grass-eaters migrate away for seasons on end. Or the rains that bring on the long grass (and better hunting cover for lions) create good grazing for the antelopes farther afield, allowing them to disperse more than usual; the lions now find hunting more difficult again. Conversely, a short-grass season is not invariably bad news for the lions, despite the lack of cover. Prey animals are then obliged to congregate around the water courses, not only for the water itself but for the last patches of vegetation. What is a fat season for one creature is a lean one for another.

If there is a whole network of circumstances that go to decide which prey species shall bear the brunt of the lions' activities at any one period, the lions nevertheless display distinct preferences for certain creatures. In Kruger Park, waterbuck prove a favorite above zebra and wildebeest and several others, despite the fact that they amount to less than one in fifty of the prey animals available. In proportion to their numbers, they are favored twice as much as any other, except for kudus (which are still a good way behind). Waterbuck are vulnerable because of their habit of sticking to the same small areas, especially along riverbanks with their ambush sites. Nevertheless, the waterbuck in Kruger Park are managing to hold their totals, and even to increase them.

In Nairobi Park there has been a decline—set off by a drought—among the wildebeest, which used to account for three-quarters of the lions' diet. Now lions are going after Grant's gazelles for the first time in years, and warthogs are coming under greater pressure, while eland are being taken nearly ten times as often as a few years ago. Yet, remarkably enough, hartebeest, which are not the most prevalent creatures in the park— they are half as numerous as the zebras, wildebeest and eland combined—sometimes rank only third on the lions' list. Only six of the thousand-odd cattle and sheep that used to live in the park were taken in eighteen years. Stock-raiding lions are a thousand times less frequent in East Africa than stock-raiding people. The same goes for leopards, whatever the furriers may say. And if lions hardly ever take cattle, there is one creature they kill even less: man. A person taken by a lion gets his name in the papers even if he does not appreciate the headline. There are many times more people who meet their ends in all manner of more sordid ways than by the distinction of a tangle with a wild lion.

How many animals a lion kills a year is a question to exercise the finest experts. At one stage the estimate centered on thirty or thirty-five. A full-grown lion in a zoo gets through seven to ten pounds of meat a day. A lion in the wild is more active and needs more food. At fifteen pounds a day, it would be getting through 5,500 pounds a year, the equivalent of rather less than twenty zebras or rather more than twenty wildebeest (a wildebeest weighs a hundred pounds less than a zebra). Lions often kill nearly twice as much in bulk as they eat; since much of the carcass is hide or guts or skeleton, a large surplus is left for the scavengers. Some experts think a predator kills a pound or more a day for each ten pounds of its own weight. This would amount to thirty-five pounds for a lioness (the female does much of the hunting), or around 13,000 pounds a year: the equivalent of rather more than twenty zebras or rather less than thirty wildebeest. Again, you can approach the problem from the opposite direction: if you know that there are around 1,200 lions in Kruger Park and that around 1,000 lion kills a year are found by patrols, and you know from other records that the rangers spot about one kill in twenty, then each lion is making well under twenty kills a year. There is a great difference between under twenty and nearly thirty; at least, the wildebeest and zebras would think so.

You can't work out the proper effects of the lions' activities without knowing how they combine with the other predators'; and it is equally hard to tell how much other hunters eat in a year. Using the basis of a pound of meat killed a day (not all eaten) for every ten pounds of predator, a leopard accounts for about 5,500 pounds a year, or thirty-five small-sized antelopes such as gazelles or impala; probably the total number of prey animals is greater considering the smaller-sized creatures a leopard takes, down to rodents and birds. But a survey in Kruger suggests that at only twenty-five animals a year the total number of kill sightings would amount to a mere one in fifty. Leopard kills are easy to see up in trees. Moreover, they stay there for several days while the leopard returns time after time to the same carcass: it does not mind how putrid the flesh becomes, nor does it have to share its feast with a group of other leopards that would finish off the whole carcass at once. If it is fair to expect that a larger proportion of kills would be found, then perhaps leopard kills number somewhat under twenty. A cheetah weighing about 100 pounds would need 3,500 pounds a year, or roughly twenty-three of the same impala-sized creatures. They eat only once from a carcass, so they waste much more than a leopard does. Wild dogs at forty pounds would need four pounds per day, or almost thirty Thomson's gazelles a year. But there is a more reliable starting point for wild dogs. After witnessing fifty kills in Ngorongoro Crater, Dr. Richard Estes and Dr. John Goddard reckoned that six pounds are available to each dog each day. This works out at around fifty Thomson's gazelles a year per dog, though packs tend to kill twice a day whether there are fewer than a dozen members or more than twenty.

From these approximations you can assess how many prey animals are disappearing in an area during the course of a year. And from that you can estimate what proportion is entailed if the park is to continue as well stocked with antelopes as with antelope-eaters. Allowing for variation among the experts, the 2,000 lions in the Serengeti are disposing of between forty and seventy thousand animals a year. This is not many out of 500,000 zebras and wildebeest (by early 1970 they totaled almost 1,000,000, but this may be a passing phase). Nor does it count the 500,000 or more gazelles, and the 100,000 other creatures, such as buffalo, elands, and giraffes, that are available to lions. Furthermore, the 3,000 hyenas in the Serengeti are disposing of a fair number of prey animals, too, perhaps around 25,000 full-grown creatures. If all the predators put together are accounting for anywhere near one in twenty in a "standard" year, it would be unusual. According to Dr. Schaller and Dr. Kruuk, they are probably managing around only one in thirty at present. The gain to offset the decrease from all causes can rise to as much as a quarter in good years and a good way beyond that in exceptional years. Moreover, at least a quarter of the lions' total food in the Serengeti seems to be scavenged off hyenas, leopards, cheetah, whatever hunter is handy. Wildebeest and zebras amount to three-quarters of the lions' total diet in the Serengeti. Zebras do not figure in as many kills as Thomson's gazelles, but since a zebra weighs five times as much as a gazelle, the zebras are supplying far more food than the gazelles.

Yet again the pattern varies from one time of year to another. When the great wildebeest and zebra herds are out on the open plains they make up almost the entire diet of the lions there. But when they move back into the woodlands they become part of the menu of a different set of lions, along with buffalo, topi, giraffe, and others. This makes for a fluctuating "predation pressure." Sometimes there are plenty of smaller creatures; sometimes there are only a few of the larger ones; either can suffice. In this sense it can be less than accurate to follow a lion and count how many kills it makes in a single month, then multiply by twelve. When there is plenty of prey the lions may account for half again as many kills as in bad times. The lion with the giraffe kill described earlier shared his carcass with two other males for only a couple of days; whereupon they left a huge pile of meat for the vultures. Another group of lions, eleven this time, stayed with a giraffe for over a week. In general lions kill only what they need and can get conveniently. Four hundred lions in the central area of Kruger Park, where there is a huge number of prey animals, are killing almost twice as many as the 500 lions in the sparsely populated area to the north. These "density-dependent" trends set off considerable shifts in predation patterns between particular places and particular seasons. The only generalization possible is that you cannot really generalize until far more is known, and then you may find you can generalize even less!

The density of animals refers not only to the creatures the lions prey on but to the lions themselves. If there are few prey, there will be few lions. If there are many prey, there may not be all that many more lions to match them. If predators do not control the prey, the prey do not always control the predators. The last fifteen years in Kruger Park have seen the prey animals increase twice over, but the lions have remained at about 1,200: if they have increased at all, it is because the park staff has stopped shooting them rather than because there has been more food to feed more lions. The Serengeti herds have apparently doubled more than once in the 1960s, but again the lion numbers have probably not changed much. Yet these two localities maintain their steady numbers for radically different reasons. Many of the Serengeti lions are limited by the amount of food available during the annual "famine" when the plains herds migrate out of one area into another. Dr. U. de V. Pienaar believes the lions in Kruger Park regulate themselves by their own social mechanisms rather than by having migrating wildebeest do it for them. Not that these factors are mutually exclusive; there is more than an element of each in both areas. Dr. Schaller believes that lions, like tigers, are probably subject to social pressure that keeps them around an "optimum" level. As soon as the prides build up to sizes that are too big for the good of the community, there is less tolerance between one pride and another. Furthermore, the lions within the prides grow hostile toward each other. Whatever the tendencies for lions to display threats toward each other rather than violence, their living space can stand only so much pressure, whether from within or without, before the males begin to regulate their numbers in the way that lions are so capable of. In Kruger Park there are only half as many males as females, which tells its story. Lions need *lebensraum*, just as much as any other species requires this indefinite quality of living space; but lions need it more than most. A creature of a lion's stature resents being crowded, long before it runs short of elbowroom. This is when it turns on its own cubs as well as on other members of the pride. Fewer cubs survive; fewer are born. When lions in Kruger Park were shot, those remaining began to produce larger litters. Eventually the prides built up to groups of twenty or even thirty. Then the population adjusted itself again. Instead of the former five or six cubs, there were only a couple born at a time; things simmered down. A lion population moves up and down in accordance with its own pushings and shovings, somewhat in the manner of other wildlife populations—but predators do not fluctuate in the Yo-Yo fashion of the prey species, even when man and his instant whims are the prevailing factor. It says something for the resilience of wild creatures that they have often been able to readjust themselves to whatever shock the environment produces.

Not that any of these factors is rigid. If the total number of lions depends on the size of territory available, together with the number of lion territories that can be spread across the landscape, the concept of "territory" is a dynamic affair that varies from time to time and place to place. There is more give and take when there are more prey animals about. Territories can even overlap. A lion does not stride up and down his borders warning off strangers. If all is well within the main bounds, he may not go near the edges for weeks on end. The territory consists of a heartland where things are sacrosanct, though whether what is being guarded is a hunting terrain or a place to protect the pride's offspring is not certain—while round about there is a hazy area where nobody minds too much who goes hunting until prey becomes scarce.

If an average pride of a male and two or three females with five or six juveniles accounts for nearly 200 prey a year, then these creatures could be supported on about only two square miles of Nairobi Park, or less than one square mile of Ngorongoro Crater. Yet lion territories usually cover twenty square miles, and often much more: one in the central Serengeti extends to ninety square miles, and two others to 150 square miles (though they overlap a good deal). In Lake Manyara Park, on the other hand, where the vegetation allows a high number of very large animals—buffalo—to concentrate in a small area, a territory may be as small as ten square miles. Kruger Park totals 1,200 lions for its 7,000 square miles, which means that an average pride occupies nearly fifty square miles. All in all, the Serengeti ecological unit totals over 2,000 lions in its 12,000 square miles, with a highly migratory prey community; Lake Manyara features one lion to every square mile, but with no migration; Ngorongoro Crater, one to a square mile and a half, with not much migration; central Tarangire, up to two lions a square mile, with immense dry-season concentrations. Looking at it another way, there is one lion to almost 300 prey animals in Tarangire at the height of the dry season; one to 1,000 or more (at present) in the Serengeti; one to 300 in Ngorongoro; one to over 150 in Nairobi Park or Kruger Park; and one to only 80 in Lake Manyara Park (where a good half of the prey animals are heavyweight buffalo). Tsavo Park is undergoing an ostensible "population explosion" of grassland animals to compensate for the bush destroyed by elephants. It is a pity that nobody is estimating how many lions occupy the landscape and whether they are increasing. It could be the first time such a fundamental change has occurred on such a scale at such a tremendous rate. There is no staff to take a long look at lions, even though this could be a phenomenon without parallel in Africa.

If ever the lions need to be saved wherever they still hold out in Africa (it is already too late in the far north and the extreme south), rescue operations would have to go beyond the lions themselves. Bringing up orphans is far from the whole story. There are no lions without antelopes. There are no antelopes without vegetation. There is no vegetation without rain and soil and sunshine, and occasionally fire. Enter man, bearing a torch.

NGORONGORO CRATER

Visitors don't begin their full-day trip down into Ngorongoro Crater until partway into the morning. By the time they are climbing into their safari vehicles the visitors in central Serengeti are looking at their second lot of lions. It is plain to the dawn-riser why he cannot set off until the world is showing a better face: 8,000 feet up on the crater rim he can't tell whether it is half an hour after sunrise or two hours, because often the sun scarcely penetrates the mist. The Crater itself is a great pit with sullen clouds billowing out of it. Only when a momentary gap appears in the shroud do you glimpse a different world down below, a sunlit land, Africa smiling. You see it only for a moment, then the mist closes in again, the clouds swirl over the bright, light world, and you are left in a dank, shivering place up above, as if you have been looking down into a Garden of Eden from Limbo.

When you eventually take off into the world down below, you bounce along a track that plunges through a gap in the Crater rim. Half an hour later you have arrived. You set off across the floor and you know you are in a crater, with a tall blue wall running around a flat plain. Ngorongoro is twelve miles across, the biggest crater of its kind in the world, unflooded and unbroken. Actually it is not a true crater; it has collapsed to form a caldera, but it is still the biggest. It is the most perfectly shaped, too: a continuous curve all the way round. It is a world on its own.

This busload had not actually driven over to harry the lioness; she had approached the vehicle to use it as cover while stalking a group of zebras. Soon there will be more tourists at Ngorongoro, within five years possibly double the present 60,000 annually, all crowding inside the 100-square-mile Crater. They will mostly be looking for more lions to photograph, instead of the "hideous" hyenas that are Ngorongoro's forte.

It has been a world on its own for a long time. Masai have probably lived in it only for a little over a hundred years, which is nothing compared with the traces in the Crater wall suggesting that man's ancestors were here as far back as the man-ape beings of Olduvai. The final configuration the visitor sees at Ngorongoro is not old as Africa goes. The material making up the basement layers here, appearing on the surface in various places, are as ancient as anything on the face of the planet; they were formed in days when this part of the world was a sea, beneath which there were great temperatures and great pressures giving birth to the rocks that can be seen on the Crater wall; they were brought to the surface when the seabed surged and swelled, forcing the land to protrude again.

All this was long before the dawning of Africa's long day: some say three times as far back, some say three times as much again. Eventually the eruptions subsided enough for the forces of erosion to set in. Over long ages the land was worn down, occasionally blasted by primeval forces more immediate than weathering, until eventually some of the bumps and ridges were flattened away and the surface became soil-like enough to support the first plant life. For the most part the region was formed by the same winds and rains that fashioned its face today, only occasionally more violent than in the present tranquil times. As the dawn of the African day came and went, there appeared plains stretching from one Serengeti skyline to another, but the great Ngorongoro massif had not yet reared out of the ground. About two hours ago in the long African day the earth fractured right along the length of the region, creating a fault like those that helped to shape the Rift Valley; much of the land subsided. These movements were countered about 5,000,000 years back (less than two minutes ago) when a final upheaval sent the land surging up again, together with a series of volcanoes erupting into these recent skies. The largest, Ngorongoro, stood for a while twice as high as it does now; slowly it settled down, forcing the lava beneath the core into the earth's interior and then falling in on itself. The final caldera of Ngorongoro had arrived—a mere half-minute ago.

The Crater could swallow a city the size of Detroit. In this enclosed space the visitor finds life in many forms—at least thirty of the better-known animals and as many again of the less common—many more than he would find in a confined corner of the Serengeti. Some of the common ones are to be found in uncommon numbers, despite the handkerchief-sized terrain. There are 15,000 wildebeest, 5,000 zebras, perhaps another 5,000 gazelles, around 70 lions, over 400 hyenas, and nearly 100 rhinos. Even in East Africa

Egrets and sacred ibises share Ngorongoro with flamingos, storks, waders, 200 different sorts in all, of which 100 are different from those at Lake Manyara thirty miles away (and Lake Manyara features another 100 that do not appear in the Crater).

there is little to equal this concentration of animals. They flock to the streams and marshes that are fed from the surrounding highlands, swamps that provide vegetation even at the height of the dry season.

A few Masai *bomas* are allowed in the Crater, with their 1,500 cattle. These communities are only a small part of the 10,000 people living in the whole area, together with their 250,000 livestock—this in a total area of 3,500 square miles. The Crater is only 100 square miles. The Masai tribesmen wander back and forth. In hard times more of them move into the Crater for the same reason that allows the wild animals to flourish—the lush swamps when all around is dry and barren. Until the late 1950s Ngorongoro was part of the Serengeti Park. The original Serengeti was set up in a rather haphazard fashion; everybody knew the great herds migrated, but nobody was sure where they migrated to. As soon as it was found they grazed across a large northern section, an extension was arranged and the Ngorongoro part to the east was lopped off. The Masai took back what they said was theirs anyway. It is a pity they were sitting on top of one of the world's marvels; still, the protection of wild country is the art of the possible. The Masai might be persuaded to look after their area better if they were invited to take part in a radical new conservation scheme. Out of the surgery of the Serengeti came the Ngorongoro Conservation Unit, the first of its kind in East Africa.

This unique undertaking aimed at bringing the natural features of the region under one authority that would coordinate the diverse forms of land-use into a single integrated entity. The Crater itself would form but a small part of the entire region; other areas would be given over to forestry, pastoralism, or cultivation; some would combine more than one use. It was to be a multiple approach to conservation, a change from the day-and-night boundaries of the usual park system, where the animals have precedence on one side and man has precedence on the other, and never the twain shall meet (in theory anyway; the practical business of keeping the two apart is not so simple, since migrating animals, like poachers and fire, do not recognize lines on a map in a park warden's office). Ngorongoro was trying to produce a plan that would mean something to everybody, a scheme where man's activities and those of the wild creatures would reflect coordination rather than conflict. To the old-time conservationists who liked their sanctuaries in neat

Right: The Lerai Forest of Ngorongoro Crater harbors an extraordinary total of twenty elephants and thirty rhinos within one square mile —far too much for its well-being, subject as it is to periodic drowning by the lake as well as ravaging by the Masai. The forest is an important feature of the Crater floor, as is the water table. The problem is how to save it, when it is already past its prime, "even-aged," with many old trees and little regeneration by younger growths. If most of the elephants and rhinos, which are both partial to sapling trees, were forcibly removed, there could be a forest by the year 2000—and the animals would recover in the meantime. Left as it is, there may soon be no more Lerai— and the elephants and rhinos will disappear with it. The problem here, as so often in East Africa, is how to keep the animals out of a favored spot —rather than bring them in, which would have been the intention if the forest had received the Treetops treatment, which was prevented only by the intervention of President Nyerere of Tanzania.

Left: Of the 26,000 grazers in Ngorongoro Crater, only 1,500 are cattle. But because domestic stock have been taught for centuries to stick together in tight formations (in contrast to the antelopes in the background), they can cause more damage to the habitat through their daily trekking than all the rest put together.

packets, it was all a revolutionary concept, but it was not so extraordinary to local people who had lived side by side with wildlife for ages. They had long combined various forms of land-use; what they looked upon as revolutionary if not regrettable was the idea of parks in segregated segments.

The Ngorongoro Masai accepted the proposals for the region because the region's proposals accepted them. It is unlikely they make much difference to the wild creatures, though their grazing areas effectively cut a slice out of the Crater that could feature more animals if they were zebras and wildebeest and gazelles instead of cows and sheep and goats. What is important is that the plan takes into account what is happening elsewhere in the surrounding country. If the Crater were a park, its boundaries would run along the rim, and then there would be little to stop the local cultivators from bringing their digging hoes right up to the edge, with regrettable consequences for the wildebeest and rhinos that migrate out of the Crater from time to time. More than that, the Crater is as vulnerable a wildlife area as any in East Africa because of its water table. The marshes are fed by catchment areas in the highland country (dozens of miles beyond the Crater) that must be protected, particularly the rain-attracting and rain-storing forests that cover one-tenth of the environs, if the Crater itself is not to head for trouble.

Meanwhile the whole populace of the region, Masai stockmen and cultivators alike, are benefiting from some of the $170,000 a year that the Crater is earning in fees alone for the rest of the community, to go with the $15,000 derived from forestry, marketing of stock, and other activities. If the Crater were to join the nation's park system, the revenue would go off to the national treasure chest hundreds of miles away, and the park would be as concerned with the people living right up against it as if they were living in another world. A little way farther over, Serengeti Park is trying to exist as an island in a sea of other activities, many of them potentially alien. Yet that in a sense has been the intention of the park: to be sealed off from the rest of the world, a haven against hostile

forces swirling about it. It declares its opposition to the ethos beyond, even if it must run counter to the main tide of things. The world is said to be against wildlife; therefore wildlife had better be against the world—and it had better build its barrier high.

Hence the crucial importance of the Ngorongoro experiment. Hitherto there has been a period of fair stability under a scheme where nobody treads on anybody else's toes because everybody is marching in the same direction. But it has been threatened, despite the efforts of Masai leaders like Solomon Ole Saibull, who took charge of the scheme when it was through its gestation period. The plan, as proposed by the Canadian advisor, Dr. H. J. Dirschl, went off to higher authority elsewhere for approval, to lie in an in-box for years on end. Other people have ideas about Ngorongoro, including civil servants in Dar es Salaam several horizons away, people who look askance at the newfangled ideas of Ngorongoro. A multiphased approach to the landscape seems two-faced at best; it does not agree with the ideas of development by compartment. Integration of land-uses runs afoul of single-purpose schemes such as officials prefer to pursue with single-minded intensity: they like streamlined schemes across the African landscape, with miles and miles of ranch fences. If the wildlife people want their animals, all right, they can have them—let them turn the Crater into a park, leaving the rest of the area to be handed over to people who know how to use it.

This in fact is a prospect that some of those parks people have long been waiting for. If they were now to get it, they would get with it something they have scarcely anticipated. The rest of the Conservation Unit would be diverted to "more practical" purposes, notably the huge lump of the Serengeti Plains that lies outside the main park (the 1959 adjustment left the park almost as unviable ecologically as it had been before). If the Unit were to be split up, the Serengeti herds migrating across the plains for their wet-season grazing might find fresh troubles in their paths, particularly pastoralist troubles. But according to the oracles of Dar es Salaam, that would be an affair for the parks people: let them sort it out as best they can. After all, when it comes to animals versus people, isn't the choice clear? Not that the oracles tell much about which people and which animals. If the people in your area are not to be compared with the eight times as many people who come to view the scene each year (insofar as they live in the area; they don't just linger there), then one might consider which animals. The wild animals inside the Crater earn over five dollars each; the livestock outside earn less than a dime. And plenty of wild animals in the area have shown their potential for cropping. During the day the visitors watch the wild creatures; then at night they return to the lodge to eat them—a little, a very little, but zebra steak is proving highly popular. Some visitors take home a tin of wildebeest stew for the evening they show their African slides to their friends. An occasional visitor even packs away a zebra skin in his luggage. Cropping 1,000 a year could bring in $60,000 profit, which would rival what is earned from all of the domestic stock in the region. A zebra is eventually worth $150, or almost ten Masai cattle put together.

One wonders what is going to happen to this serene, secluded world. At present it seems more secure than at various stages in the late 1960s. When you are on safari there it seems like an enduring offshoot of the ancient Ark. Possibly this will be another instance of the earth's old order having to be sacrificed to the twentieth century and its "modern" demands; in which case one might wonder whether it would not be better for the twentieth century and its modern methods—the really modern methods—to be allowed to safeguard it from old-fashioned proposals and their still-fashionable methods.

As shown in the map on page 91, Tanzania Masailand contains an array of parks and other wildlife areas. Again, the diversified approach to conservation here includes the idea of protecting your park as something which may not be altogether at harmony with the outside world, even though it is heavily dependent on the outside world for its borderland "breathing space" (for example, Serengeti), and at the same time preventing the environs from becoming a noose around the park by trying to live at terms with the world and its constrictive ways (for example, Ngorongoro). The Ngorongoro Conservation Unit recognizes that its tourist-draw Crater is dependent on the hinterland, notably for water from catchment areas as much as thirty miles away, so it shares the Crater's revenues with the entire area while insuring the Crater derives support from the rest of the regional block: the various activities are intermeshed in cooperation, instead of locked in struggle. Lake Manyara Park is already severely reduced in the seasonal outlets for its herds; its wildebeest probably could not sustain a comeback even if their grazing areas in the park were restored. Tarangire Park acts as a dry-season gathering ground for huge assemblies of animals, 250 to a square mile, which in the wet season depend for reserve grazing on broad dispersal areas that cover several times the size of the park— or they used to: since the time twelve years ago when Dr. Lamprey was noticing how the Tarangire environs were so ravaged by the Masai that they could support as little as one-fortieth as many creatures as similar savannah country in Serengeti (safeguarded from human inhabitation by tsetse and other factors), the situation has grown even worse under the impact of more Masai, more cattle. When Tarangire Park was set up in the 1960s, it employed a framework of operations that worked well in the preservationist days of the 1950s; a more accommodating approach to the world will be required in the 1970s, or the park may find the world's response to Tarangire will be less tolerant in return—and the world isn't likely to go away.

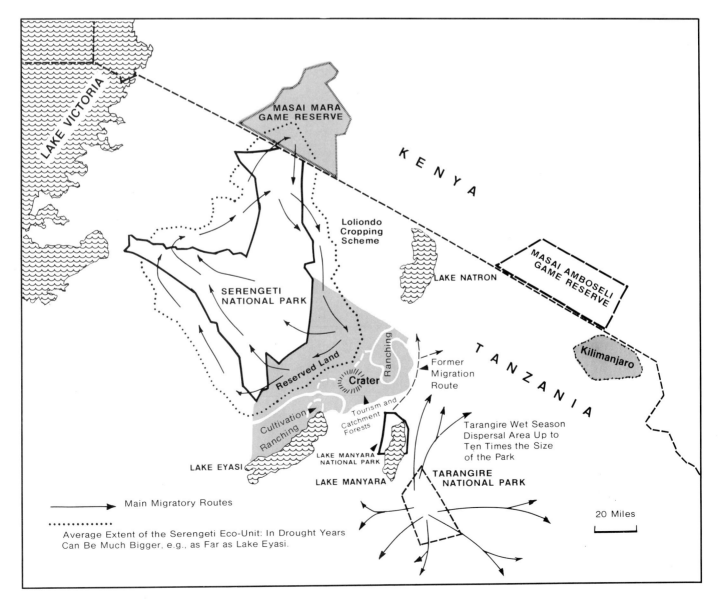

BIRTH OF A ZEBRA

Left: The zebra mother-to-be had already started on her final labor when she was troubled by a passing rhino. But she merely got up and cantered away a few steps, then lay down again.

Left below: After the first few moments of the final process, the front feet appeared, kicking to be free. Three and a half minutes later, the nose appeared, then the whole head.

Middle below: In only seven minutes the birth is complete. The mother lies back exhausted, but the zebra foal is immediately on the move.

Right below: Struggling round toward the business end of its mother, the foal is encouraged by her licking.

The wildlife-watcher on the plains at the right time of year, particularly in January or February, may see something special: the birth of a zebra. He must watch out for a zebra showing signs of discomfort, one that lies down every few moments; she has trouble keeping up with the herd, since she can only manage a few steps at a time. She may not eat, no matter how long she nuzzles the grass. She shows every sign of not being her usual self.

This particular zebra lay down for her final labor during the early morning, a time particularly suitable for a zebra—if, like a wildebeest mother-to-be, she can defer things to the best phase of the twenty-four hours—since it allows most daylight for her and her offspring to recover before nightfall. Only a few moments were needed before the preliminary white sac appeared. A few moments again, and the front feet arrived, soon followed by the head and shoulders. Another couple of heaves and the foal was half born. A pause, a final shove, and there it was: the birth was complete. All in all, it had taken just under seven minutes.

A few seconds in the light of day, and the foal shook its head. It was still entangled in the membrane, but if this was a new life, it wanted to get on with it. The newcomer twisted and wriggled until it got its head clear, then took a look around and sniffed. The world was wet with dew and none too warm. But this was an independent life coming into being; it felt how long it was, it nuzzled its mother, it held up its head and looked out over the grass. At $1\frac{3}{4}$ minutes old it felt alive.

The mother raised herself and smelled at the foal, trying to draw it from the sac with her mouth as she cleaned its fur. At $3\frac{1}{2}$ minutes old, the infant wanted to stand. It tried its forelegs first, but that was no use. Then the back legs, but that was no good either. The forelegs again, and it got one shaky hoof to prop itself up for a moment. Crash: that didn't last long. But there was no stopping it. First one leg, then the other, each was tried in turn; crash, crash, the foal fell a dozen times inside a couple of minutes. Then up on

both back legs at once, and it half-rolled, half-fell a few feet forward. Time for a rest. It had achieved a lot in its first $5\frac{1}{4}$ minutes of life.

By now it was holding its head up all the time. Its mane grew frizzier as the mother dried it out, and the fur became more like the soft woolly pattern of a young zebra, with brown stripes that would stay brown for several months. The foal experimented again, and found what a lot of strength it had gained in its half-minute rest. It struggled; it quavered less. Its falls now were not so frequent; things were getting altogether firmer. It could coordinate two legs, then all of a sudden tried four. A sort of spring, and it could stand.

Six and a quarter minutes old now. Bang, a fall, this time from the full height of its being: it needed a moment or two to get its breath back. Then another struggle, and the foal managed to stay upright, body swaying backward and forward, head weaving around, long spindly legs trying to decide if they were made for standing or not. The view seemed an improvement on the grass-level perspective, because the foal bent its neck this way and that to see in every direction. It wanted to turn around and see what was behind it, but this promptly returned it to the grass-roots view. Another try, and it moved forward; it reversed; it moved forward again; it accelerated; it stopped. It lay down, in careful control this time. It got up again, or rather it leaped up—no more labored heaving itself off the ground. After only eight minutes of life it could move all four legs at once.

No matter how many times it fell, it struggled up straight off to have another go: three jumps in a row. It suddenly realized how far it had strayed into the world and made haste back again. This time it had to fall back rather than jump. It was tired by now, so it took another rest. Time, too, for a feed. This meant more exploring, spending time hunting around for the right place until it could take its first sustenance.

The nourishment livened it up. It began springing about with added abandon, all four legs at full strength. A series of capers took it right round its mother. Except for a tumble when it was cornering at speed, it used those legs as if they had been working for days. A pause in between laps, and it was off again, a sudden sprint that could not be stopped

Far left: At under five minutes of life, the young zebra is trying its legs.

Middle: The first strides are brought to a crashing halt by the umbilical cord, which is still attached.

Near left: At only seven minutes, the zebra foal stands for the first time—though it doesn't remain standing long.

Below: A quarter of an hour from the first stages, and both mother and foal are ready to move off with the herd.

without a few stiff-legged jumps. This time it arrived a good twenty yards away in the long grass. It wheeled around and came prancing back. No need for a rest now, so it took off on another canter in the other direction. A quick break for more sustenance and it was off again.

A young zebra, like a young horse, has legs which look unusually long for its body. But without those spindly legs to run with, right from the hour it is born, it might not survive. When the foal suddenly found itself face-to-face with another zebra, it was strong enough to come back at a steady canter. Now there was a lengthy inspection by other members of the herd, snuffling it all over. The foal paused, then made up for lost time by finding out just what was around the next bush; and the next. There was no stopping for rests; they weren't needed any more.

The mother had now been on her feet for several minutes. She was ready to move on. The smells around were attracting unwanted callers such as jackals—they themselves would cause no trouble, but they could be the first in a long line of callers. The foal set off with its mother for the nearest rise, following the rest of the herd. Halfway along something startled her, and she shifted into a trot. The foal stretched out to keep up. It disappeared over the top of a slope, not quite twenty minutes old.

RHINOS

Something strangely compelling about a rhinoceros (apart from its charge) makes one stay and watch it when it is out and about in the hours before the sun gets high. There is three times as much chance of coming across a rhino before midmorning. After that its bulk absorbs a lot of heat, and the rhino is inclined to disappear into thicket patches. It lumbers on its way with a shambling dignity, oblivious to the world it casually crushes aside. For all its reputation, the rhino is not so much mean-tempered as unpredictable. When it feels at bay it has only limited means of weighing up an intruder. So it is hardly to be blamed for being somewhat fractious. If it is uncertain of its ground, it takes a stance of undiluted belligerence; and a rhinoceros, with that volatile temperament on the edge of instant attack, is something out of more formidable times.

A rhino sometimes gets trapped in the mud. It may drown. It may get jammed between two rocks. But it has little to fear from other creatures. In normal times a rhino can live for forty years. Not that these are normal times; many a rhino nowadays ends up on a poacher's spear. A little care and the hunter can get close enough to a rhino with its near-useless eyes. (A single spear thrust to the flank usually does the job. If it does not reach the heart, it will puncture the rhino's lungs, which lie surprisingly far back.) Throughout its many stages in the long African day, the rhino has had time, more than most, to evolve defensive devices against whatever may threaten it from its environment. But the few moments it has been hunted by humans—the mere 2,000 years since rhino horn came into fashion—have not supplied a fraction of the time necessary to prepare a defense against the one predator that hunts it more widely and more efficiently and more uselessly than any other.

Yet even the rhino is a recent starter compared with the stretches of Africa's prehistory. Its first beginnings were something like 70,000,000 years ago, or nearly four hours ago in the long African day. At one time or another, there have been thirty-four different species, some far different from today's end-product. One of its ancestors was a small, fleet-footed creature with a flattish head and no horn that trod the earth, or rather trotted over it, during the Eocene, 50,000,000 years ago. Some time later a more suitably bulky beast emerged, nearly thirty feet long and standing as tall as a modern-day giraffe. It was the largest land animal that ever lived: the earth would not mistake its passing as it

trundled about its affairs. It still had no horns, but it sported a pair of tusks no creature meeting it could ignore. Somewhat later the two horns appeared, side by side at first instead of one behind the other. This shift from tusks to horns gives rise to a number of queries. If a creature has horns, does it have less need to develop teeth for defending itself? Yet this approach could apply the other way round. Some of the earlier rhinos had formidable teeth such as are generally evolved for tearing and chewing—and not just at vegetation. Horns are fine for defense, but not so suitable when there is more involved than self-protection. Of course, an elephant did not develop its teeth-tusks for anything other than warding off whatever threats might appear. Presumably the rhino developed its horns for a similar purpose. At any rate, the teeth of a modern rhino have become broad and fitted for grinding up vegetation.

According to the Masai, there is another story of how the rhino got its horns, or at least how they came to be where they are. Once upon a time, they were where they belong, on top of the head. One day the rhino came across the elephant. The elephant did not mind the horns, but it was emphatic that it did not want to find rhino droppings around like its own. The rhino was affronted and told the elephant what it could do with itself. It chose the wrong beast to tell that to. The elephant seized the rhino's horns and forced

A three-month-old rhino may suckle every half hour, though it might be seeking security as much as sustenance. It is as alert as its mother to the antics of the egrets and other tick-seeking birds, should they fly up in alarm.

them down onto its nose, so that it could use them to scatter its droppings about and leave observers in no doubt whose was what. Which is why you see rhinos using their horns to root around in their dropping sites.

These horns have further purposes. A rhino uses them for the extended greeting procedure, which involves rubbing cheeks together, followed by a bit of "jousting" with the horns. The horn has served the rhino well enough for ages; now it has suddenly become the rhino's downfall. The Asiatic male in his inscrutability has a craving for phallic symbols, a curious need in a continent of such teeming millions. For an aphrodisiac he might just as well grind up his toenails. The poacher in the African bush may get only a half dollar per pound for his trouble, but the price on the Mombasa wharves is up to fifteen dollars, five times the rate of ivory. A twenty-pound horn can bring $2,000 in the Far East, making it one of the most valuable animal products on earth. A recent dhow shipment totaled almost 300 horns. Ominously, the horns are becoming so scarce that any part of the rhino will make a tolerable substitute, even phials of urine. But as the trade gets tighter and rhinos get fewer, Oriental tastes are shifting to reindeer horn. If the Asiatic in his wisdom can be persuaded this is just as potent a prop for sexual prowess, there might be a new day for the rhinoceros and a new profit for reindeer owners.

It should rank as a miracle that this throwback to remote eras has lasted long enough for man to set eyes on it, especially when, in the view of some people, the rhino passed its peak of evolutionary development a good while back. Like other outsize creatures, it produces an offspring far less than once a year, which means much less scope for evolutionary forces to concentrate on the ones best suited to changing circumstances, and hence less room for "survivorship" in the whole species. This is a dangerous situation for a creature that has already become specialized into something so refined as a rhino: it needs time to maneuver. Which makes no difference to man's reaction to the extreme chance that has allowed him to set eyes on such a remarkable relic; he pursues it wherever it goes. If our descendants ask what happened to the rhino, they will not get the reply that people were hungry. The three Asiatic species of rhino are down to miserable totals, about 800 altogether. Those in Africa are lucky; they number in the thousands.

The two types, white and black, are both battleship gray and share other features of a battleship as well. The white rhino lives entirely off grass, using a strip of cartilage in the

Rhinos rarely fight. Rather, they engage in a lengthy weighing-up of each other, then depart in different directions and in apparent boredom. These two males presented fine displays of ferocity to each other, occasionally emphasized by a charge, during a period of about two hours, before going their separate—and moderately bloody—ways.

lower lip for cropping grass very short, like a hippo. The black rhino generally lives off shrubs or bushes, and only small amounts of grass. Because of its catholic tastes the black rhino can feed off 100 different plants in a day, and throughout the season it may sample almost twice as many. According to Dr. John Goddard, the rhinos of even the scrub areas in Ngorongoro Crater make up half their diet with legumes. Those in the open grass plains or the swamps find still more. But rhinos vary enormously from one place to another and one season to another. It is not easy to describe a "typical" rhino diet. In Ngorongoro a regimen of legumes is feasible considering the exceptional year-round moisture draining into the Crater from the surrounding highlands. Even though there are plenty of other herbivores, the rhino's diet rarely leads to conflict with the rest of the community. Rhinos largely keep off the more plentiful herbs that make up a fifth of the total cover. The only creature that might compete for the same food is the Grant's gazelle; but a mere 1,000 gazelles do not make much difference to well under 100 rhinos.

At Olduvai Gorge, only thirty miles away, there is a different habitat. The rainfall is not much over a half the Crater's, so the rhinos have to get by on less than a third as many different plants. An Olduvai rhino needs more than two square miles of living space, twice the area that suffices in the Crater. Yet despite the harsh environment of Olduvai, the rhinos stick it out there. Even at the height of the dry season they prefer to stay and semistarve. But some of them seem to get by well enough with virtually no surface water. Different rhinos, different habits.

No rhino, however, likes to move far. It is this hyper-reluctance to shift, the rhino's inability to adapt, that has induced some people to say it is short on "survival value," running out of evolutionary steam. If the Lamarckian urge for creative change cannot help them, the Darwinian removal of the unfit is settling them. But such an outcome is not imminent. The most sudden "flash" extinctions, like those of the dinosaurs, took millions of years. If man gives the rhino a helping push down the slope, it will be a demise such as has never been achieved by the most cataclysmic forces of nature. Meanwhile, the Olduvai rhinos make out as best they can, using all manner of special tactics. They rear up against low branches of euphorbia trees till they can reach the more succulent material higher up; or they wedge a branch between their horns and drag it down. The euphorbias, rich in latex, may be a source of water toward the end of the dry season, when the rhino makes up three-quarters of its diet with this plant as compared with only one-quarter during the wet season. Rhinos are sometimes seen chewing at very woody vegetation and spitting out the tougher material, and when things get really dry, and all those legumes are finished, they go to an emergency source of nitrogenous intake, their own dung.

It was legumes and the rich protein that allowed rhinos to flourish in the late 1960s in Tsavo after the better rains. But if a rhino sticks to its own familiar area through thick and thin, then the 1971 drought made things really thin for the Tsavo rhinos. They were not directly catching the heavy end of affairs as a result of the elephants' depredations, despite what many people suggested; the two hardly competed. The elephants were causing such damage to the environment that the plants rhinos need were left with less protection against the sun. They became desiccated, while sun-loving plants, such as the rhinos find of little use, started to flourish. There was no real shortage of water, whatever the pleas about water for wild animals. Many of the 600 rhinos that some observers believed died were found lying in water holes. Others were found with their stomachs full of what amounted to wood. As the habitat underwent such radical changes, the elephants could tolerate less succulent material; the rhinos could not. A rhinoceros must have green vegetation or it ceases being a rhino. If drier times have indeed returned to Tsavo for a lengthy period, then the tremendous number of elephants are probably eating their way down through the spectrum until they are taking the legumes as well. The indirect competition could be turning to direct conflict, a crisis of more durable if desperate kind, especially for the hundreds more rhinos that are threatened in the impoverished environment if the drier phase persists.

In other areas rhinos prefer coarser vegetation, the prickly stuff generally disregarded by other creatures. They like to feed, for instance, on gall acacia trees. If one rhino eats from 250 trees a day, which may be a conservative estimate, one can imagine their influence. If the rhinos were eliminated for whatever reason, the gall acacias would thrive, to the detriment of a range of plants that other animals prefer. On the other hand, this habit of rhinos could occasionally lead to trouble. In Nairobi Park the gall acacias are also browsed on by giraffes. If more and more rhinos were to be released into the park following further capture campaigns, there might eventually be too many creatures around with the refined taste for gall acacia spikes. The rhinos would probably not want to move on: how about the giraffes? The park does not want to lose its giraffes either. Giraffes can cope somewhat better, and sometimes wander off for many miles; but they like to come back again. There could be a prospect of problems as large-sized as these two creatures. The gall acacia bushes are already down to three or four feet, as compared with those over the park fence where they are not browsed by any feeder and reach twice as high— although that does not necessarily leave them any more flourishing. But John Wyatt has found that while the rhinos spend much time near these "whistling thorn" bushes, they are not always feeding on them. They are, rather, after plants underneath the bushes. This is the sort of problem that is not properly surveyed in advance: there is a shortage of funds and of staff, as everywhere in East Africa, despite what rhinos and giraffes contribute to this unique park so close to a big city.

If a rhino can live in rough scrubland and lush forest alike, maybe it is not so inept at survival after all. What counts is whether it is given a chance. One might say that its extended history, primeval to go with the best, amounts to good cause for allowing it living space—it has been here a lot longer than its sole persecutor. Rhinos remaining are remarkable; rhinos vanished would be regrettable. It is difficult to see what advantage

there would be: a world without rhinos would have lost one of its subtleties. It will be a comment on the world if a corner cannot be found for the rhino somewhere within its natural environment rather than in some museum.

UGANDA KOB

In Africa one cannot see one antelope and see them all. There are dozens of kinds. Nor does seeing one individual make another less worth looking at. Some of them are such splendid-looking creatures that you look and look; and when you have seen enough of one you do not have to look far to sight another—the second could be only a few yards away. And often enough, to see one is to see hundreds, if not thousands. Which is a sight of its own again.

Uganda kob are to be found in several parts of Uganda. But in the Semliki Reserve there are open plains where you *can* say that when you see one you see them all (or almost), and you are glad you can. They are rich red-brown, sleek, and gorgeous. At midmorning they are returning from their drinking, thronging along their traditional paths in herds that look as endless as you hope they will be.

Back at their grazing grounds there is more to watch at this particular time of day. Each group is making for its own locality. Certain of the males go to special patches of ground to take up positions in the closely packed and closely guarded breeding grounds. A male's territory may be twenty or forty yards across. It is circular, the ground trampled until it is flat and almost bare. Nearby, in fact so close as to be touching, will be another such territory with another male standing in the middle. There may be a dozen such territories in one area, or there may be forty. The entire territorial ground may be two or three hundred yards across. At Semliki there are thirteen of these territorial grounds; all the kob in the area belong to one or another, roughly 1,000 or 1,200 to each. Each kob knows where it belongs. If it is captured and taken as far as forty miles away, it will be back in a few weeks, if not a few days. On the way it will pass through communities of other kob in their hundreds, but it continues until it finds its own proper spot.

Some of these territorial grounds have been an identical part of the scene for thirty years. Wildebeest are attached to their territories too, but they do not perpetuate the same limited grounds year after year. Moreover, they tend to take up all the space available, staking out larger areas for their territories than do kob. The wildebeest pattern more nearly approximates the idea of what a territory should be. Yet the kob is much more "territorial" than most antelopes. In fact, one might say it displays territorialism to the ultimate degree. An antelope territory is usually large enough to allow the creature to get most of its daily food needs (except for water) within its confines, although it is primarily a place where the male can assert himself and safeguard his females. A waterbuck maintains such a territory, as does a wildebeest, though in a different manner; so does a lion in a peculiarly leonine manner, though it may require the assistance of the waterbuck and the wildebeest. By contrast, a kob stations itself in an area that could not sustain it, even if the grass were lush and growing (the vegetation is in fact worn away by all the trafficking across it). The male does not try to keep females within these close limits; it would be even more difficult to keep several females well fed in such a tiny patch.

When a female is ready to go in search of a male, which may happen at any time of the year (another peculiarity of the kob), she makes her way to the breeding grounds. She mates with several males, and then goes back to her herd of fellow females some distance away. Near this female group may be a bunch of males who are too young to compete for a breeding ground. They make no claims on her. Nor do the breeding males attempt to set up further breeding grounds closer to the female herds. All is tradition; all is stability.

Despite much talk about conflict between rhinos and elephants for food, the direct confrontation inclines to the sort seen here: this elephant's track to the water hole took it through the middle of the rhino's dust bath, and the dust flew up tree-high. When it had cleared, the rhino had withdrawn ten yards, but the elephant was going round another way. There was not much for this particular rhino to fear from an elephant; but shortly afterward she had a tangle with a poacher that left her a decided loser—permanently.

Perhaps the system has evolved to insure that the huge kob population is spread across the Semliki flats, not concentrated just in the most favored parts. Or it could be that this social sanction on breeding procedures prevents the herds from growing too big; the numbers are kept limited, hence stabilized.

Possibly the kob community has stories to tell other creatures. Their system insures respect for one another's property, and permits outlets for disagreement before they become disputes, and disputes that stop short of debilitating or destroying the antagonists. When one of the territorial males is challenged by a usurping male, the defender puts up a show that is vigorous enough, yet not too vigorous. It is a contest rather than a conflict. The two push, forehead against forehead, horns interlocked. They do not use their heads as battering rams, since the object is a show of dominance rather than direct injury. When it becomes plain which is the fitter, the vanquished turns to leave. This would be the moment for the victor to inflict damage on the unprotected back end of his opponent —an outcome that has never been known to happen.

Having established his territory, the male waits for a female. Mating among wild creatures frequently becomes a violent affair, with much "displaced behavior." Among kob, with their restricted mating grounds, certain rituals inhibit any latent aggressiveness released by sexual activity. The male approaches the female with forelegs rigid, in a prancing gait that perhaps induces him to hold his vigor in check. He holds his head high, revealing a white patch on the throat that matches the black and white on his forelegs, a gesture to indicate that his intentions are anything but aggressive. All is placatory posturing, a standardized ceremony to show how everything is getting along. The moves are more formalized than for any other antelope. Indeed, most antelopes do not engage in any form of ceremony at all once the initial overtures are completed. But then no other antelope is like the kob.

Kob communities have been the subject of study for several years, notably by Dr. Hal Buechner and Dr. Walther Leuthold. These studies have led some people to ask what benefit arises to conservation overall from investigations of how the kob propagates itself: all of great interest to the survival of the kob, no doubt—though the kob seems to manage its affairs successfully enough—what does it contribute to the survival of wildlife at large? It now turns out that such studies lend themselves to a process that could hardly be of more relevance to the future of wildlife in East Africa. They help the East African to be better fed. Kob in the Semliki Valley are now being cropped at the rate of 1,200 a year. They easily make up this number by the following year. Their social structures and habits make it easy for the cropper to find the kob he wants. It is an undertaking of little appeal to the man who thinks of that red-brown coat spattered with red-brown gore, but it is an approach that is vital if there are to be any kob left in twenty years' time to admire, sentimentally or not. Man has always taken these kob, whether with bows and arrows or with more Stone-Age implements. Perhaps man has constituted another influence in keeping the population stable, a balancing factor that was allowed for while kob were evolving their breeding procedures. The hunter nowadays finds each kob produces over a hundred pounds of meat. Visitors come to see the remaining kob, oblivious of whether those are the year's full total. No watcher could ever tell what is going on by the disturbance, because there isn't any. Since males don't participate in the breeding process until they are over three years old, considerable numbers can be eliminated before then, especially after the first year, during which they have put on most of their weight. All this is fine enough, provided one can determine how many to remove while maintaining a sufficient supply of fresh blood. The bachelor herds are easy to find, since they stay in much the same place. Still more resident, however briefly, are the breeding males, who, standing in their tiny circles, make easy targets. Fine for the less-than-competent cropper, but less so for the kob. There is cropping and cropping, and crude slaughter is no good to anybody.

A male kob in his prime makes a striking sight; and the white patches and black stripes must add something in the eyes of a female kob, though their purpose is not apparent to the human watcher during the stately ceremonies of mating.

CHEETAH

Every safarist in East Africa wants to see one of the big cats making a kill. Only with much luck and much more patience will he see a lion or a leopard in action. The chances are slightly better of seeing a cheetah at work.

A cheetah needs daylight to exploit its running power. At any time of day the cheetah is a creature of grace and elegance, but at speed it puts its powers to full use. Little puffs of dust rise behind a blur that covers the ground with hardly a trace of jerkiness. A lion is a muscle-bound incompetent by comparison. Seventy miles an hour is said to be not beyond a cheetah flat out. A cheetah in full stride defies mere numbers and becomes a creature of its own. The vertebrae in its back are articulated until they allow the whole animal to flex like a bow. As the hind limbs reach far forward to get leverage for their thrust, the body winds up into a circle. Not that its muscles are large; in fact, a cheetah borders on the scrawny. But that hundred-pound frame releases energy that in proportion far surpasses that of a racehorse with its seized-up stride.

A horse has a much more powerful backbone, yet it is a far less flexible animal, and its shoulder blades rotate only a fraction as much as a cheetah's. The horse reaches into a stride four times as long as its body (less the head and tail), but a cheetah stretches half as far again, size for size. In terms of body bulk a cheetah is twice as efficient as a horse. A horse has to support itself against the ground for a greater part of its galloping cycle, in fact for most of the time except for a brief phase in the middle of the stride; the cheetah leaves the ground for two separate phases, amounting to half the total time instead of a quarter. The horse, like the cheetah, can manage two and a half strides a second, but makes far less use of each stroke. At its best a horse can move only a little faster than a greyhound. Once the horse has hit full stride, of course, that powerful back comes into its own; it can keep going far longer than a cheetah, and if it drops top speed a little it can stick at it for miles. A cheetah rarely travels less than flat out, and rarely goes more than a

Far left: A cheetah on the hunt uses hillocks, tree stumps, whatever is handy for a lookout post. If it spots a possible prey it may try a semi-stealthy approach before starting the final chase. While it waits on top of the fallen tree, it sometimes marks the spot by spraying urine or leaving droppings. But it is unlikely to maintain territorial rights in the manner of a lion or a leopard; the scent-marking may be for its own orientation on future forays, as well as to indicate to other cheetah in the vicinity that this particular area is occupied at this time.

Middle: Two minutes earlier the cheetah was poised in midstride as it froze to avoid being spotted by the gazelles; the gazelles lowered their heads to graze again, the cheetah started to lope, then it was leaping over the plain after a gazelle that was leaping faster than any other African antelope can manage, but not nearly fast enough to out-flee a close-range cheetah. Cheetah in the Serengeti may make up over 90 percent of their food with Thomson's gazelles, which means that all the cheetah together are taking less than 20,000 of the Serengeti's 500,000 gazelles a year. American gamehunters, on the other hand, have been taking as many cheetah a year as would cover a patch of Africa greater than New England, or the whole of Uganda.

Near left: A cheetah may abandon its kill at the approach of the first couple of vultures, but this one defended its carcass for two hours. Much probably depends on how hungry it is. Some cheetah may have found, too, that a vulture appearing on the scene can lead to other creatures appearing on the scene: vulture movements are watched by hyenas, even by lions.

few hundred yards, which is, nevertheless, farther than a lion or leopard could manage even if not nearly so far as an antelope runs.

The greater the advantages, the greater the drawbacks. The cheetah would have to give up after what a gazelle would consider only the start of a chase, so long as the gazelle were still in the running (so to speak). If a gazelle spots a cheetah a couple of hundred yards away, it takes little notice. Even if the cheetah gets near enough to launch into full chase, the watcher still cannot say the hunt is over before it has begun. The gazelle may have enough presence of mind to dodge aside at the tactical moment. The cheetah cannot do much about it except go tearing past and feel frustrated. Of course, the gazelle does not always have the sense to dodge aside, otherwise the predator-prey balance would be upset.

The structure that gives the cheetah such surging power in a single direction prevents it from slowing down in a hurry, or turning aside in more than a hurry. A cheetah can hardly turn fast enough to make any difference. Its tail may be of some help, since it is long enough to act as a counterbalancing rudder. If the cheetah were an out-and-out sprinter, its tail would in time have disappeared as a useless appurtenance, or it would have been reduced to the size of a greyhound's. Yet some cheetah learn a thing or two about dodging. Ron McLaughlin has noticed in Nairobi Park that they sometimes leave the plains to go prowling around the forest area, so they must find it tolerable terrain for hunting. Yet a tiny dik-dik has only to scamper around the nearest bush to get clean away. The savannah and its open spaces are the main place for the cheetah. But even there you do not see grossly gorged cheetah, with fewer and fewer gazelles; that would soon mean fewer and fewer cheetah.

To see a cheetah on the move, you must first find a hungry cheetah. That spotted coat makes good camouflage. By the time the heat haze starts up around midmorning, it is more difficult to make out. You may be lucky and spot a hunting cheetah early in the day, but a hunt right after dawn is unlikely unless there has been moonlight to help the cheetah sight its prey. If the cheetah is hard to spot, you can try using the gazelles' eyes. They can see a cheetah a good way off, provided it is on the move. A group of gazelles staring in one direction, stamping and snorting, is a sure sign of a hunter abroad. The cheetah, sensing that they can pick out a moving shape, freezes when they look in its direction. This is a rudimentary sign of catlike stealth in an animal that, all too often, acts in a manner more doglike. A cheetah rarely attempts to use bushes for cover even when there are plenty around. Yet the sort of creature a cheetah sometimes goes after suggests that stalking counts for more than one would expect. In Kruger Park there are reedbuck, waterbuck, kudu, and tsessebe by the thousand and impala by the hundred thousand. Impala make up by far the greater part of the cheetah's diet, though they are a long way from being favorite when their numbers are considered in proportion with reedbuck and others. Impala congregate in herds while the other antelope are more solitary. Groups of impala all standing together offer a multiple target, notwithstanding all those watchful eyes. Yet they turn out to be a more difficult prey for a hunter that apparently does not rely on speed alone, perhaps because a multiple target represents a confusing target.

The cheetah must depend on its eyes to get near its prey. It spends some time in a careful approach before it is in position to make its strike. Again, its camouflage suggests that it cannot depend entirely on open running like wild dogs, especially since wild dogs depend on stamina more than sheer speed. Just as a gazelle cannot make out a cheetah when it is still, so a cheetah can pick out the prey only when there is some trace of movement. But if the antelope heads are merely flickering as they graze afar off, the cheetah will spot them. Human eyes need binoculars to pick out the same creature. Yet few animals that a cheetah hunts put their faith in freezing as a safety device, except a newborn gazelle, which cowers in short grass while the cheetah passes by a dozen yards away. As long as the tiny creature keeps its nerve it has a sound chance. But too often it waits until the predator is almost past, and then leaps up to make a dash for it. A survey by Dr. George Schaller suggests that a cheetah in pursuit of a gazelle fawn hardly ever misses, whereas it does well if it makes a kill around half the time if it is after a full-grown gazelle.

The antelopes of the open plains generally use flight as their only method of escape, flight as immediate and as fast as they can make it. A gazelle produces more than half a cheetah's speed, so the cheetah has to be close before it launches its rush. I once watched a cheetah trying to approach a solitary gazelle. The cheetah was sighted before it got anywhere near, whereupon it lay down by a bush. It bothered with the flies instead. The gazelle wandered off a short way and took to grazing. It glanced every now and again toward the cheetah, but as long as there was that eighty-yard gap, things were all right. Three hours later the cheetah got up and stretched itself. It started to amble over toward the gazelle. The gazelle watched. Suddenly the cheetah burst into full speed. The gazelle realized that this was action, and action for real. It took off—too late. The cheetah had closed a fraction too much of the gap.

Sometimes there is more attempt at a true stalk. But how far is the stalk a real attempt to get close, and how far is the cheetah somehow stimulated to unleash its sprint only when the prey flees and triggers the pursuit reaction? Often enough the antelope that the cheetah singles out is the one that breaks away first, even though it has the best start. Often enough again it is more likely to be a female. Females have a greater "fleeing distance," which does not always serve them well. In fact, some cheetah take twice as many females as males. Not much is known of how predators "choose" their prey. Does a lion or a leopard mark out a particular unfortunate before it charges from ambush? Does a cheetah in fact find itself hungry and then look around for a gazelle, sensing that there walks a meal, or does it follow a series of intermediate reactions before it finds itself with a pile of food at its feet?

Once into its final sprint the cheetah finishes the job off quickly. It needs a grip on the throat, but it cannot risk a straight strike at the animal's neck in midflight—that would be too dangerous. A cheetah with a slight injury to that lithe body is a cheetah starving.

Cheetah regularly drink after feeding—but they also lap up blood from the carcass, which probably helps them to survive in arid areas such as they often frequent.

Instead it aims a clawed blow at the rump. The prey is unbalanced; it falls, and that is that. A large Grant's gazelle can get to its feet again with a cheetah hanging on to its throat, but that serves no purpose. The jugular is soon severed and the trachea crushed, apart from whatever strangulation goes on. A cheetah's jaws are not strong enough to bite through the vertebrae as a lion or a leopard can; nor are its forelegs powerful enough to do much damage—even if the claws could be retracted and thus kept from blunting. Yet cheetah have been known to kill buffalo calves, even on occasion a young giraffe. They can manage waterbuck or full-grown roan antelopes four or five times their own size, though that probably requires several cheetah in combination. On the other hand, a cheetah has been seen chased by a roan antelope for half a mile, only escaping when it took refuge in a tree. So much for endurance!

Having made its kill, the cheetah's problems are far from over. It must dispose of the carcass as fast as it can. There are all too many creatures ready to share the meal, and most of them might not mind including the cheetah as well. Dr. Schaller has found that a Serengeti cheetah may lose one kill in ten to lions and one in twenty to hyenas (a hyena can sometimes drive a cheetah off a carcass just by putting in an appearance a hundred yards away). So a cheetah with a fresh kill must either hide it in what cover there is around, or eat it in a hurry. If the kill is only a gazelle, a cheetah thinks nothing of dragging it 200 yards away, a task as exhausting as the chase itself. And if other carnivores do not hesitate to appropriate another's kill, or consume various kinds of carrion, a cheetah hardly ever touches anybody else's leftovers. If it loses its own food more than most predators, one would expect it to take whatever scraps come its way; but perhaps it does not get a chance at extras often enough to grow accustomed to the idea.

If the cheetah is fastidious about what it eats, it is not about the way it eats. Of all carnivores the cheetah makes the most mess of a carcass. It takes the stomach and intestines out, but, unlike a lion or a leopard, it makes no gesture towards burying them. Nor does it have the powerful teeth or jaws for biting off lumps of flesh straight from the carcass; it grasps a chunk with the side of its mouth and then twists it off, or it gnaws at the tougher portions, leaving a wreck of a carcass. There may be plenty of flesh remaining, but the cheetah does not return. One cheetah with two cubs, watched by Dr. Schaller for three weeks, killed an average of twenty-three pounds a day, yet the three of them ate only twelve pounds. A lion or a leopard would eat a greater proportion unless prey was very plentiful.

The cheetah is hardly catlike in much of its daily round, while retaining something of the measured power of all cats. On the other hand, its small head, slender legs, and non-retractable claws make it more akin to a dog—especially when it brings these assets to bear in the hunt. But it is a distinct cat for all that. It can purr if it cannot growl; its strange chirrupings sound something like a high-pitched bark. As Dr. Richard Estes has pointed out, it has the speedy reflexes of a cat, and it has muscles that are more quickly exhausted than a dog's. Its jaws are not elongated, and they carry canines that are stronger than a dog's even though they are not much good at rending flesh. It does not have such powerful molars, nor so many, as a dog; nor does it have the same need for them, since there is not so much chewing and grinding to do. Like cats, it can hardly chew at all; it bolts its food in lumps. Chewing needs a pair of jaws that move sideways as well as up and down. Dogs can manage it; humans too, but cats cannot. A cheetah has the same number of teeth as a cat; hence the shorter jaw, and hence the greater leverage—of great advantage when making a kill. Wild dogs or other pack-hunting animals like hyenas or wolves are more inclined to rely on several sets of jaws worrying at the prey and tearing out lumps while it is still alive. But the cheetah's shortened jaw means a shortened nose, hence a limited sense of smell (it sometimes hunts downwind), and is rarely found following a trail, nose to the ground, as a wild dog will. Any hunter, cat or dog, has eyes farther to the front of the head than the creatures it preys on. An antelope eats food that cannot run away, though it has to be able to spot danger coming from any angle, so its eyes are at the sides. A cheetah, like other cats, has eyes farther to the front than a dog. It has binocular vision for judging distance when preparing the sudden strike and the overwhelming attack. But its body is more of the lean doglike build. Like the dog, it rarely hunts at night, presumably because its eyes are not sufficiently catlike. Yet, like the night hunters, it tends to be solitary, if not as supersecretive as a leopard. Even when several cheetah make up a group, they rarely join together in a hunt; instead, the rest sit and watch while one does the work, even though an attack that depends on pursuit is much more efficient if shared among several. Primarily a loner, the cheetah does not produce the huge litters dogs do, which a mother on her own would be less able to look after; on the other hand, a cheetah litter is usually larger than a leopard's and larger than the average for lions— though fewer survive. In fact, its whole life is somewhere on the border of the cat world and the dog world. At some time in its past it moved away from the normal cat routine to take up a separate route to survival. A mere 3,000,000 years ago, ten minutes back in the long African day, this process culminated in something much like a modern-day cheetah. Its adaptations have equipped it for an existence that can exploit a niche where it enjoys much of the canine way of life while remaining a cat.

The watcher can make out all this when he comes across a cheetah, whatever it is doing. He does not have to look for a cheetah stretched out in full flight to see a thoroughgoing cheetah. He would not be able to see much of it anyway in that blur. He should have a look at it just lying in the shade of the bush. It is phenomenon enough.

ELEPHANTS

During the early hours of the day the elephants are active. They are out and about, and this is when they are easy to observe. Later on you can still find them if they haven't disappeared into the swamps, since an elephant standing under a tree is not the sort of thing you can miss—much less a herd of elephants. But they will be resting. From dawn until midmorning is the time to watch them going about their affairs. Nobody ever gets

Left below: Elephants are capable of all manner of amiable gestures. This way of viewing them would no doubt be decried by anti-anthropomorphists, but to watch elephants is to wonder at their social systems, full of delicate idiosyncrasies.

Right below: This tree probably required a combination of several elephants lunging at it with their foreheads to push it over. They removed almost all of the bark, but ignored a lot of the twigs that they could eat with little trouble. Amboseli's fine fever trees are slowly disappearing, as are trees in many elephant areas across Africa: a felled tree satisfies the elephants for a few days, but it stays felled forever (except in parks that prop them upright again).

tired of elephants. Lions and rhinos and zebras tend to get predictable in their patterns, but elephants are always different. Watching them never becomes a repeat process.

Elephants do not live to be a hundred, nor do they go to special cemeteries to die, nor do they fly. They can pass messages to one another through the merest twitching of the trunk. They go looking for food that ferments in their stomach, which they seem to enjoy in fuzzy-eyed fashion. They can move through thick bush as silently as an antelope herd. To watch them going about their daily business undisturbed, there is more to these creatures than bulk. Not that there are many fully-grown bulls anymore; they have been mostly shot for their full grown ivory. Now you are lucky to see a male much above middle age. At Mkomazi, southeast of Kilimanjaro, there is hardly a bull much beyond a teen-ager. According to those who work out the dynamics of animal engineering, an elephant is about as big as a land-living creature could become, given that a doubling of body weight requires far more than a doubling of leg size, and given that modern environments do not lend themselves to such outsize creations as dinosaurs—which had swamps to give them buoyancy. The pillars an elephant uses for walking are devoid of any spring at all.

It is not the elephant's show of size and strength that attracts attention so much as the smaller revelations of an elephant's nature. Elephants are capable of a whole range of characteristics, as if each possessed some rudimentary form of personality or was an elephant unto itself. The instances of elephant loyalty are legion. A shot elephant in its last throes will not be left alone; its companions try to lift it up with their tusks, straining so hard they may snap one off. There are records of two elephants actually supporting a wounded comrade between them and helping it to make off. Such idiosyncrasies in such a ponderous beast make it all the more remarkable. Sometime it seems massive to the point of being trapped within the limits of its lumbering nature, resigned to elephantine ideas, incapable of the finer points of life. But its basic intelligence can hardly be doubted, surpassing that of most animals. Its brain size is considerable, a foot long. Not that this is big in comparison; in proportion to body size, it is only one-tenth the size of the human brain. Moreover, what counts is not so much outright size as complexity—how convoluted it is, how much surface area it affords. Whichever way one looks at it, an elephant's gray matter is relatively bigger by far than a rhino's or a giraffe's or a buffalo's.

An elephant is a creature of some sensitivity, receptive to the moods of its companions. It is not a troublemaker, and is altogether careful not to tread on other creatures' toes. It treads softly in the literal sense, too, when it has to. If danger is suspected, the lumbering shamble is dropped; the feet have soft spongy soles that absorb undue noise. Moreover, it is a marvelously adaptable creature in terms of habitat. Elephants are found in East Africa all the way from the equatorial coast to the heathlands 12,000 feet up on Kilimanjaro and Mount Kenya, a range matched by very few African animals. They like to go up Mount Kenya for the fruits of the mukaita tree, very popular with local people for treating stomach disorders. Possibly the same applies to elephants.

Although it is the biggest animal of the plains and forests, the elephant does not make a nuisance of its strength, even if it occasionally uproots sign boards in the parks. Not for nothing are signs posted on park tracks: ELEPHANTS HAVE RIGHT OF WAY. They particularly like water installations and occasionally an elephant has learned how to turn a tap on—though not how to turn it off again. By and large they are remarkably pacific, although an irate elephant makes quite a sight. The ears flap, the feet stamp, the trunk comes up in a scream of anger—and it is all show. Not until the trunk is curled out of harm's way, the head turned sideways to get a better view of the target, and the elephant is standing quite still with tusks raised, is it time to put a lot of Africa between you and the elephant. Something reaches the flash point and the elephant sets off with a lunging gait that reaches full speed almost straightaway. Not that an elephant runs; it can manage only a fast walk. For a person on foot, with an elephant after him, it is a very fast walk indeed. Some people

say an average man could get away from an elephant provided he is something of a sprinter, has a flat stretch of ground to run on, and has remembered to bring along his track shoes.

Parks are the places to see elephants. There they are accustomed to autos, and they tend to grow larger than outside. An elephant is in its prime for fifty years or more, tusks growing all the while. Over a lifetime six sets of foot-long teeth appear (very occasionally seven), until the last lot wear out. After a lifetime of grinding thousands of tons of food, the elephant can no longer sustain itself, for want of a few pounds of dentition. This is when it makes for a swamp and its softer grasses. Eventually it may get stuck in the mud, as so many of its forebears—and that is the end of the elephant, and the start of tales about elephant cemeteries. More interesting, and more probable, is that an elephant's life span is limited by its feeding equipment rather than by straight old age, which partly explains the "phenomenon" of elephants' breeding right up to their final years, which in turn means that those elephants that stay out of most trouble produce most calves: a factor of natural selection that makes for elephants experienced and wise.

A fair amount of vegetation passes through the vast cavern of an elephant's stomach, an average of 700 pounds a day for a six-ton elephant; in good country, half as much again.

This elephant had plenty of food within trunk's reach wherever it stood in the swamp, yet it moved around constantly for three hours, apparently highly selective. At some seasons, an elephant is partial to papyrus, even ducking under to dig it out with its tusks. Swamps are also favored by elderly elephants when their last teeth get worn out and they can chew only soft material. Eventually they get stuck in the mud; that is the end of the elephants, and the start of legends about elephant cemeteries.

A female eats more in proportion than a male, probably because she is often either pregnant or rearing an infant. Any elephant eats incessantly: its life is one long, stand-up feast, amounting to 4,000 tons of food or more. Yet it is not particularly efficient with its food. It digests less than half, since it has no complex system of stomachs that enables a ruminating animal, like a buffalo, to extract more nutriment from the material. (On the other hand, an elephant needs less proportionately than a buffalo; care and maintenance are not so demanding for such a large animal.) The elephant's stomach sometimes gives off prodigious rumblings, not as loud as those similar sounds that are more abandoned and more disgusting, which are presumed to be rumblings of pleasure, because the elephant produces them only when everything is going well, and they stop instantly if it senses something wrong. The elephant produces these powerful sounds through its throat; a human ear can pick them up at half a mile and an elephant ear presumably at much greater distance, so they may be a means of communication. Those ears have other purposes. As the morning progresses they begin to flap. Inside is a network of veins to keep the owner cool. Constantly flapping ears are not a sign of perpetual frenzy as some people suggest. Throughout the long hot day the ears beat backward and forward. Not until the cool of evening do they become still again.

When an elephant is fully fed, its weight goes up by at least 5 percent over what it is when it is really hungry, and it has to fill that stomach twice over in twenty-four hours. Its feeding habits are a world apart. It exploits a wide variety of foliage, grasses, leaves, fruits, seeds, bark, and roots. In Tsavo, elephants have been seen to feed off a hundred species in a day, and it is likely they range over an even more extensive spectrum during the year. With the onset of the rains they enjoy a wider regimen, revealing itself in wider "tusk rings," which, like tree rings, indicate the rate of growth. At Murchison Falls Park the elephants eat a tremendous amount of grass. It is scarcely accurate to say this must be what they prefer, because there is little else for them. Elephants no longer roam right across the landscape in search of what they like. They have to take what they can get. There is hardly a park in East Africa where they can feed on everything they would take in truly natural conditions. The areas are too limited, even though some of them cover thousands of square miles, so there is less choice of food than normal, and more elephants than normal to feed off what little there is. And the parks restrict the one predator that is able to do much about controlling elephants. Elephants throng into the parks from outside to escape harassment from poachers and cultivators alike. On their way in they meet other elephants that would be on their way out if they had anywhere to go. The story is much the same throughout Africa. In Kruger Park there were 10 elephants in 1908. By 1947 there were 560. In 1964 there were well over 2,000, and now, with international elephants thronging in from Rhodesia and Mozambique, there are well over 10,000, requiring a crisis cropping campaign to remove at least 2,000.

In Lake Manyara Park the elephants live in prolific forestland, around 400 of them in only thirty-three square miles. The researcher who has been watching them, Ian Douglas-Hamilton, finds they show a predilection for a particular sort of tree that covers only a tenth of the park, the *Acacia tortillis*. It has a bark that is easier to strip off than most, which may be part reason for their preference. It comes in for worse treatment during the rains, though nobody is sure why. During a period of ten years this forest canopy in parts of Lake Manyara has been reduced by almost a third, and this over roughly the time the place has been a park. As the elephants have become yet more confined, the damage has increased to 5 percent a year in some places, 8 percent in others, which means that none of these trees will be left in fifteen years at the most. How to protect the ones still alive? It is not much good fastening wire around the thousands of trunks, since the elephants still gouge the bark away with their tusks. If it is calcium they are after in the bark, calcium piles could be scattered around the park. But would the park still be a park if one starts "feeding" the animals like that? The elephants at Lake Manyara are not

An elephant's trunk is one of the most versatile instruments in the natural world, rivaling even man's hand. It is used for far more than getting food to the mouth (though without it an elephant would be almost as incapable of reaching food on the ground as twenty feet up in the air). After watching a group of elephants engaging in their social interactions, when the trunk conveys all manner of subtle communications, one can visualize what an elephant is like with its trunk severed in a snare; there are plenty such in Africa.

apparently suffering any real deficiency in their diet insofar as they are still breeding fast enough, making this one of the very few parks in East Africa where elephants are still thriving in this way. Moreover, the *Acacia tortillis* trees are mainly overage anyway, and would disappear in the next thirty years, elephants or no elephants—and the remainder of the forest, much the larger part of Lake Manyara's habitat, is actually expanding. Most elephants elsewhere are on a limited diet and a cutback in their breeding rates—sometimes by well over half. Are the two related necessarily, and directly? Nobody knows what is good for an elephant—what it really needs. You could spend a series of seasons finding out, maybe a ten-year cycle, but by the time you get your answers there could well be no forests left—and then how many elephants? If the shortage of cash and scientists is critical and chronic, the shortage of time is worse. At this stage of the long African day there is hardly one five-hundredth part of a second left.

To see what elephants can do in a congested environment one should go to Tsavo. Fifteen years ago it would have been difficult to walk through much of the area at all. Now there are parts where one can walk across plains that are half grassland or more. Of course, the change has made it easier for the visitor to see what else is going on, if that is to be counted a factor for the last great gathering place of elephants on earth. Or at least it was considered an advantage at the start. The present stage is not a start of the cycle from

bushland to grassland, and it hasn't been a start for a long time. The main trees are *Commiphora* thorn trees, which can ordinarily maintain themselves in company with plenty of other vegetation. As soon as they are thinned out, the isolated remnants do not prosper half so well in a half-grassy habitat, since they cannot stand up to the competition from sun-loving plants like legumes nor from most grassy plants which compete directly with *Commiphora* more than with deeper-rooted trees. Moisture is limited in a parched place like Tsavo, which gets well under twenty inches of rain a year on the average. As long as there are plenty of *Commiphora* they monopolize much of the water. A tree newly smashed over is a hefty proposition; dead and dried out, you can pick it up with one hand. The main ravaging started at a time of drought, ten years back; perhaps the elephants were tearing the thorn trees apart to get at the moisture stored inside. By 1964 the worst of the destruction was over and better rains had arrived. But now that other plants have taken hold, the balance may have swung against the *Commiphora*. A second wave of destruction started in 1968, followed by yet another in 1971.

The elephants have meanwhile been wrecking the baobabs as well. One might say that elephants and baobabs go together: both huge, both gray. One might also say a baobab is a tree that is nothing but bark and yet anything but bark. It can grow to a pulpy thirty feet across. African legends say they are trees planted the wrong way up, with their roots reaching toward the sky. They are soft and fibrous right through—three-quarters moisture. A bullet fired at a young baobab will come out the other side. It is easy for an elephant to gouge one to bits. There is a lot of calcium inside, and presumably elephants need a lot of calcium to keep their bones and tusks growing in the lifelong process (though Dr. K. G. McCullagh suggests that Murchison Falls elephants get quite enough calcium even from a grass diet, from a size-for-size comparison with elephants whose calcium intake is known). Baobabs grow in scattered ones and twos, and live hundreds of years, and occasionally thousands. There may even be baobabs as old as the oldest redwoods, and just as striking, which in itself should be reason enough to protect the baobabs, if anyone can devise a way of stopping elephants from doing what they want. A park is supposed to protect all natural features of an environment, especially those of unusual interest. In Tsavo the baobabs have been undergoing extermination at a rate of one in twenty a year, and as fewer are left, the rate goes up; at other places, such as central Ruaha, the rate is worse.

In the view of Dr. Richard Laws, who, together with Ian Parker, was responsible for most of the investigatory work, Tsavo Park without trees may well be headed for Tsavo Desert. Rainfall on the open grassland is more prone to evaporation. It runs off more easily; there is no longer the drip-drip from spreading branches to insure that the ground gets watered slowly and steadily. On the other hand, grasses provide more root systems than woodland trees, and hence allow more inlet-points for percolating water. During the late 1960s Dr. Philip Glover has seen springs coming to life in Tsavo after standing dry for years, though that could also be a temporary result of the better rains meantime. An arid spell, to match the drought of the early 1960s, has begun. Possibly the grasslands will hold their own, or even prove a more stable vegetation. But grass is generally more vulnerable to poor rain than is bushland, and this is an area where normal rain is poor rain. During the earlier drought few grazing animals died in Tsavo, while grass-eaters died by the thousands in other parts of Kenya. In those days there were not nearly so many grassland animals in Tsavo, because the "herbivore explosion" following the tree damage had hardly begun. Now that there are more grazers, there will be more competition when times grow hard. Tsavo's ecosystem is swinging up and down in a manner scarcely ever witnessed by scientists or safarists, and on a scale that can hardly be imagined. It is a pity there are not more scientists to witness it; at present there are only three to keep an eye on what is going on in an area the size of New Hampshire, while the scientific community elsewhere busies itself with the thousandth piece of research on

Elephants will go to any length—or height—to get the food they need. Many elephant areas in Africa feature trees with plenty of foliage above twenty feet and little at all below, a "browse line" that indicates clearly what the elephants are up to. Such areas soon have more trees than usual upended.

white-tailed deer, disregarding an episode that must rank as a major phenomenon in the whole history of large mammal biology.

To find answers to the massive problems that only elephants can supply, one has to know just what they need to eat. Brief experiments by the Tsavo warden suggest they can get by on as much as 90 percent grass. But one would have to watch many elephants for many seasons to get any realistic idea. Elephants have been "adapting" trees for as long as there have been elephants and trees. Whether you look on the present pattern as destruction or merely as modification depends on your point of view. A giraffe or a kudu may regret losing the more vigorous and taller growth; a dik-dik may not object at all, especially since its smaller appetite will take a long time to work through all the fallen foliage; a plant that needs extra shelter may find the wreckage makes the difference between surviving and shriveling. This is no great matter overall, as long as only a few trees, a "natural number," are upended. But elephant country is hardly ever natural nowadays. Dr. Laws has worked in several elephant habitats and believes an optimum diet would include at least 40 per cent browse material the whole year round. As grass becomes more withered during the long dry season, it grows more fibrous, with only 2 percent protein as compared with 30 or 40 percent still to be found in trees and bushes. When the rains return the grasses suddenly produce far more protein: for a brief period the elephants possibly subsist more than half off grass (which is why elephants in Tsavo are more dependent on browse material than those in Murchison Falls, where there is three or four times as much rain a year). The huge amount of browse forage that elephants seem to need partly explains why they need less total food, in proportion, than most animals; their diet is unusually high in quality, provided that browse material is available.

Some elephants spend several hours a day sleeping. This bull was well known in Amboseli for his outsize tusks, and he must have been one of the most photographed animals anywhere. His fame led to his undoing; one day he stepped a few strides outside the Reserve, and there was a hunter waiting. The skill needed to shoot an elephant with modern weapons may be measured by the capabilities of one expert who can account for ten in less than a minute (when he is eliminating surplus elephants); a girl barely in her teens has been known to accomplish the task.

It is not so much the patches of woodland that elephants smash down, as the fringe material surrounding the thicker growths. A grassland plain does not suddenly end and a forest begin. In between there is a zone of shrubby stuff, narrow and necessary, which forms a thick, tight barrier held together by creepers. It can't flourish inside the forest, since there is not enough light, and it can't flourish out in the plains, since it needs the shade of the forest to keep from withering in the sun. In turn, this zone protects the forest by forming a natural firebreak. In ordinary times the elephants are not numerous enough to destroy the barrier altogether, and it renews itself while it renews them: they have little need to go devastating trees on every side. But as soon as they become too numerous, the thickets disappear and the forest is opened up to herds of elephants seeking substitute forage.

It would not be convenient to discover what elephants eat by watching them endlessly, since they go at it day and night, and even a team of observers would not get far in the dark. Not that a team of observers is available in Africa, despite the teams of teams that do similar jobs on other animals elsewhere. One way to check on what is happening to an area is to look at it after the elephants have worked it over, and also to look at their droppings. This was tried by Dr. Larry Wing and Dr. Irven Buss in Kibale Forest of western Uganda. They worked out that the 216-square-mile forest must contain around 250,000,000 plants, and that more than 400 elephants are feeding on around one plant in five. They also noticed what destructive feeders elephants can be, especially on woody material that they have tried to break up—they make a thorough job of it. The plants are either used heavily or not at all. When these two researchers checked on the droppings, they found a surprising amount of grass remnants in them. Elephants digest only a part of their food, so the droppings tell a fair story, more so than a rhino's, and much more so than a buffalo's. Several hundred droppings in the middle of the forest suggest that well over 80 percent of the food is made up of grass, despite the woody forage around. So perhaps elephants feed on huge quantities of grass not only when they have to, but when they choose to as well. Other people have seen elephants chewing at aloe leaves and sansevieria, then spitting out the debris—perhaps to get at the moisture. Yet elephants in Tsavo Park, with rain pools at their feet, do the same thing. Many theories, no certainty. It will require many more observations and many more elephant droppings swept into sacks before there are any precise indications.

Meanwhile, it is apparent that elephants carry much of their environment from one place to another. These droppings average seventeen pounds and are deposited an average of seventeen times every twenty-four hours, or about 300 pounds. This means the elephants of Kibale Forest are shifting well over 100,000 pounds of material every day, nearly 23,000 tons a year, or 105 tons for every square mile of forest. This represents not only a huge turnover of vegetation but a huge turnover of energy as well. One can hardly begin to visualize the effect elephants must have on their habitat. Seeds sometimes germinate twice as well when they have been through an elephant's gut, and a set of droppings can contain hundreds of seeds. Elephants tear trees down and rip up the soil, aerating a whole microcommunity that might stagnate without its macrocompanions. Elephants act as vast pruning shears for a wide range of vegetation, engineering tracks through thick-grown environments (and elephants are proficient at navigation, selecting the shortest routes with the easiest gradients—by "critical-path analysis"?), which allows a host of other creatures to move about and spread their effects in turn. As Dr. Wing and Dr. Buss have observed, elephants trample down much vegetation with those ponderous feet while trekking around to meet the daily needs of a diet that is remarkably unrandom, if remarkably unknown. Like their droppings, the trampled vegetation acts as fertilizer, as well as producing a protective mat or litter to shade the soil and reduce rainfall runoff or to prevent leaching of unwanted salts to the surface. All goes to build up a soil fauna that in turn builds up a richer biotic community. In Zambia there are signs that when elephants are eliminated from a forest the whole scene starts to decline as the land dries out. Modern Africa makes for too many elephants or too few. The old balances that were calibrated over millennia are being upset in an eye-flicker of time before anyone has a chance to find out what they amount to: all one can judge is that elephants are enormously useful. The present prospect is bleak. Elephants are thronging into the few remaining woodland patches of their environment and destroying them as only elephants can. The processes of elephant style of living that can be so constructive are now turning highly destructive.

Elephants are among the most adaptable creatures on earth. Within their limitations they show a capacity for resource and resilience to surpass all except the one being adaptable enough to outmaneuver all others put together. Evolutionary forces have constructed a world subtle and sophisticated for an array of life that man is not yet ready to document, let alone appreciate. Evolution and elephants alike are running up against forces with an unprecedented impact. Whereas the earth's upheavals put an end to the dinosaurs in an immense and instant-long "great dying" that lasted a few million years, the cataclysmic changes now under way last no longer than a part of the lifetime of the visitor who travels to Africa and looks at elephants and marvels. It is a change that is silent, and insidious, and swift like no other. If the elephants are to survive, it looks as though it will be under conditions that are far from natural. The signboards on the edges of the parks saying PRIVATE FARMLAND, KEEP OFF are as powerful as iron bars. Tsavo Park is the size of Vermont and is in danger of being reduced to an enlarged zoo, so inadequate is it for protecting the wild scenes of Africa. Worse than an enlarged zoo is the prospect for Tsavo of an impoverished zoo. What elephants were like in their wildest of wild states, what they ate before they were afflicted with malnutrition because of malnutrition in another more proliferant being in the environment, is something we may never know. An obvious answer would be to feed some of the excess elephants into the outsize numbers of local people. But at present there is no elephant specialist available to recommend any solution at Tsavo, or Murchison, or a dozen other places in Africa with an elephant problem.

This is one way to get rid of ectoparasites at the base of the trunk. The rubbed-smooth bark shows what a favorite tree this must be; sometimes a less sturdy tree is knocked down by overvigorous rubbing.

NAKED MOLERATS

Sometime toward the end of the early morning period the wildlife-watcher in the drier parts of East Africa may come across a sight that is more bizarre than many he will see during the day. Certainly it is more characteristic of Africa than elephants, rhinos, or lions: most of these creatures can be found on other continents or have appeared elsewhere at some stage of their history. To see a truly African animal, like the lungfish or the aardvark, one should take a look at a naked molerat. It is only a few inches long, and it is one of the prodigies of the continent.

A naked molerat is hard to come upon, since it is almost always underground. It is most active around midmorning and in the late afternoon—especially in the period just before the rains; its habitat receives less moisture than much of East Africa. There are other molerats that live in damper areas and are several times as big, but they are not adapted to the specialized underground life of the naked molerat in hot country. If you are very watchful and very lucky, you may see one emerge briefly from its tunnel to peer around on the surface. It does not stay above ground, since its skin has no protection from the heat and glare, no hair or pigmentation, and it cannot sweat—which is partly why it does not need to drink. It cannot see very well; its eyes have been almost "evolved out" over the course of time. Eyes are not much use in the molerat's world of permanent darkness; it might be even better if they were to disappear, since there would be less possibility for getting sand in them.

Left below: As soon as the naked molerat is brought above surface into the sunlight, it immediately starts to dig down again. With back feet braced and front legs shoveling the soil away, it doesn't take many moments to disappear.

Right below: There are other molerats in Africa, not all so naked. They all have the same elongated incisors for digging.

You can't watch a naked molerat long: almost immediately it dives down again. It is powered for extremely rapid tunneling. The massive incisors do the digging, and the hind legs scoop the soil away while the animal balances itself on its tail; or the hind legs form an arch for the front legs to do the work. Once the molerat disappears, it is not long before there is a conical mound several inches high with soil erupting from the top several inches higher. The molerat progresses underground at a speed that is incredible until you see it.

A man digging with a spade can scarcely keep up with it. Miss J. Jarvis has observed them for two years and finds that a colony can set up corridors and shafts hundreds of yards long. She follows them with a Geiger counter, keeping track of specially impregnated animals.

Molerats require long tunnels to find their food. They also prefer colonies of twenty or so to help locate food, which can be scarce in their parched country. Molerats that live in wetter areas do not have such a problem finding food, and they generally live singly, a life-style possibly appropriate to their extraordinarily aggressive nature— whether toward other molerats or whatever. The naked molerat lives off succulent roots and bulbs that it finds primarily by bumping into them. There is not much of their kind of food in dried-out soils (except during rains, when their activity increases), so a molerat is always on the go while it is awake, restless and energetic, probing around to investigate whatever fresh patch of ground it finds itself in. It is probably one of the most mobile animals of the savannah—much more so size for size than the wildebeest with all its trekking to and fro, during the day and during the year.

A naked molerat seems grotesque until you look at it in its environment. Its skinny shape is most efficient for roaming around underground. There are no bits and pieces sticking out, such as ear flaps. Its legs are as small as they can be while still able to do their work: they are not projections so much as minimal appendages. A molerat is not a mole gone wrong. Instead of the padlike feet with claws that a mole uses for tunneling, the molerat has developed incisors like long chisels. They grow throughout the molerat's life; they are constantly being worn away at the tips from so much work, which keeps them always at the right length and maintains them as some of the sharpest tools in the animal world. There is a fold of skin in the cheeks that can be drawn into a tooth gap between the incisors and the molars, sealing off the front part of the mouth so that while the molerat is working its way through tough soil it is not bothered by mouthfuls of earth.

There is little about a naked molerat that is not useful to its life beneath the hot scrub-lands. It is an example of evolutionary forces that have dispensed with what does not help. Surplus features have deteriorated over the ages until there is a sort of "progress through regression." Such is the phenomenon the visitor sees with his eyes as the soil spurts out of the ground, and sees with his imagination as he follows the busy, out-of-sight tunneler. For once he can talk as loud as he wishes about what he is watching. The molerat can scarcely hear. But it detects the stranger's presence through vibrations in the ground. If he moves about, the sand-spurting stops. To watch a molerat even at one remove, you must enter a molerat's world. It is no good watching from your own elevated stance: the molerat will soon enough become aware of your world to counter it.

VERVETS

By ten o'clock the sun is soaring. The safarist is less likely to notice how high it is than how hot it is. The animals notice, too. By now the early-morning activities have shaded off into others, although it is still too early for the noontime retreat into the shade.

This is a time to watch for vervet monkeys. They are leaving off their feeding and making ready to head for the trees. It takes them a long time to make the shift. On the way they indulge in a good deal of social activity, searching around in each other's fur. It is now, when they are busy with the "grooming" and very much involved with each other, that they can be most easily approached. At other times they are too alert to tolerate strangers; they have to be suspicious if they are to continue being vervets.

No vervet does not enjoy being groomed. One of the troop may approach another while feeding; or one comes and lies down in front of another, expecting to be stroked with all the gentilities of the ritual. A third vervet may assist. An expression of beatific

An infant vervet is very dependent on its mother for a long time, as well as on the protectiveness of the rest of the troop. When it starts to get its black adult face it attracts less attention, and less tolerance too.

contentment spreads over the face of the monkey getting the treatment. After a while it returns the compliment, or it goes and passes on the consideration to another. This ritual may have originated from the need of vervets to rid their fur of the blood-sucking insects they pick up as they move around in the grass; and from this origin of mutual help the gesture expanded into a practice of great ritual significance. By and large, any vervet can groom any other vervet. This is a factor of no small significance. In vervet society everyone knows his place and better remember it—or else. But grooming often cuts across many of the social barriers. In a community where powerful forces emphasize the hierarchy during the greater part of the day, random grooming must build up a sense of acceptance that acts as a strongly cohesive force. Without it the community could become prone to divisive tendencies. It might even fly apart. This would not help in a world where protection is largely a matter of being with plenty of other vervets. A glance at a troop suggests there are outbursts and sporadic fighting going on all the time, all as haphazard as can be. But these flare-ups are nothing compared with what might happen if creatures like vervets tried to live together with no bonds to counterbalance their inclinations toward individualism. Members of the troop rub shoulders constantly. In many an activity of the daily round a vervet reveals what could well be a measure of intelligence greater than a lion's or an elephant's. There is a probing urge to adapt and adjust the prevailing state of things, together with a strong instinct to dominate others. In very broad terms, there is a need among creatures of such mental agility and nervous energy for a system that establishes the social scheme of things. This communal pecking order, to which everyone submits, is balanced by the communal scratching order, which actually implies less order, since anyone can pretty much be groomed whenever he wants to be.

Life in a vervet troop is not all that unpredictable. It doesn't take long for a watcher to pick up something of what goes on. Watch two monkeys going for the same piece of food: one seizes it; the other may have been in the act of reaching out when it was superseded, but pretends he has not noticed after all. If the relationship is not so clear-cut, there might be a brief conflict, which soon emphasizes who is superior. The lower-rank monkey makes no further attempt to retaliate. Instead, it goes away and passes on its annoyance to some monkey a notch further down the scale. This one passes it on again, and so on until the frustration reaches a miserable wretch at the end of the line. Status does not altogether depend on age or sex. Occasionally the leading male is far from the oldest; he might even be subordinate to several females. Nor is social standing dependent on sheer strength. What counts is confidence. A monkey with a steady gaze and a demeanor of imperturb-

An infant vervet usually clings onto its mother's stomach, though it occasionally rides on her back, as does a baboon baby after a month or two. Patas monkeys, which are much more adapted to living in the open grasslands, always carry their infants underneath, since they would be too prominent on top for a monkey that places a premium on concealment. Vervets never stray far from trees, which allow them some immediate protection.

able superiority can outface one that is bigger or merely a "tough." A stray baboon, even a small one, in the middle of a vervet troop stands out as far bigger than the rest, but as soon as it senses it is in a foreign environment it becomes unsure of itself and quickly shows it. It promptly loses face and has to give ground. A vervet of the lower echelon is easy to spot. It is a shifty creature, constantly looking over its shoulder for the doom it fears is going to strike. It expects the worst, which helps to draw disaster down on its head. A well-bitten monkey is not a social outcast: it just feels it is, and so behaves in a way that leads to its being treated as such. A monkey of superior status does not need to maintain its position by constantly defending itself through combat. A single look, and aggression from another quarter promptly evaporates. Authority has its own rationale.

Among young vervets the system works to protect the weak and helpless, and hence to assist the survival of the species. Until a vervet infant reaches eighteen months or so it can snatch food from any superior. If there is retaliation the outburst brings the rest of the troop to the rescue: resisting an obstreperous juvenile is just not worth it. Generally a vervet youngster is appreciated by all and sundry. By virtue of its special position it is assured its own well-being. There is also a strengthening of the cohesive forces that hold the troop together. A shriek from a youngster, and everyone looks up. A year later nobody will notice what noise it makes, unless it is a warning of threat from outside. A soft call—loud enough to warn the troop, but not noisy enough to put the interloper on its guard—means danger at a distance. A loud cry, harsh and urgent, means it does not matter if the intruder gets the message too, since it is already too close for comfort. All these forms of communication can be picked out in a single half-hour's watching. Usually the sounds and screeches express the subtleties of the vervet social scene, accentuated by facial expressions that also have their purposes. When the face is relaxed it is all over black and all over normal. When the monkey gets angry or alarmed the face goes taut until a pale strip stands out under a fold around the eyes, emphasizing the beetling effect of the eyebrows. The new mood is obvious. At close range, the stern aspect discourages an opponent before it escalates to final violence. This is a feature common to many primates: the face acts through gestures or sudden coloring to show what has supplanted the previous peacefulness, and signals to an attacker whether the situation is worth pursuing further. It is only when primate combatants devise a system of fighting at long range where they cannot see each other that such safety devices break down.

Many of these features of troop organization, however, vary from one locality to another. The vervets on Lolui Island in Lake Victoria, a land of milk and honey for vervets (and with few predators), flourish within a network of territories that are small, but strongly defined and defended. At Chobi on the River Nile in Uganda, by contrast, an area made half barren by excess hippos and elephants, the vervets are harder pressed to survive; they are much less numerous and must range far more widely to find food. They do not demarcate their far-reaching territories through nearly so much scent marking; a good part of their daily routine is radically different. The same applies to vervets through-out the huge segments of Africa which they have made their habitats: the local conditions make for variations in vervet life-style, until it is not nearly so simple to say what a vervet is—even in one area from season to season. What suits the troop one year may have become fundamentally changed a few years later, leading to fresh troop organization, new patterns of social behavior, whatever else allows the vervet to feel tolerably at home in the world.

Most monkeys keep to the trees. The vervet is one that has managed to adapt itself from a life in the forest to one in the open woodlands, even part way out into the savannah grassland. The creature is worth investigating to see if it gives any clues as to how a more capable primate once made the step from a life in the trees to a life on the ground. But the supply of vervets for such an investigation is not as plentiful as one might think; just because you see hundreds in the parks does not mean there are thousands in the much larger elsewhere. Vervets used to be the most numerous monkey in Africa, possibly in the world. But they are not hard to trap. And they are needed for experiments on how medicines repair one's insides, or how cosmetics enhance one's outside. Vervets can be captured in Africa only outside the parks and reserves. One such unprotected area near Nairobi was not long ago losing 150 a week. Now a trapper would be lucky to find five. But he would not be allowed to export the animals from Kenya anyway. The trade, which was up to 18,000 a year, has been stopped, despite the usual arguments about animals versus people. The vervet is now better safeguarded in many of the areas where it still survives. The "rescue," which was a rescue before a rescue was finally needed, was instigated by the World Wildlife Fund, which, to its credit, decided to help an animal that was only in danger of danger. There had once been hundreds of thousands, and now there weren't. Funds are usually available only for creatures far closer to ultimate disaster. When a species is on the brink of extinction it is more than threatened, and there is more threatened than just a species. This is what wildlife and conservation should be about. Someday that is what it will *all* be about: conserving, not salvaging.

MAN

The visitor to East Africa has the opportunity to view a scene that has been of immense significance to whatever wild world he sees during his safari: the site of an earlier primate that took a more adaptable route than the vervet. If the safarist spends an hour at Olduvai Gorge he can consider some of the origins of the creature that has done as much as all the other creatures put together to shape the recent savannah scene: man. He has purged it with fire and opened up the grasslands. He has hunted animals far and wide, possibly helping to push some of them toward extinction. He has developed special hands, special feet, a special brain. He has even discovered a special way of adapting: instead of waiting for biological change to adjust him to his environment, he has broken out into a cultural evolution that allows him to adapt his environment to himself. At first he achieved this revolution by picking up bits of the environment, stony bits, and using them in an original fashion to fend for himself. Over long stages he learned how to manipulate the habitat until it followed his bidding more closely. Over the final very short stages he has learned how to control many more aspects of the environment—although not nearly as much as he likes to think. No other animal has ever learned more than the barest rudiments. All this he has done without changing himself. Instead of becoming physically specialized for some particular role, he has remained the compleat generalist. He can exist on the equator, and he can exist at the poles. He can exist as a more or less complete vegetarian and as a more or less complete carnivore. He has never thrown off a subspecies, since he has not had to. Far from producing modifications in his own body, as all other creatures in all other ages have done, he has produced changes outside his own body by fabricating tools and fire and clothing. He alone has developed capacities for consciously exploiting the ecological network that had been developing for at least 1,000,000,000 years before he arrived; he has also developed capacities for ripping to shreds the entire fabric of life. On a cosmic cinder revolving around an insignificant star in an inconsequential galaxy, he has brought himself to near-mastery of creation. He may still have time to recognize just what he is—barely enough time. He is still an animal, if a precocious one. He still has to eat and excrete. He still has to breathe oxygen. He reproduces his own kind like other animals, though he is far more adept when it comes to keeping his progeny in being, if not in balance. The visitor at Olduvai is seeing one of the main sources of this phenomenon. Visitor, know thyself.

The early man-form at Olduvai lived by a lake, benefiting from a sheet of water that

Hand axes at Olorgesaillie in southern Kenya indicate the sort of technology that enabled primitive man to cut pieces of meat off another carnivore's carcass, or to make his own kill.

appeared nearly 2,000,000 years ago and disappeared only a few seconds ago in the long African day. Here dwelt a creature whose skull, found by Dr. L. S. B. Leakey, dates back to about 1,750,000 years ago, just under six minutes ago on Africa's time scale. Other hominid remains found at Lake Rudolf are almost 1,000,000 years older still. Among the creatures living at Olduvai were some that were proficient at making stone tools; you see hundreds of them around. Some of them were proficient at catching animals; there are plenty of bones there, many of them split open to get at the marrow. These hominids all lived side by side with creatures that disappeared while the man-forms, or their successors, were evolving—creatures such as buffalo-sized sheep and the hippo-sized pig with three-foot tusks, along with a few kinds of pig, including the warthog, the bushpig, and the giant forest hog that the safarist sees today. There were several different kinds of elephant, one with tusks in the lower jaw that curved downward like those of a walrus. There were crocodiles half as long again as today's largest. The biggest tortoises in the world today survive on islands off the East African coast, but there were once tortoises here with shells seven feet long and two and a half feet high. Man himself was possibly not more than four feet tall. He had no forehead, but a bony brow and a bony ridge along his skull. He had a brain only about a third the size of the visitor's. He sported a massive lower jaw that together with its large molars gave him the name "nutcracker man." Possibly his dentition went part way to leaving him little choice but to be a vegetarian; there are no signs that he could make fire.

There are plenty of signs that he was one of the most advanced ape-men—or man-apes—to emerge on earth. It is not certain how close he is to the climactic missing link. Some people say it is not the link that is missing, but the chain: how to relate the various parts? Among the other creatures found at Olduvai, contemporary with the Australopithecines to which this creature belonged, was a being that has sometimes been named *Homo habilis*, or "skillful man." He was probably a direct ancestor of the safarists who come to look at the place where he grew and lived and fought and died. Both these strains stem from a stock that originally shared one lineage with the great apes, possibly as far back as 25,000,000 years ago, before the parting of the ways (although biochemical research now suggests the breakaway could have been far more recent, a trifling eight or only five million years ago). The ape line went on to produce chimpanzees and gorillas; the other produced the sub-man hominids. Some people believe that one of the first hominid creatures was the Proconsul discovered by Mrs. Mary Leakey at Lake Victoria and reckoned to be 20,000,000 years or more. Others place Proconsul in the other camp, while still others place him just before the parting of the ways. At any rate, Proconsul was an apelike creature with teeth that were sharp for fighting and hands that were flexible for grasping. His physiognomy shows how the scene was set not only for the apes and the monkeys but for the forerunners of man.

Proconsul was also one of the first beings that abandoned the runalong action of the tree-living primates. Instead of holding on with feet and hands as they moved along the branches, they took to swinging from branch to branch using a special structure of the shoulders and chest and elbows and wrists. The safarist, too, could indulge in brachiation somewhat like the anthropoid apes and unlike the monkeys. Possibly the larger primates had become too big for easy scampering along the slender branches. They had to take to a modified life in the trees, and even to a modified life on the ground. As the forests of Africa declined in the drier periods 25,000,000 years ago, there would have been a greater need to attempt ground-living in savannah style. On the grasslands there were more carnivores than among the trees, and only an ape that was large enough to look over the grass tops or perch up on its back legs to see what was going on (supposing it weren't so small, like the patas monkey, that it could easily hide in the grass) could survive. Slowly this became a way of life for some; it was the first time any creature had achieved it while being advanced in other ways, that had fine muscular coordination from its earlier stages in the trees where any slip meant that the line would be carried on by those that didn't slip. This was a creature, too, that had developed no mean brain through the delicate deployment of complex muscles for tree-living.

The start of bipedalism was an advance of the first order. Living on one's back legs means one has more time to use one's front legs for all kinds of other activities. They hold things; they manipulate things. They become hands, and then tool-using hands, and finally tool-making hands. Not that modern man with his adept forelimbs has altogether left his four-legged life—he is still prone to ruptures, flat feet, and other liabilities of a not-yet-natural way of moving. Over the first few millennia of this development it might even have been no great advantage unless it was counterbalanced by advances in other directions. Possibly this was the time when the brain was growing more rapidly, working out not only how to make tools but how to apply them in a range of situations: planning ahead for tomorrow and the day after tomorrow, for a food-source it could not yet see and on a horizon it could not yet discern. An Egyptian vulture is a tool-user (it picks up stones for breaking open ostrich eggs), and a chimpanzee is a tool-maker (it adapts twigs to extract termites from their holes); neither is a visualizer of tool-needing situations at more than one remove. A gorilla's brain, less than a third the size of a man's, cannot grow any bigger as long as the gorilla needs large teeth and heavy jaws with heavy muscles that have to be attached to a strong support on the top of the head; hence the thick bony crust and the beetling eyebrows of a gorilla. Somehow the hominid creatures of the other stem dispensed with the massive jaws, though some of them had a chin that looks more like a chimpanzee's than a man's. As soon as the teeth had become smaller and the jaw lighter, there was less need for a fixed skull structure. The brain could expand, and the tongue could develop in the more refined mouth with its greater space: one of the starting points of language?

It is doubtful, however, that the Australopithecines could communicate much except by grunts or gestures or by knocking each other over the head. But they could walk upright, and fashion rudimentary tools by flaking slivers off stones, and survive in the savannah plains. Most important, they could do all these things at once. It is not so much the individual items that count as the combination in a single creature. They could organize their lives in a range of specific directions. When ape-man left the forests he took with him a set of teeth and a set of habits that were suitable for eating fruit and fungi and leaves, but in the savannah he found far less of his usual diet. There was protein aplenty, but it was in large lumps and on four legs. For a while he may have contented himself in part with the life of a scavenger. His teeth would have been little use for tearing at the tougher parts of a carcass as it lay on the ground, so he would have had to get used to the idea of picking up scraps from a lion kill before the hyenas got at it, and then running off with them: that takes sound hands and sound feet. Slowly he would have started using his flesh-ripping tools as prey-killing tools, perhaps picking on one of the hyenas that challenged him for a carcass. (These manlike creatures were perhaps the only ones ever to eat hyenas, except other hyenas.) Dr. Leakey has illustrated how man, nevertheless, may not have been driven to use his tools as killing implements for some time: a person known more for his prowess anthropological than athletic, he has shown that he can catch a gazelle with his bare hands. But eventually man must have learned how his tools were better at providing him with a kill-carcass of his own. Perhaps he learned on one of the more fragile creatures: perhaps on one of his own kind.

Man has been a cannibal for a long time and with a larger appetite than many other creatures. Ever since he first became a hunter, this puny creature must have found he could best operate in packs, and these packs must soon have found they could best insure their prey supply by protecting their territorial rights against the pack over the hill. Within the pack, too, there would be friction and fighting, especially among creatures that were developing inclinations to violence along with their new hunting life. Among

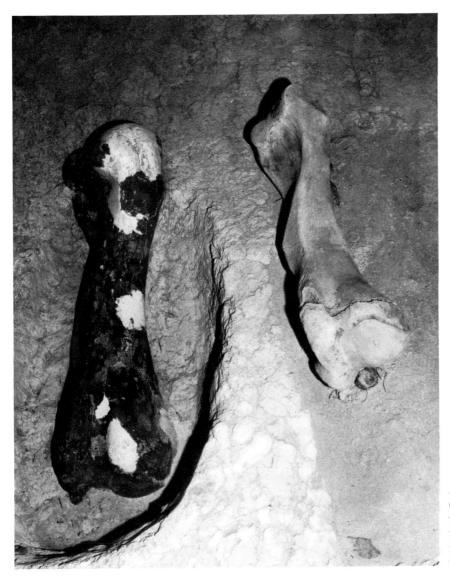

A primeval elephant's bone (left) shows how much larger were some of the prey animals that primitive man came upon, in comparison with today's variations.

other predatory carnivores there have gradually grown up social systems to limit the damage they can do to each other with the powerful claws and fangs that they were developing. Lions show strong inhibiting tendencies to prevent their threat-displays from escalating; it is not always lionlike to go further, unless there is little alternative. But in many respects manling had scant time to allow instinctive sanctions to grow up in balance with his other changes. It would be faster for him to devise his blunt instrument and take aim at his brother than it would be for restrictive tendencies to grow up in his nature. In a sense man has still not grown accustomed to the power afforded him by his tools for modifying his fellow men. He wages war and claims it is a law of nature—which is just what it isn't. Nor is it a protective device for keeping the population in balance. During this century, a period of the biggest wars in history, the population has far more than doubled. Yet the creature that has learned to be a hunter better than most, by virtue of the tool in his hand and the brain in his head, was also learning a thing or two of a different kind. He learned the advantages of cooperation and communal living. Was this the start of the more flattering features of man's nature?

The whole story of tools is a complicated affair. It is hardly true to say that ape-man developed a large brain and then the spark struck. Evolution does not work that way. An animal picks up a fresh characteristic, such as a lot of gray matter, only if there is a definite and immediate advantage. The brain would not arrive by accident. Some of these hominids had brains not much bigger than a modern chimpanzee's, yet they had tools. Did they develop brains to go with the tools, then better tools with the better brains, and so on? If man has been the maker of tools, tools have been the making of man. A chimpanzee can use a tool, but it has not developed the angled foot structure for upright running that characterized the hominids; it can only hobble. Nor has the chimpanzee developed a hand with a precision grip for making a chopping axe, even though it has developed a powerful grip for using the chopping axe on an animal's tendon. Gradually the tools became more refined and more varied—cleavers and choppers of divers kinds. Hand axes came into vogue six or seven hundred thousand years ago, and were being used in much the same way as recently as fifty thousand years ago.

This stage brought spreading of the implements that the visitor can see scattered on every side at Olorgesaillie in Kenya. Gradually they spread across the savannah lands of Africa, around the Mediterranean, along the Atlantic coast of Europe and into India. If, as seems more than possible, the original starting point was the savannah stretches of Africa, it was an area suitable in ways that the safarist can see for himself. The plains are dotted in every direction with animals. In prehistoric Africa there were more; this was not bad country for gangs of hunters who could catch their prey as it came to drink in huge herds. Bison country in Wyoming, which may represent something of what prehistoric America looked like, can at best manage only half the living animal weight, more usually a quarter, that average African savannah sustains. Europe was a forested place and would hardly support more than a tenth of what bison country attains. The steppe country of southern Russia, with its saiga antelope, averages less again.

Meanwhile, man was learning more techniques that may have resulted in the still greater change wrought by this upstart creature. Before he had fire, he had tools that had become sophisticated weapons, suitable for whatever animals he set eyes on. Possibly he chose larger animals, since they could not run so far nor hide so well, and they supplied a larger pile of food when he got them to the ground. No animal would be too large for a pack of hunters with their axes and bolasses and two-edged "knives." These primitive progenitors gazed out over at least a third as many more species as can be seen today; most of the missing ones are the larger beasts of the Pleistocene. Their bones have been found in hunters' homes at Olduvai and Olorgesaillie and Kariandusi. Over the earlier period of 1,500,000 years the process of elimination was very gradual; nineteen genera of large mammals. Suddenly, during the brief period from 100,000 to 50,000 years ago, there was a regular orgy of destruction: twenty-six genera gone in a flash. The larger animals in present-day Africa tend to have a slow rate of turnover, which may partially explain why the larger animals of bygone days were suddenly exterminated. It would be a good deal easier to eliminate the approximately 15,000 elephants and hippos in Queen Elizabeth Park than it would be to eliminate an equivalent weight of zebras and wildebeest from the Serengeti, where there are ten times as many animals and much faster ones at that. Neither before nor since that Pleistocene slaughter of the megafauna has there been such an outbreak of catastrophe for the larger mammals. Although the last 1,000 years have seen a sudden unleashing of forces across the African landscape that transformed the place even more rapidly, and the last 100 years have seen the ultimate upheaval, the arrival of Western civilization, in neither of these periods has Africa lost a single complete genus. (The last thirty years of this century might tell a different story.) Some people think that man played only a small part, if any, in the wide-scale destruction, and suggest instead that the main factor may have been drought. But, as Dr. Paul Martin has observed, it must have been the only drought of such a scale. It did not affect Madagascar, whose onslaught coincided with the arrival of the Malagiche people, when two out of five of its species suddenly disappeared. If mainland Africa lost a good third, North America lost two-thirds at a single sweep, when the Baleo Indians appeared. All three waves of extinction did not occur at the same time, not by thousands of years, which makes climate an unlikely factor. On the other hand, one might wonder why the African animals did not disappear as widely or as swiftly as those of North America. If they were growing side by side with the new predator that was slowly finding its feet, they would have time to develop defenses against what was to become their scourge. In North America the disaster was as instantaneous as the invasion (yet since those early times the Indians have not accounted for a single species, not even after they acquired horses). Possibly climatic changes made the larger, less adaptable creatures more vulnerable to the new threat.

By the end of the Early Stone Age, 50,000 years ago, the slaughter had come to an end. Things were getting very recent, down to the last ten seconds of the long African day. Man was starting on a series of leaps and bounds that would take him to his present elevated stance—if not to falling headlong over his teeming talents. He had already mastered fire, and fire was mastering new methods of producing tools. Fire was also allowing him to cook things, food for his stomach and poison roots for his weapon tips. He was also learning how to use fire for scaring animals into traps. This increasingly expert hunter remained a hunter until the arrival of new tools and new ideas, which allowed him to turn to agriculture in the last one-hundredth part of his existence, 10,000 years ago. By 4,000 years ago there were domesticated cattle. By 2,000 years ago the first Bantu-speaking people were on the spread, rather under half a second ago on Africa's time scale. It was a last-moment assertion of ascendancy over nature.

Some people think that now, in this last-moment flickering of the last moment, there is a mounting counterassertion by nature. Man does not inhabit a remote planet of a remote system in a remote galaxy. He lives on a wafer-thin covering around his earth home, wafer-strong, too. The most trifling ripple of the cosmos would erase it, but maybe it won't have to wait for cosmic calamity: it can find one nearer home, such are the predatory assaults on it by this creature that can be a power second to none and a parasite second to none. If he is to make a further adjustment to his surroundings, it will have to be a quick one and a big one, an adjustment in his style of living that will be as great as any precipitated by the greatest revolutionary changes of the past. To tackle the challenge he will have to use the mechanism that is the finest product of evolution. Man's brain could not be matched by a computer except one too big to be accommodated on the planet. His Stone-Age brain is enough; there has been no advance in size since primitive days: the Bushman and the Berkeley professor share much the same equipment.

MIDDLE DAY

The sun soars. Everywhere there is glare. You wonder if it can get any hotter—and it does. But what strikes you most is the way the sun presses down. It is never as oppressive anywhere else. Other creatures feel the heat, and they make for whatever protection they can find. The elephants disappear into the thickets and swamps; so do the rhinos. The hippos have long since submerged in their glorious mud; now they lower themselves that extra couple of inches. The buffaloes join them. The lions are usually nowhere to be seen; they are lying up in tangles of undergrowth. A leopard is getting what breeze there is high up in a tree. The cheetah seeks out the cool of a bush; like the other great cats it pants and pants throughout the heat. Hyenas, jackals, foxes, all have disappeared long ago. The savannah is still. Even the birds are silent until the harsh time has passed.

But this is also the time when many animals go to drink. They have already set off in

long treks to the watercourses, line after line of antelopes moving languidly through the shimmer. Not every beast that drinks comes away again. While the noonday sun makes any lioness anxious to avoid activity, a hungry lioness is something more than a hot lioness, and she makes what use she can of the water holes. Other predators, too, may be on the lookout for midday kills. Vultures are soon on the move if they catch a glimpse of a struggle beneath them. The giraffe does not seem to mind the heat despite its bulk, and it remains more active than most. But all in all the bush scene is not nearly so alert and alive as it was earlier on, nor as it will be when the late day arrives.

There is still plenty to see. Africa presents a different face, though it is far from asleep. Africa is never dozing, except perhaps around the safari lodge where the afternoon torpor is more apparent than out on the plain. The savannah activities merely take on a different form. An antelope standing still is not "doing nothing." Nor will it stay still for long; it soon goes back to what is more characteristic of it, feeding. Meanwhile, its mechanisms do not come to a halt. It has had many a long hour throughout its African day to become adapted to the African heat. At noontime it brings other subtle devices into play to make it even more of an antelope. The watcher might wonder how it has learned to survive with more composure than he himself is feeling. If African wildlife represents some of the

Far left: One way to pass the sweltering hours.

Above: Few creatures enjoy themselves so much at the water hole as elephants, and few elephants make such a thoroughgoing job of it as an elephant young enough to delight in such things and old enough to do it on its own.

Top: Thomson's gazelles can go for a long time without water, Grant's gazelles for a lot longer, even months. You have to watch more carefully than for most animals to catch them at a pool, and then more quietly than for most: the camera click sent these two far out into the plains again.

Bottom: Zebras keep away from the shade sanctuary of thickets and brushwood patches at midday: they might not come out again.

most remarkably varied forms of life, they are equally varied in what goes on inside—this variation is not so easy to discern, but it is there many times over.

And hot Africa gets hotter. You can hardly bear to look at the sky, but the clouds make a spectacle of their own, with banks of cumulus piled up in huge downy masses. They float around, showing there is a breeze somewhere up there. The crests spill over as if they were foaming with life from deep inside. This is something that really looks whiter than white: they are incandescent. However much they cover the sky, they never seem to obscure the sun. All is very fine at morning time and one says, "how wonderful"; by midday one wonders again.

The snows of Kilimanjaro sparkle with a harsh glitter. Below them an inert peacefulness settles over the wilderness. In a sense it seems a little less wild, as if the normal vigor of free nature has disappeared. But it has not; the plains are not unmoving or lifeless: they are just hot. However things may appear, this is Africa too—and Africa alive. It is not a suspension of the normal way of things, just another aspect. The man who wants to go to Africa should experience Africa in all its forms, Africa the extreme as well as Africa the benign. You brave the midday sun and you remember it—not altogether with regret.

LEOPARDS

Every safari expert in Africa has his own idea about how the lion hunts. Some say a lion pride working as a team can devise subtle traps: one roars, to stampede the prey toward the others. But anyone who has the luck to watch a lion roaring during the day finds that the animals roundabout do not take much notice. If you play a tape recording of a lion only a few yards away from them, they go right on grazing. You hardly ever hear a lion roaring by day; far more often at night, which suggests that a roar is a territorial warning, or a means for one member of the pride to keep in touch with the rest.

One has to be extremely lucky to see a lion on the attack, and far more than lucky to see a leopard—just to see it at all, let alone see it on the hunt. Leopards are solitary and secretive as well as nocturnal and shy. In any case, over the last few years their numbers have been falling in the face of the fashion trade. Now it is quite a privilege to find a leopard in broad daylight. People have lived in Africa for years without ever seeing one— even though it is quite likely that many a leopard has seen them. Only in the central Serengeti can you reasonably hope to find one, and here a leopard is almost as easy to spot as a lion; they are plentiful and assured, safe from the hunter.

Around the later hours of the morning you may glimpse one as it goes on its prowl. A leopard starting its hunt is silent and efficient, ignoring all else. It may use your safari truck as stalking cover, and peer around the fender with supreme disregard for the creature on the other side of the glass. Whereas a lion may make several attempts before bringing off a kill, a leopard sets about it as if it manages every time. Of course, it often misses, but it looks the consummate hunter. A lion depends more on sheer strength, and does not altogether need the sinuous stealth of a leopard, silent and unobtrusive though a lion tries to be. A leopard is a powerful creature, too. Pound for pound, it is perhaps the strongest of the cats. It has been known to pull down a 400-pound antelope and drag it into cover. A giraffe calf has been found high up in a tree: what else could carry it there but a leopard? The leopard is specially adapted for its role, just as a lion is specially adapted for its different role. The leopard is a tree-climber and is more lithe than a lion or a cheetah. But did leopards learn to climb trees because their light build had already adapted them for various activities on the ground, and allowed them to make part of their habitat above ground if need be? Or did leopards find they *had* to learn tree-climbing because of over-intense competition in the predator spectrum of those prehistoric times, and so developed a body structure appropriate for tree-climbing as well as helpful in various other activities? This is no mere academic point; it tells what slot the leopard occupies in the ecological scene. From some angles its role is clear; from others it blurs off into the field of other predators.

But "ecological separation" need not be confined to the animals a predator hunts. The leopard can hunt the same animals as others; in East Africa it takes a lot of gazelles, just as do lion, cheetah, wild dogs, and hyenas. Lions, however, hunt gazelles only for the part of the year when there is little else available; it is certainly not the lion's number-one choice, as it often is for the leopard. Wild dogs hunt gazelles, but they have a diversified diet, and only overlap slightly—or briefly—with the leopard. Cheetah hunt gazelles, but mostly females and fawns, especially pregnant females that cannot last out the chase. (In this sense, cheetah may be more of a limiting factor on gazelles than leopards, which take more gazelles altogether.)

While you are watching the leopard on its stalk (it is a lengthy procedure), you can speculate on what fresh signs of the leopard's standing may be drawn from its camouflage. The spotted coat is admirable in the bush savannah, whether to the safarist observing it or to the antelope not supposed to be observing it. It matches the various clumps of vegetation that dot the grasslands, especially around the rock outcrops, the kopjes, in

A leopard on the stalk moves from tree to tree looking for a vantage position, using the side of the trunk away from its prey. Having made a kill, it may hoist the carcass up a tree as steep (and branchless) as this one, even with a carcass heavier than itself in its jaws.

places like the Serengeti Plains. It is an equally fine disguise in a forest where the dappled light-patterns conceal the leopard at a few yards. This, together with the technique of instant attack at close quarters, allows the leopard to be at home in a forest as much as in the grasslands. A lion cannot operate among the thicker vegetation, whatever jungle movies suggest. It cannot twist like a leopard in a confined space, nor can it deploy its strength so well; moreover, its coloring is perhaps not as suitable among the green tangles of a forest environment as in the yellow grasslands. Yet a lion has a common ancestor with a leopard, as is indicated by the spotted patterns of lion cubs before they grow up. The watcher may ponder whether the lion was obliged to abandon the forest because that environment did not suit its powerful assault technique, and hence slowly assumed a better savannah camouflage as well; or whether it avoided close-grown environments where its coloring rather let it down, and then steadily developed the hunting practices (and the body to go with them) of the open country. Again, there can be no answers until there is more information on which predator is the most successful in which habitats, and for which prey species—and in what seasons, in competition with which sorts of predators, and so on. There is a fair amount of information on lions and cheetah and others, but more in isolation than in relation to each other; but next to nothing on leopards. Until the day when the interrelating factors as well as the basic facts are established all the theories will remain less than theories and authoritative assertions will be guesstimates at best. In East Africa there have been people studying birds, rodents, small mammals (none of them endangered) for years; only in the last year has someone started studying leopards anywhere in its range from West Africa to East Africa to South Africa.

There are one or two broad ideas that offer remote clues, together with such interpretation of the scattered facts as anyone may wish to try his hand at. The same rule of thumb that is used for the lion—that predators hunt creatures of roughly their own size and weight—can be applied to the leopard. It hunts antelopes around the 150-pound class, such as impala or young wildebeest. Or it takes smaller creatures like oribi, dik-dik, or klipspringer. A leopard can turn its paw to a wider range than any other of the great hunters, even subsisting on rats and birds if need be. That is why there are leopards closer to Nairobi than the Nairobi Park, half a dozen miles out of town. Leopards rarely starve, not in the way lions do in the Serengeti when their usual prey has migrated beyond the horizon. On the other hand, a leopard hunts the larger animals much more seldom. Wild dogs hunt creatures many times their size, but they do not hunt alone. To a lesser degree the same holds for lions. Cheetah, on the other hand, can sweep a wider stretch of country with their far-ranging tactics; they are not territorial in the same manner, either. Yet wild dogs tend to pick up small creatures that the bigger predators do not notice. As a pack goes foraging across the plains, a dozen or so together, they are more likely to spot a gazelle fawn hidden in the grass than are two or three cheetah or half a dozen lions (which do not go in for much marauding across the countryside anyway). A lioness can pass a few paces from a young gazelle and never suspect. A leopard, watchful and alert as it is, has been known to spend a couple of hours consuming a Grant's gazelle while a fawn lay huddled in the grass a few strides away. Neither infant would have escaped a band of wild dogs or a pack of hunting hyenas. In this sense, as Dr. Richard Estes has observed, wild dogs may exert a greater effect on gazelles than lions or leopards, even if there are generally far fewer of them.

Of all the great hunters there is none so solitary as the leopard. It is a cat that walks by itself. It is independence unique. Its hunting technique reflects its nature: it works by surprise, the stealthy stalk. In some dialects its name means "the one that kills with a single leap." It gets as close as it can, then a step or two closer. A leopard has been known to rear up out of the grass and seize a buck right above it—striking *up* at the creature rather than at it. Secretive and solitary, that is the leopard. But, again, which comes first? Is it solitary because a hunting companion might not be any advantage? Or is it stealthy

Above: The kill made, the leopard gets its gazelle into a tree as soon as it can. With the carcass wedged in a fork, the leopard is safe from most carnivores. Even vultures do not bother it, though they perch in a nearby tree waiting for the leopard to finish. If the leopard moves higher up the tree to rest, away from its kill, the vultures still keep off—an angry leopard is quicker in a tree than a vulture.

Right: Temporarily gorged, the leopard rests—although it will return to what is left of the carcass even several days later, when there may be as much flies as flesh. Meanwhile, the gazelles down below are not aware of what is watching them; they rarely look above head-height, and they would be unlikely to spot an inert leopard anyway.

and sly because some other facet of its character makes it unsuitable for living with other members of its kind? So little is known of this creature that fascinates so many but whose workings elude even the most experienced in the wildlife world. Ask fifty wildlife experts in East Africa, and all of them together do not know as much about leopards as any one of them knows about elephants. People talk knowingly of the lion's way of life and the secrets of its domestic arrangements; you can make out what a cheetah is up to because it is an animal with a disposition as open as the plains it frequents. But the leopard is a law unto itself, and nobody else knows the laws of its game. It comes and goes in a manner known only to its individual self, possibly not even to another leopard. They are never seen together, except at breeding times, or when a full-grown cub has not yet gone off to follow its own solitary existence.

The leopard hunts to live. Watching it you might think it lives to hunt, as if it spends the time between hunts just waiting for the next opportunity. A leopard was once seen relaxed in the late morning sun on the branch of a tree, gazing at a herd of Thomson's gazelles near a river. The gazelles were not coming to drink, since they do not need to bother much with water, but were seeking out the greener vegetation along the river banks. This was the place for a leopard, with plenty of cover, and a leopard knows how to make use of every last clump. It did not rush in for a hurried botched-up attack. It waited and watched. It sensed which direction their grazing would take them. Finally it slipped down the trunk on the side away from the gazelle herd. It used another couple of trees as further check-points, closer in. Then it crossed over to the thick growths of the riverbank. The gazelles moved closer. Finally they entered the taller tangles, the danger zone. Nothing happened. Half an hour, and still nothing happened. Suddenly there was a spurt of dust, the gazelles scattered, and there was the leopard with a kicking carcass dangling from its jaws, silent as ever, impassive and implacable.

You can sometimes find out what makes a creature what it is by finding out what it isn't; or you might say you cannot really know about leopards without knowing about many other creatures as well. In the long run you can only describe a creature by describing other forms of life it shares the environment with. In this sense a leopard's life impinges directly on numerous others', more than does a lion's or a cheetah's. Its hunting tally can spread across forty different creatures. It preys on guinea fowl. Since it also preys on several other small mammals that take guinea fowl eggs and chicks, this might mean a leopard results in more guinea fowl, not fewer. A more familiar example of how a leopard lives with its environment is its supposed predilection for baboons. If local farmers kill off leopards for their skins, they may find a plague of baboons raiding their crops. How many baboons are regularly taken by leopards is open to question. Hardly anyone sees a leopard with a baboon carcass in a tree, even though kills in trees are not hard to notice. In Kruger Park less than one leopard kill in a hundred is a baboon. A baboon carcass probably does not last as long as a reedbuck, so there would be less chance of spotting it. But baboons have highly developed social systems, a purpose of which is to supply joint protection for members of the troop. A single male is capable of driving off a full-grown leopard and its offspring, provided he is backed up by other males close by. A baboon kill is probably rare, though an authentic occasion was once observed: a baboon troop ranged out, foraging over the plain; a lion happened by, and as the baboons came pelting back to the trees one of them ran into a leopard concealed in the grass; the rest apparently viewed a lion and a leopard as too much of a combination.

Baboons or not, it is the leopard's capacity as a cat for all seasons that marks it out in the carnivore community and keeps it from conflicting with others—or they with it. It specializes in being a generalist. And if its role is best seen through that further generalist perspective, the total scene of a wildlife area, then there is only one place so far where it can be considered in detail, Kruger Park. Records of assorted kills by assorted predators have been collected over twenty-five years. Forty-six thousand kills may seem like a mass of data that could become a mass of muddle, but in the hands of Dr. U. de V. Pienaar it tells a superb tale of what goes on in the wild. Two-thirds of the kills are the work of lions. There are 1,120 of them, and they get through roughly 20,000 a year of the 200,000 prey animals. Over the whole period the leopards have accounted for one in six of the animals killed, but during that time their share has risen from one in ten to almost one in four. Presumably the leopards have been increasing until their present prosperity of 650, a little over half as many as the lions. In the interim the park has been undergoing a rapid expansion of its bush cover, a result of too little fire to regenerate the grasslands, and too many animals from outside joining the too many inside. Extra bush means more hunting country such as leopards revel in. They are getting through a conjectured 16,000 animals a year, mainly of the smaller sorts. In the meantime, cheetah have come on hard times, and they account for a mere one in twenty of the kills each year, 6,500 animals or less. The wild dogs continue to flourish insofar as they ever flourish: over 300 of them are accounting for one kill in eight, almost 12,000 animals a year. Hyenas and others do not seem to achieve much beyond one kill in a hundred. There is a good deal of variation from one part of the park to another. Wild dogs account for one in three in some areas, less than one in twenty in others (a reflection of the maneuvering space allowed by the vegetation for those far-seeing and far-chasing hunters); while cheetah range from one kill in eight to one in seventy, and lions from seven kills in ten to less than four in ten. Leopards vary from one kill in three to just under one kill in five; hence they appear much the most able to operate in whatever sort of habitat is available.

These seemingly huge kill totals—estimated at approximately 55,000 a year—are taken from an assemblage of 200,000 animals or more. Despite the attentions of all those predators, the prey animals have doubled their numbers over the past fifteen years, and at the same time as the shooting of carnivores has been stopped, and an anthrax epidemic has decimated the herds, followed by a drought. Proliferating faster than most are the impala, which thrive on the same bush vegetation that helps the leopard: they make up well over half the prey animals in the park. Not surprisingly, they make up three-quarters of the leopards' diet, as compared with less than a fifth for the lions, two-thirds for the cheetah, and five-sixths for the wild dogs. An impala, at 150 pounds, is a suitable size for smaller predators than a lion. In accordance with their larger appetites as well as their larger numbers, the lions take almost all the wildebeest killed each year, almost all the zebras, buffalo, giraffe, eland, and sable antelope, along with four-fifths of the roan antelope and waterbuck, roughly three-quarters of the kudus, tsessebes, and—oddly enough—warthogs (perhaps warthogs are too ferocious and well armored for any but the biggest predators). The lions face little competition for all these prey creatures. They have the field to themselves, and they do not squeeze another predator out of its "ecological hunting space" by their powerful pressures. Leopards, with their greater tendency to hunt impala, occupy a different niche; and when it comes to a whole range of smaller animals, which might not count for much by their numbers but count for a lot in the increased elbowroom they afford leopards, there is another broad field they can work across largely undisturbed: they take almost as many reedbuck as all other hunters put together, even if reedbuck amount to only 1 percent of kills for all predators ($2\frac{1}{4}$ percent for the leopards). Similarly, leopards take a half or more of the bushbuck, duiker, steinbuck, grysbuck, klipspringer, oribi, and baboons; these creatures make up only another 3 percent of the total intake (8 percent for leopards). It is marginal, but it matters.

The overall figures can be perused endlessly for fresh insights into who kills what and when. In the face of the recent upsurge of impala numbers, every predator except the cheetah is now taking a quarter as many again as twenty years ago. This means that lions are taking proportionately fewer wildebeest, the wild dogs fewer waterbuck and kudu, the leopards far fewer bushbuck. On the other hand, the lions are taking nine times as many buffaloes, if still only an eleventh of their diet; so what prey animal is released from lion pressure to be exploited further by which other predator? Leopard patterns vary from place to place: impala average three-quarters of their total diet, but amount to only a half in some areas, while other creatures—minor parts of the diet—are preyed upon twenty times as heavily. When you look at leopard kills in relation to the number of animals available of each species—the "preference rating"—the bushbuck comes out on top, followed by the waterbuck (which has the misfortune to be second for cheetah and wild dogs too, and first for lions). Impala, which are so heavily preyed upon by the hunting community altogether, rank fourth for leopards, twelfth for lions, fifth for cheetah, and number one for wild dogs. The preferred species for the cheetah is reedbuck, the creature

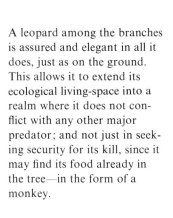

A leopard among the branches is assured and elegant in all it does, just as on the ground. This allows it to extend its ecological living-space into a realm where it does not conflict with any other major predator; and not just in seeking security for its kill, since it may find its food already in the tree—in the form of a monkey.

so heavily preyed upon by leopards, but it still makes up only a twentieth of the cheetah's diet.

Just as important are shifts in hunting from season to season. A sustained assault in the birth season can be as drastic in its consequences as what goes on over all the rest of the year. Cheetah step up their predation on impala half as much again during the calving period, though largely on adults—twice as many females as males. During the dry season with its great concentrations around the water holes, the lions kill a third to a half again as many of the zebra, wildebeest, kudus, and buffaloes. Sudden rains out of season can leave any hunter watching its usual menu march out of the area overnight. At times like this it is up to each hunter to shift its pattern as fast as it can, and there is little doubt which is the most adaptable.

Even if the leopard is all that competent, it is probably no more capable at its job, all considered, than are the other predators. If it were, there would soon be far more

The crater of Kilimanjaro may seem a strange place for a leopard. But leopards are by far the most wide-ranging of the big cats, and have been found high up on Mount Kenya and the Ruwenzoris; they also flourish farther into the deserts than most lions want to go.

leopards around. Possibly the same restraints apply that limit lions. Does a leopard feel that another leopard this side of the horizon amounts to crowding, and goes to do something about it? And if so, which leopard—the male or the female? If it is the female leopard that discourages intruders, there could be consequences for the breeding patterns—fewer females than males in congested areas—that would not help much in the leopard world. Places where there is a fair idea of how many leopards constitute capacity suggest they are generally much thinner on the ground than lions. Conversely, their food tastes, as well as their food-getting techniques, enable leopards to flourish all across the length and breadth of East Africa, in human habitats as well as wild. There is a Leopard Point on the Indian Ocean and a Leopard Point at Kilimanjaro's summit. If a leopard can exploit a wider variety of terrain, it can exploit all manner of minor complexities that altogether amount to a substantial advantage. In rainy weather a cheetah may be at a disadvantage on slippery surfaces; to a leopard the weather is always fine. Lions like to hunt more in wet and cloudy conditions than fair, though nobody is sure why. Possibly the circumstances, whatever they are, benefit the leopard, too. Nobody knows.

In one sense the leopard occupies a distinct, if regrettable, position in the wildlife community. It can be robbed of its prey by lions and frequently is. It can be robbed by hyenas, and it is, even more frequently. It takes its prey into trees to get out of the way of interlopers. Even up there the prey is not safe from lions—nor is the leopard itself—though lions do not have a fraction of the climbing ability of leopards. Although those massive lion limbs are better for action on the ground than thirty feet above it, the lions are not deterred. They clamber up any tree they can with the smell of meat in it. Hyenas are yet more inclined to plunder another hunter. They monitor a leopard's movements, just as they do with wild dogs and vultures. They recognize the familiar pattern of a leopard on the stalk, and they sit and wait. For all its terrible ferocity (and a cornered leopard can hold several lions at bay for a while), the leopard comes well down in the hierarchy of hunters. It can rob a cheetah, and that is all. But what does it matter if it is not right at the top of the heap? It clearly survives well enough. The predators do not direct the system, whatever their dominant demeanor may suggest. They are part of a myriad of beings that live off each other, with each other, through each other.

This does not mean that a leopard in late-morning isolation on a bush track is any the less a creature to wonder at. When it is not "relating" to others in its own intrinsic manner, it is still a creature to relate to the viewer. A man eyeing a leopard eyeing him back might feel he is nearer to the wild world than elsewhere. The leopard looks out from somewhere behind those green eyes, and the gaze is not the lion's gaze. It communicates something else. Perhaps it communicates that the leopard is a being apart, with nothing in its nature that speaks to a mere visitor in its domain. As it pads on its way, the onlooker knows he has seen something different.

LIONS IN TREES

In two parts of East Africa there are no lions to be found on the ground after midmorning. The lions of Lake Manyara Park and Queen Elizabeth Park climb trees and spend much of the day reclining among the foliage. Down below there is sometimes little shade for a heat-suffering lion, but aloft they enjoy a nice breeze. The odd flick of the tail to swat the flies away, an occasional eye cocked at the cigar-chewing camera down there making a lot of noise, and the rest of the day they snooze in repose.

At Lake Manyara there is a semiforest type of vegetation, and the lions probably climb trees to escape insects and biting flies in the grass. They have less need to find adequate shade, for there is plenty of that below. In Queen Elizabeth Park, on the other

Overleaf
Left: Lake Manyara lions like to get out of the way of flies. They also like to get out of the way of elephants and buffaloes, which sometimes cause lion cubs to come to a sudden end. Things get congested in this 35-square-mile park with its 400 elephants, 1,500 buffaloes and 35 lions.

Right: This Queen Elizabeth Park lion obviously has something to digest. A fig tree with broad spreading branches low down is not hard to climb, though there are particular ones—perhaps every twentieth tree—that the lions seem to favor. From up there, they can spot which way the plains herds are moving—although they have not been known to drop out of a tree onto an unsuspecting antelope below.

hand, there is open savannah grassland with just an occasional fig tree about the plain. There the lions have more need to climb trees to find refuge from the sun—except that the same conditions prevail in other parts of East Africa without the lions' feeling the same urge.

Hauling three or four hundred pounds of lion aloft must be quite a job, even in a big tree with its spreading branches low down. And if getting up is quite a problem, getting down again can be almost as difficult. With a few grunts the lion comes down at a rush, half leaping and half slithering. One lioness once came down so quickly that she lay on the ground for a quarter of an hour, out to the world.

Lions in other areas have been known to climb trees in emergencies. In Ngorongoro Crater the 1962 floods brought on a plague of flies—nine generations in a single season. The multitudes attacked any lion they could find, leaving the only escape twenty feet up in the trees, where the lions were clear of the worst swarms. The lions declined from something over sixty to less than a dozen. Now they have recovered. In the Serengeti there are lions that climb trees from time to time to get at a leopard with its kill. But for a siesta they prefer to climb the kopjes or great rock outcrops that dot the plain. They sprawl around on top, getting whatever breeze there is and using the rocks as lookout posts. You might wonder how they bear the open sun up there. All of which seems to indicate two things: that lions can climb trees when they need to, and they may do it to get out of the way of flies. The visitor seeing a lion on the ground is often struck by the insects pestering it. It is hard to see what good the flies could do the lion—except, as someone suggested, to keep it from brooding too much on being a lion. Much else is mystery, just as the look in the lion's eye as it gazes down from its lofty perch. He looks at the tourists and the tourists look back, each as mystified as the other.

The tree-climbing lions in Queen Elizabeth are especially capable as crowd-pullers. Already they attract visitors by the hundreds each week; before long it should be by the thousands. These dozen lions could soon be some of the most valuable animals in the world—if they are still around. They live on a narrow salient of park land, the Congo on one side and a Uganda hunting area on the other. The trouble is that there are only a few square miles for these few lions, and there isn't enough of either land or lions. The pride used to consist of a black-maned lion, a few lionesses, and an assortment of cubs. Their range could not be confined to this one small strip. Sometimes they strayed over into the Zaire, though in the main they sensed that was a country better to stay away from. Or they moved into the Uganda hunting area. The pride was all too easy to recognize, since that magnificent black mane was known far and wide. One day a white hunter heard of them. He was determined to go and put that proud head on his wall. All he had to do was wait. Sure enough, it wasn't long before his patience was rewarded, his courage, too—behind a high-powered rifle. The local people took note. The famed tree-climbing lions were not so sacrosanct after all. Several of the pride disappeared in quick succession. The rest moved out of the area. A good while later they returned. But for a time things were not what they used to be. Sometimes it would be weeks before anyone saw more than an occasional lion. If those particular lions had had the sense not to be something special, not to supply new insights into the wildlife world, as well as some remarkable photographs, they might not have been so notable. This is not always a world to be special in.

CROCODILES

By midmorning the launches on the River Nile in Murchison Falls Park are travelling up a stretch of river where you can see more crocodiles at close range than anywhere else in East Africa, probably in Africa. It is a good idea to take one of the earlier launches to see

When the crocodile needs to get back to the water in a hurry, it "sledges" along the sloping shoreline before taking the final plunge. A ton-weight crocodile taking off from a river bank occasionally twenty feet high is something to imagine. And that is largely what it is, a sight scarcely to be seen any longer—any more than ton-up crocodiles.

the crocodiles in their Mesozoic multitudes, since by the time the late-morning launches arrive most crocodiles have taken off into small inlets or other places where they can get out of sight. No visitor wants to look at a crocodile at a distance idly lying there; he wants a photograph close up, and he wants action, preferably the crocodile plunging into the water. So the coxswain is urged to drive his craft as close to the bank as possible and race the engine until the crocodiles perform. The tourist feels gratified if not edified, and the boat moves on to the next lot. A few crocodiles haul themselves out onto the bank till the next launch turns up. Repeat performance, another in a series of dozens that go on throughout the day.

There may be an answer in time if the crocodiles get used to the boats (they haven't managed it after ten years). They are timid creatures anyway; and perhaps they recognise that a boat is as likely to contain poachers as tourists. A better answer would be to explain to the tourist that he is contributing to the demise of an animal which is already in critical straits. Tourist disturbance is greatest during the peak season from January to April, just the time when the crocodiles are protecting their nests. Unguarded nesting grounds are exposed to rapacious plundering by a host of creatures that are not so fearful of boats as are crocodiles. In any case, a troop of baboons working through a nest of crocodiles' eggs makes an unusual picture for the camera addict. Out-and-out tourism, allowing the demanding viewer everything he demands, tourism going in up to the hilt and deeper still, is not the same as conservation through tourism, despite the numbers of times tourists are upheld as the saviors of wildlife.

But explain all this to the tourist and he may ask how an aggressive monster like a crocodile can possibly be timid. Besides, a crocodile may be fascinating to gaze at, but it is still somewhat repellant, isn't it, not really one of the nicer creatures? It is hard to work up much sympathy for a beast like that—if it is going to present such an appearance to the world, it had better learn to look after itself. Well, the crocodile has done a pretty good job of looking after itself; it has had plenty of time to work on the problem. It was here 100,000,000 years ago, which is roughly 95,000,000 years longer than a modern elephant or a hippopotamus, and 99,000,000 years longer than a leopard or a baboon, and many million years longer than the Murchison Falls themselves. It has devised a way of living that is highly successful, except for the late twentieth century. Until quite

On the Nile in Murchison Falls National Park, there are often over fifty crocodile eggs to one nest. But over half the nests are opened up by creatures other than the mother crocodile, while one in three of the remaining nests is overtaken by disasters such as flooding. An average of only two eggs out of a whole clutch may eventually produce full-grown crocodiles—which is no more than is generally needed, unless the adults are being decimated by poaching.

recently it was impossible to swim in most lakes or rivers in Africa. Now the tourist can plunge into almost any stretch of water throughout the continent.

Along this seven miles of Nile in Murchison Falls Park, there are slightly over a thousand crocodiles. According to two of East Africa's leading ecologists, Ian Parker and Murray Watson, it is doubtful if there are another thousand within the rest of Uganda, a country the size of New England. Some say it is equally doubtful if there are an additional thousand along all the rest of the Nile, all 3,000 miles of it. But if there is something appalling about the crocodile, is it not in the grand manner? And is there not something exhilarating about standing in modern Africa and sensing you are back in dinosauric days? This is one of the most striking ways you can get a sense of an era as remote as that, way back in the earlier half of the long African day. Yet crocodiles hardly accord with our tidy idea of what is right and proper. The ancient Egyptians felt they had to propitiate them in temples, eventually embalming them and placing them in sacred repositories. The monuments at Abu Simbel were saved at much expense by help from every land, while the creature to which some of the temples were dedicated is now being driven from the scene—precisely because of its unique appearance, if you listen to the cries of some vermin-hunters. Far from being a reason for the outright destruction of this magnificent monster, that should be a reason for its protection in a world of bland conformity. Few creatures have been so revered and reviled.

But if the crocodile is more popular dead than alive, it is helpless against the appetites of a fashion trade whose demands are voracious in a way no crocodile could match. Its skin is too fine for this world. This is refined plundering of a kind the greatest rogues and robbers could scarcely exercise so efficiently or so suicidally. Uganda's trade used to be worth the best part of half a million dollars; now it is a mere fraction of that, and plunging. Botswana sold 3,000 skins a dozen years ago; in a recent period of four years they dwindled to 500. Hence the significance of bans on the trade in several centers overseas; the legislators achieve so much, they know not what they do. There was a time when a crocodile count across Uganda would have been impossible—there were too many; now it is all too easy. But as fewer legal skins become available, many more dollars are pursuing the illegal ones. When the resources of the United States cannot protect the alligator in the Everglades, one wonders what chance the crocodile has in emergent Africa.

The crocodile is now considered an endangered species in much of Africa. It has never been an endangering species. It takes an occasional cow or goat, but, despite claims to the contrary, it does not always go for many fish of the sorts that humans take. While it is a master of hunting and scavenging, it does not harm man's activities—rather it helps him, by taking the large predator fish that eat into man's food supply in many lakes and rivers. It is such an all-rounder that it straddles much of the ecological spectrum, having learned how to fit into the community without making a nuisance of itself. It was learning its place a long time ago, and a long time before that. The forerunners of crocodiles were among the first creatures to establish a beachhead after leaving the primordial seas; this was over 200,000,000 years ago, when the vegetation of the earth was developing into ferns, and landscapes were becoming covered with coal forests. More and more plants were spreading that had only recently begun to trap the sun's light in chlorophyll. Perhaps another 100,000,000 years elapsed before the crocodile finally emerged as one of the most advanced of reptiles; perhaps this is why it survived the catastrophes that lay ahead for the reptiles. A crocodile is a fairly advanced creature, the only lower vertebrate to possess something approximating a four-chambered heart—a great help in sorting out the blood at a critical stage of its circulation: in most reptiles there is some mixup during the pumping process, when oxygenated blood going out meets exhausted blood coming in. To separate the chest cavity from the abdomen, the crocodile also possesses a structure resembling a mammal's diaphragm. And it has a brain more developed than almost any other reptile, though its intelligence does not account for that leering look.

Yet, as reptiles go—or rather as they went—the crocodile may have remained more rudimentary than some of the outsized dinosaurs that took to the land. The larger saurians perhaps evolved such complex circulatory systems during the 100,000,000 years of their rule over the earth that they could regulate their blood temperature better than the water-dwelling crocodile—and then they ran into the climatic changes of the late Cretaceous, when seasonal shifts started to replace the permanent summer: such switches could have seemed decidedly wintry to animals too large for hibernating. The crocodile nowadays holds its temperature at around 78° Fahrenheit, with a variation of only five or six degrees on either side. Its day-long routine matches the changes in its environment. It comes out of the water at daybreak and basks in the sun. It stays there until late morning (launches permitting), and then returns to cool off for a spell before hauling itself out onto the bank in the early afternoon. As the earth's atmosphere undergoes a rapid cooling toward evening and grows steadily colder throughout most of the night, the crocodile returns to the water to a more constant, hence warmer, temperature. This routine is supplemented by the crocodile's habit of lying with its jaws open during the hotter part of the day to allow evaporation from the mucous parts of its mouth. It even takes to lying half in and half out of the water so that part of its body absorbs moisture while the other part releases it.

Despite the hours a crocodile spends on dry land, it is primarily a creature of the water. As the crocodile submerges, a "curtain cover" allows it to maintain clear sight. Since it gets most of its food under water and at night, its eyes are able to take in whatever light is available: they have a pink pigment that helps it to get around better in the dark than most creatures—they glow, but with refined vision rather than blood lust. But no matter what time or place, crocodiles are at home in the water: they have been seen miles out at sea, and even tangling with sharks. As they swim along they use only the tail; the legs are folded close against the sides. The tail is so massive that if it were not for the hind legs it would be difficult to tell where body ends and tail begins. It is powerful enough to sweep a large animal off a riverbank, perhaps breaking its legs on the way. It is also strong enough to enable the crocodile to surge a good way out of the water and strike at a bird on the wing. A creature with a body so large and legs so small is—like the hippo—built for a water world. It needs the buoyancy. When it is in the water the crocodile weighs only a twelfth of what can amount to a ton for a full-grown male. Sometimes, however, it weighs too little. When it dives it "pulls in" its chest and abdomen to reduce its specific gravity. Then it just sinks. But it might lose stability and even float upward again like a cork, if it weren't for the stones in its stomach, up to thirty pounds of them for a big crocodile, averaging 1 percent of its dry-land weight. In its early years the crocodile swallows pebbles or even broken glass or bits of pottery to increase its weight to about one-eighth in the water. This provides ballast for hydrostatic balance. Before they find their stones, young crocodiles tend to be top-heavy or tail-heavy, and they cannot lie on the surface like their elders: they roll over. A grown-up crocodile has been found with twice as many stones as usual in its stomach—but it had lost half its tail.

A hippo can stay underwater for a good four minutes. Seals can manage longer and whales a lot longer. But a full-grown crocodile can stay under for an hour—some say much longer—without undue trouble. Yet for all its equanimity in water, there is water and water. The crocodile likes to rest just below the surface with its snout just above to breathe. It does not like rough water, which may be why it avoids the open areas of lakes, or in fact any unsheltered shorelines. On Lake Rudolf the 12,000 crocodiles are largely concentrated away from the western side where broad beaches with little vegetation are exposed to the surf whipped up by the winds across the lake. Sheltered water may also be favored by more fish. Crocodiles like sloping beaches that make life easier getting in and out of the water. But this sort of shore is preferred too by hippos, especially those with calves. Along the banks of the Nile the hippos seem to monopolize the best areas, while

Wherever there are crocodiles there are usually birds, and not just the tooth-peckers of legend (of reliable experience too, even if infrequently). Some river birds, especially the cormorants and darters, account for more fish than all the crocodiles on the Nile put together.

crocodiles have to settle for second best. There may be no other way but to forcibly persuade hippos to allow extra living space for less fortunate creatures. Crocodiles and hippos, however, are not the only ones that like sloping beaches: humans do, too. This is probably another major factor in the crocodile's decline in Africa, where human populations are expanding into every last corner of the landscape. It is one thing to try to control poaching or restrict an international fashion trend, but it is another to find *lebensraum* for crocodiles when there are other contenders more vigorous. Just finding a lake or a river in which to throw artificially hatched crocodiles is not enough. In the old days you could swim around in the middle of Lake Victoria and not get taken by a crocodile in a year; now you can do it along 700 miles of shoreline too.

On land the crocodile is not a fraction so rapid as in the water. Stories of sprinting humans being overtaken by a fleet-footed monster are the prerogative of films. The crocodile usually staggers around with its body arched high over the back legs, since they are longer and have to take most of the weight. These stout hind limbs suggest that the crocodile is probably descended from an ancestor that walked around partly upright. When it is in a hurry, and especially if it is going downhill—which is the route the crocodile generally takes when it is alarmed and trying to get back to its water refuge—it takes to a "belly run," sledging over the ground and using its tail to scull itself along, with the legs acting as oars. There is a third kind of movement that younger and lighter crocodiles use when they are frightened and there is no slope handy to the water: they "gallop" along with the body bucking like a bronco, a sight to be imagined—and better seen.

Occasionally a crocodile is caught a long way from water. It may wander inland across patches of flooded country, only to find that the rains have receded and the water is a dozen miles or more away. If the distance seems too far for the crocodile, it digs a tunnel under a bank and settles down in its underground chamber. And if there is no bank handy, the crocodile goes straight down. It works its way into mud, digging lower and lower until it is five feet down. In this self-inflicted confinement it subsides into a stupor. By the time the rains come again, five months later, there are plants growing across the entrance.

One solution for the crocodile's bleak future is to set up crocodile farms. One is being tried in Uganda. It will be a long process. According to Dr. Hugh Cott, newborn crocodiles are less than a foot long. A male puts on about ten inches a year for the first seven years and a female two-thirds as much. After that they slow down until they are growing at most an inch a year, the female even less after she starts breeding. The farmer has to wait far longer than farmers are generally prepared to. But it is a growing process to which there may be no end. A really big male measures twenty feet and a female over fifteen feet. In the roaring reptilian days of the Mesozoic there were crocodiles fifty feet or more. By the time the modern midget gets up to twenty feet it may be a hundred years old, and some of the largest crocodiles may be well into their second century. But no one now alive is likely to find out even roughly how old they can grow. The biggest crocodiles are the ones hounded down first by the hunters.

A female crocodile does not usually produce eggs until she is nineteen, but then she produces fifty at a time and up to twice as many as she gets older. The Nile crocodiles seem to produce more eggs than at Lake Rudolf, where conditions may not be as favorable—or they may be so favorable that there is less need for large numbers of eggs. Laying is timed for a stage in the dry season when there is a prospect of lower waters and no flooding during the three-month incubation period. Hatching is timed for the return of the rains, when the young will have plenty of shallow places in the flooded plains to get away from the older crocodiles, which are not indifferent to a youngster or two. The flooding waters also bring a fresh supply of insect food for the infants. When the female crocodile scoops out her hole, she may dig only six inches down or several feet, depending on how hot or moist the atmosphere is. She covers the eggs with sand, rather than with grass as an alligator does. Then she settles down nearby to wait. She does not hatch them so much as guard them. If the site becomes too dry, she may let water trickle off her body after she has been in the river. During rainstorms she may shield the nest from getting too soaked. Generally she just watches. She spends her three months virtually without food. She falls into a sort of trance. This is the time to try approaching a crocodile on foot—a breeding crocodile takes little notice. She abandons the nest only if she gets chased away by something so unearthly as a tourist launch.

But as soon as she is gone plenty of creatures are waiting to pounce. Monitor lizards and baboons lead the way on the Nile, with mongooses, honey badgers, marabou storks, and vultures all willing helpers. Nests that escape predators or flooding may still fail to hatch, because they are too damp or too hot. Others have no female on hand to open them up when the young ones down below croak to get out. The top of the nest can get so hard that a man needs a knife to chip away the mud-brick earth. The tiny crocodiles emerge, snapping at the world and each other. Yet they seem to like each other's company for protection, and they do not lose their gregarious instinct until they are much bigger. They lie on top of one another in piles, perhaps to keep warm, too: their small bodies do not conserve heat so well as when they are bigger. For a long while they need plenty of protection. They climb up on top of the female's head or shoulders, often several families together, while she slowly enters the water and helps them get the hang of it by gently submerging and surfacing again. They do not need to eat much for several months while they subsist off the yolk enclosed in their bodies when they hatch. Slowly they take to a diet of insects and small water creatures. During the first month they hide away in swamp patches or weedy shallows. They avoid the usual basking grounds more and more until eventually they seem to disappear altogether. They may hardly be seen again until they are five years old! By that time they have outgrown predators that would swallow them up when they were small, such as storks or herons, eagles, kites, and egrets, as well as monitor lizards and the smaller cats like serval. The only threat they haven't outgrown is another crocodile. A twelve-foot adult has been seen with a four-foot young one in its jaws, maneuvering the helpless wriggler until it had it just right for swallowing whole.

While at this tender age the crocodile feeds on other smaller predators, invertebrates such as freshwater crabs, giant water bugs, dragonflies whether nymphs or adults, water beetles, or aquatic spiders, all of which are notorious feeders on fish fry. If it weren't for these young crocodiles, there would be fewer fish in the Nile. By the time they are middle aged, the crocodiles have shifted to a diet of underwater prey, mainly the larger crabs and gastropods or fish. But the fish they take are mostly worthless in direct economic terms; indirectly it is the crocodiles that can be worth a great deal to the local fisherman. The fish they take are generally the larger predatory fish such as Nile perch, barbel, catfish, and lungfish, rather than the tilapia that make up most commercial fishing. But although the crocodile is a creature for all seasons, there are different crocodiles for different places. At Lake Kioga, a hundred miles away, the crocodiles make up three-quarters of their diet with fish. At Lake Rudolf it is nine-tenths fish, and mostly tilapia at that. They have little choice; there is far less prey on the lake shore since the area is exceptionally arid, but the fish are so plentiful you could almost walk across the lake. Here the crocodiles might really be a threat to the fledgling fishing industry, which is at last giving the local Turkana people a way of life that is no longer a struggle to find the next meal. Even on the River Nile the crocodiles below the Falls eat twice as many fish as those above. This is not so much because they take fish that are stunned from the Falls, but perhaps because the water cascading down is better aerated, and hence better for fish. What presumably decides a crocodile's regimen is what there is to eat round-about, just as a lion in Kenya often follows a different diet from one in Uganda.

In later life the crocodiles on the Nile move on to mammals such as antelopes that come down to drink. Or they take to reptiles such as lizards and turtles or an occasional cobra, or puff adder, or even a python. By this stage they are not eating very much since their growing has slowed almost to a standstill. And if it is difficult to say what the typical crocodile eats, it is also difficult to say how much it eats. Dr. Hugh Cott, who spent years looking at crocodiles in Uganda, Zambia, and elsewhere in Africa, believes they do not eat very much except when they are small. A crocodile's life is a tranquil one requiring little energy. Its stomach need be full only once a week or so, whatever its reputation for an insatiable appetite. In fact, a crocodile may spend four or five months before it eats its own body weight, whereas a pelican can get through a third of its own weight every day, mostly fish of the kind humans eat. In southern Africa, on the other hand, it has been

Monitor lizards, together with baboons, wreak havoc on crocodile nests during the day, accounting for over two-thirds of the predation that goes on along the River Nile. At nightfall, hyenas arrive to account for many of the rest.

found that a young crocodile eats nearly 4 percent of its body weight every day, a stagger-ing ratio for a carnivorous creature; for an adult it would amount to around 750 pounds per crocodile a year—enough to make a crocodile farmer blanch.

The methods the crocodile uses to get its food are notorious; they are also efficient. It is so swift that it can take a tiger fish in mid-air. It can occasionally catch a full-grown buffalo or a lion—though one battle among a lion, a buffalo, and a crocodile left all three of them dead. Now and then a camel is welcome. But crocodiles are not the scourge of human populations they have been made out to be. This is as great a myth as the legends of underwater "larders," where a crocodile keeps its meat until it has putrefied enough. Crocodiles can feed off fresh carcasses, although they have to slash at the meat with their jaws and get a grip until they can "corkscrew" in the water and twist a lump off. But when they submerge, a special flap seals off the esophagus as well as the gullet, so they have to surface before they can swallow. If crocodiles cannot chew, how do they get those bits of meat stuck in their teeth for the famous birds of Pliny and Herodotus to come and pick at? Birds have actually been seen at such work, though very rarely. The most likely candidates are spurwing plovers and common sandpipers. More important, the birds act as sentinels while the crocodile is basking; a single call by the bird and the crocodile is alert if not already on the move. A bird has even been seen to bang itself against a dozing crocodile's head, just as ox-peckers do with rhinos.

The crocodile is really only a villain to its own kind. One crocodile in five among the older ones on the Nile shows some injury, especially the males. Generally the tail has lost a chunk, but sometimes a jaw is bitten off short or a limb ripped out. Fights among males are more frequent at breeding times. They display a territorial aggressiveness that has been described by M. L. Modha on the small central island in Lake Rudolf. The three-quarters of a mile of shore may be split up among only a dozen males, the more dominant ones occupying 200 yards and the others only 75. Periodically the defending male takes to the water to patrol his area a few yards off shore. As is usual in a territorial system, the males do not practice "herding" groups of females. The same stretch of beach at Lake Rudolf can feature over 400 other crocodiles: some of them are males that have not yet risen high enough in the community rankings; the more lowly ones seem to offer sub-missive gestures when they encounter their superiors. And if these breeding crocodiles are a sight to watch, they are also something to listen to. The males give off tremendous roars like rolls of thunder at the bottom of a well, at least as stirring as an elephant trumpeting or a lion sounding off. The roars are possibly not so much a warning to another male as a "come-on" to the female: she responds with a hiss.

To inflict such terrible injuries on the armor plating of another crocodile those jaws must be among the strongest in nature. While a hyena can leave toothprints on an iron bar, a crocodile tackling a piece of steel snaps so hard it can drive its teeth back out through their sockets. A human finding himself attacked by a crocodile is advised to dodge the first stroke, then seize the jaws while they are together. He can keep them shut with one hand, according to theory. Kipling's tale of the elephant's child is not without basis; more than one crocodile has been seen taking hold of an elephant, an adult, let alone an infant. One elephant retaliated by plucking the crocodile out of the water, knocking it around a few times, then wedging it in the fork of a tree—as a warning to others?

Stories become legends, until the crocodile is a creature of myth and mystery. It is one animal that goes far to substantiate its fables: the high rate of moisture exhaled through the mouth causes salt to be concentrated in the bloodstream and then disposed of through "crocodile tears." This is a creature of marked sophistication if not marvelous refinement. Even its name reflects the creature, sharp and businesslike at one end, and elongated at the other. In the few places where you can see them teeming, a bank relaxed with reptilian composure is a spectacle to watch; as soon as they are disturbed the whole bank slides into the water. These sights are now very few and far between. One of the last places is the northeastern corner of Lake Rudolf, where there is the best part of 100 crocodiles to a mile—mile after mile along the shore. The whole lake totals over 12,000: it must be the finest scene and the last of its kind. Lake Rudolf is an immense sheet of water, but insofar as the crocodiles spend most of their time within a hundred yards of the beach, they congregate in only one fiftieth part of the lake. So concentrated are they that their biomass there rises to well over 50,000 pounds a square mile: all the pronghorn or bison in the richest square mile of North American wildland cannot achieve half as much.

Alastair Graham believes that they are not in as good condition as they might be. There are plenty of them, possibly too many. They produce fewer eggs than they could, they grow more slowly, they feed less often than do crocodiles elsewhere, they are smaller; all of which could be a way of saying it might help to thin them out a bit—and if one could produce enough skin, there might be ways of cutting the ground from under the poacher's feet. Despite a blight of "button growth" on many skins, Graham believes a good-quality fifteen-foot hide is worth around $75, while one half as big (though well under half the age of an adult) would fetch $35. If an average of nearly two-thirds of the twenty-odd eggs a Lake Rudolf female lays each year are hatching, then 14,000 infant crocodiles appear every year. If they could be cropped at a juvenile stage when the slower growth rate is setting in, they could produce upwards of $130,000 a year.

Crocodiles prefer flat sandy beaches such as these at Lake Rudolf, especially areas with offshore vegetation to protect them from squalls. But crocodiles favor more land vegetation than is seen here, not only for their own shelter but because it supplies more animal life.

Beyond that, of the thousands of young crocodiles that see the light of day, possibly only one in a hundred reaches adulthood, though that seems to be enough to keep the population going. If this perilous growing-up stage could be freed from predators, or if the infant crocodiles were to be raised artificially until they could look after themselves, many more crocodiles would reach the stage where they could earn money for the local Turkana people. The whole scheme would need particular care: taking a lot of crocodiles at, say, seven feet runs the risk of taking too many females by mistake, since they grow more slowly and hence amount to a higher proportion of that particular size group. Probably there should be more males taken; but how can you tell whether a crocodile is a male just by looking at it?

Lake Rudolf is still considered "infested," as if it were infected with some sort of disease, though it is the crocodiles themselves that do as much as any creature to keep down disease through their scavenging habits. But crocodiles across Africa are on bleak times. A few years back there were hundreds on the Nile below Paraa Lodge, rivaling the hundreds above; now they are largely gone, and the breeding grounds at the sites of the greatest concentrations have been largely destroyed. The crocodile has never before experienced such an overkill. The start of a fashion fad in 1954 led to 60,000 wiped out in East Africa in one year; one white hunter dispatched over 1,000 in one month but bemoaned the fact that he could hardly find one over four feet (probably because there weren't many left beyond four or five years old). Other white people once mounted anti-crocodile campaigns on Lake Victoria on the grounds that the earth was to be cleansed of this plague; every year they destroyed eggs in the thousands. Twenty-five years ago crocodiles were being shot on Lake Kioga at the rate of 30,000 a year; now there is hardly one left in the lake, and the few that have survived the holocaust are being knocked off by Africans: who is to say them nay? Experts believe there should be a ban on hunting for fifteen years at least, even though the skin merchants protest that their way of life would be ruined. These same traders are not allowed to traffic in other limited trophies like rhino horn, and there are probably far fewer crocodiles in East Africa outside Lake Rudolf than there are rhinos. Rhinos have been a topic of much consternation, not to say confusion, whereas a strong dose of protection for crocodiles *now* could bring greater prosperity to traders and local communities in a few years' time. The old argument of "animals versus people" should be one for the conservationist to fling in the face of the indiscriminate exploitationist, rather than the other way around, dated and delusive as that argument has now become for the no-holds-barred hunter.

The crocodile has revealed many of its secrets, while still retaining many more. The visitor watches the crocodile gliding away under the water: the armor plating flows from one side to the other before it disappears. Which way did it go? Nobody knows. The crocodile is silent and silurian.

MURCHISON FALLS NATIONAL PARK

The visitor watching the crocodiles in Murchison Falls National Park could well do what not all visitors do—take a look around the rest of the park. The Nile boat trip is an experience in itself, but it reveals less than 1,000 of the 50,000 creatures of the park, and an even smaller part of their variety. Traveling further afield he can see animals ranging from white rhino to oribi, which he is less likely to see elsewhere. He will also see various other familiar features of African safari country, some of them less fortunate than others.

Murchison Falls goes far to representing in microcosm the promise and the problems of the parks in East Africa. It is a somewhat large microcosm, 1,500 square miles, though little more than average as parks go. It is the hub of Uganda's tourism and all that that

Few places in Africa have such a concentration of elephants and buffaloes and hippos too—as Murchison Falls National Park on the Nile in Uganda. And there can be few places with such a potential, and such a need, for continuous cropping, large-scale as well as long-term. If the animals could be persuaded to supply meat to the environs, beyond the 6,000,000 pounds they have already produced through crisis-cropping, the people of the environs could perhaps look more agreeably on the park, instead of seeing it as a huge chunk of land set aside for foreigners—white foreigners, affluent foreigners, well-fed foreigners. The park might even be able to make its peace with the environs, which are now swiftly suffocating the park.

holds for the future. Already it attracts over 70,000 visitors a year, not many as compared with places like Yosemite, which can beat that total in a single day at the height of the season. But some people say that Yosemite is on its way to becoming urbanized during the great migrations, and that one can enjoy all the delights of the suburbs there—which may be why some people go. Prospects of hundred-seat launches on the Nile with loud-speaker commentaries on the tranquil scene are still remote for East Africa, although Murchison Falls draws more tourists than any other park in East Africa (except Nairobi Park, which is close to the big city). If, in a few years' time, Uganda's tourism is to bring in $25,000,000, rivaling cotton and coffee, it will be Murchison Falls that does it. Queen Elizabeth Park does not draw nearly half as many tourists; a whole year of the brave experiment of Kidepo Park hardly matches a busy weekend at Murchison Falls.

Murchison is close to a major breakthrough: showing a profit. Uganda's parks altogether earn about $2,000 a square mile, making them one of the most profitable land-uses in the country. The Budongo Forest near Murchison Falls is so productive that it is renowned across eastern Africa, but it produces less than half as much a square mile as the park; subsistence agriculture, such as occupies much of Uganda's territory, generally earns only a quarter as much, and rudimentary stock-raising, such as surrounds much of Murchison Falls, even less. Tourism could well be producing four times as much in the

Below: A spectacle central to the park is the falls themselves. Actually there are now two falls, following the 1961 floods; but both would be severely diminished by the hydroscheme once planned for this area. How far the park's attraction would be diminished (or the wildlife herds, and all those workers in the park for twenty years) is no engineer's guess. Nobody expects the developed world's yearning for untrammeled nature to stop in an emergent nation with overwhelming yearnings for higher living standards. Far right: The hippos at Murchison Falls cannot spread far and wide, as they can at Queen Elizabeth where there are water-sheets on every side; they are mostly confined to the single strip of the Nile. Until the mid-1960s, a 55-mile stretch of river above the falls featured 10,000 hippos at increasing cost to the river-bank zones. Four thousand have now been removed, drawing people from 100 miles away to the meat.

not too distant future. Fifty years ago the human inhabitants of the Murchison Falls region moved out when the tsetse fly moved in; the tsetse is still flourishing. Yet so pressing are the demands in a developing country with its people waiting to be fed and housed and educated in a way that befits people emerging into new-found independence, that when on one occasion, the Uganda parks asked for a few thousand dollars to assist development, they were awarded a mere $3 (*sic*)—enough, as someone remarked, to erect a memorial.

The onlooker might consider such factors when he speculates on what makes a park run. Figures for finance do not always scintillate with interest, but they go to the heart of wildlife in East Africa. Especially important is the 50 percent share of the gate fees at Murchison Falls that finds its way into local coffers. Of equal importance are the non-paying visitors, the Africans who would find the parks far too expensive to enter—but which they are grandly told by foreigners are part of their heritage. Wildlife depends on public opinion, and public opinion in Africa is African. Most of these free-entry visitors are schoolchildren, the new generation that will decide how things should go. Such factors are just as important as the poaching problem, which generates more sympathy and dollars from overseas. Yet what poachers do to the animals is generally nothing compared with what they do to the ecology of the area. They light fires outside the park to lure prey onto the fresh grass that springs up after a day or two. If the fire burns on across the park, what is that to the poacher? But it could be a fire to wreck the whole burning system for the park territory, since a controlled-fire plan is a basic practice in a park nowadays. Honey hunters light fires in the middle of the park, leaving them to burn out in their own good time. Other people light fires because they know it will harm the park: they have not yet been reached by the sketchy publicity programs. The ecological damage from random fires goes far beyond that of poaching an elephant or two. Murchison Falls has only 300 men to manage the entire area, not all of them fire-fighters or rangers to chase after poachers. The staff is greater than in any other park in East Africa, but it is not nearly enough for an area almost the size of Delaware.

The prime problem is not so much poachers and too few animals, as too many animals

and too few people able to do much about them. An elephant is an excessive-sized animal in itself; when there are excessive thousands of them, there is a problem. These gargantuan feeders, together with the fires, have reduced the park to a monotony of grassland from one skyline to the other, especially in the country south of the river. The safarist arriving at the south entrance might take a look at the landscape before he looks for many animals in it. Winston Churchill stood at this same spot fifty years ago and looked out on a "wide sea of foliage, thinning here into bush, darkening there into forest." Now there is a less diverse tale to tell, and less diverting, too. The decline has been halted in recent years by cropping elephants, but the problem was ripe twenty years ago, before the place ever became a park. Is this in fact what one wants, a stereotyped vista of unchanging grasslands (or is wilderness never a stereotype—does it need a wild sense in the beholder to be appreciated for what it is?).

The park plans to modify the vegetation again, this time in the opposite direction. The underlying policy of the park is "to maintain and create by natural means as diverse a habitat as is possible and natural to the area." Splendid as it is to find a park with a definite policy, one pauses at this pregnant statement: does "natural means" include bullets? And to perpetuate what is "natural to the area," does one post rangers around borders to keep out elephants fleeing into the park from harassment outside? And "create": does that mean "recreate" and "restore," or does it allow for new ideas about fresh combinations of flora and fauna that have not grown there before? After deciding these preliminary points, how does one go about inducing more vegetation on those southern stretches if it is to be more varied? A prime problem—and a costly one, entailing lengthy fences and ditches to keep elephants out of rehabilitated areas, and reinforced firebreaks to keep out an even more wayward intruder. It will mean planting trees (in rows, to use the space more efficiently?) and waiting until the trees are safe from destruction: they are not proof against fires until after five years; how about elephants? Is the entire area to be covered with trees, eventually, if that means fewer grassland animals like hartebeest and oribi and kob? Probably the aim should be something of everything. Would a more varied vegetation mosaic produce a greater assemblage of animals altogether, apart from just different ones?

The problem in this form applies south of the Nile; a different approach will be required in the north, where the vegetation has not been altered so much by elephants or fire, and where climatic differences may have helped to maintain a richer array of wild creatures. Or did these differences, rainfall for example, arise after the forests of the south bank had disappeared? Not that there is all that much variation in rainfall between the two areas, but possibly more runs off uselessly south of the river. Elephants on the north bank have a more rapid breeding rate, as do hartebeest; the river has long been a barrier enough to keep the two populations apart. In fact, Murchison Falls Park is really two parks.

But there is no doubt it is a single park when one is trying to cope with problems from outside. Again, the Murchison Falls region is something of an epitome—and an unfortunate epitome—of the pressures besetting most wildlife areas in East Africa. Yet, once again, it is a region with a plan. The plan has not yet been adopted, but the blueprint stage is far ahead of most areas. The park's creatures need much more than the park's territory to keep them going, and they are threatened more and more as human activities continue to crowd up against the park's borders: cultivators constitute a threat more than poachers or fire-makers, inducing more animals from outside to squeeze into the overcrowded area. Of the 200-mile border, two-thirds is threatened by types of land use—mainly cultivation that amounts to little more than subsistence agriculture—that are far from in harmony with the park's needs. There are proposals for tobacco and sugar, which would bring some degree of control, though in the long run they would only contribute to the same creeping paralysis. What is wanted is a range of land uses that would not compete with the park's interests but coordinate with them. A park does not exist within its boundaries, it exists within its region. This factor has led to a proposal for a buffer zone around the park where the environs can supply a breathing-space instead of a nooselike no-man's-land. The plan could be a landmark in conservation for this part of the world, emphasizing how conservation aims at rational protection of the entire environment, not just places where wild animals live. It would provide security for one of Africa's finest wildlife assemblies and far, far more besides. The area surrounding the park would be utilized in support of the park itself through a combination of stock raising and game cropping. The scheme should bring in over $2,000,000 a year, or around two dollars an acre, more than a good enough return by most standards in East Africa. Even more important would be the approach: an integral region would be protected by a single conservation authority, a tremendous advance over the fragmented administration of other regions where local authorities proliferate and the area's right hand may not know what its half-dozen left hands are doing.

The 1,500 square miles of Murchison Falls National Park are only part of a greater ecological bloc comprising the entire region. An imaginative land-use proposal sees the area as one conservation unit under a single integrative authority, allowing a range of activities—wildlife, tourism, large- and small-scale cattle ranching, game cropping (and perpetuation of the park)—in coordination rather than in conflict with each other.

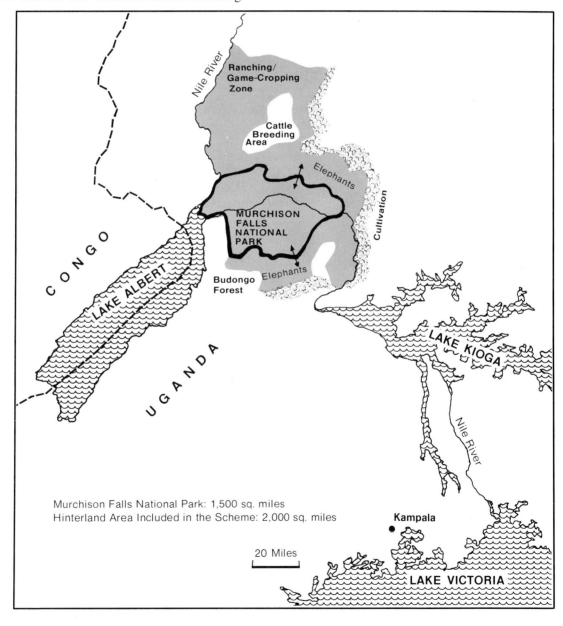

Murchison Falls National Park: 1,500 sq. miles
Hinterland Area Included in the Scheme: 2,000 sq. miles

20 Miles

Those opposed to the plan doubt whether livestock and wildlife can be run side by side: "You cannot farm in a zoo." But possibly the animals could be kept separate by a method just as effective as fencing or the most attentive herder: nature itself. Separation by fences is not so detailed in its operation as separation by factors of ecology, and in fact could be more wasteful of the savannah's resources. Most species of wild animals do not use identical areas at identical times in identical ways; could not this principle keep cattle and wildlife apart in view of their different needs? Moreover, when elephants migrate they do not move across a constant broad front, but follow regular corridors, just as they migrate only at certain seasons. Differentiated habits such as these could amount to "fences" without resorting to complete mutual exclusion in time and space.

The game-cropping plan envisages the wild animal throngs extending on both sides of the park borders. The scheme would regulate the total populations in the entire eco-unit, with the cropping territory acting as an overflow area for the park. A safety valve of this sort is essential to relieve pressure inside the park itself. The overall total of 20,000 elephants could produce 600 a year at their usual breeding rate, or a rate of 3 percent; 15,000 hippos would yield 750, or 5 percent; while 30,000 buffalo would allow an off-take of 4,500, or 15 percent (buffalo are shorter-lived, hence breed more frequently). Apart from the meat from an elephant, there is $150 worth of ivory and hide; a hippo produces an extra $100 in similar fashion, though a buffalo produces a mere $5 for the skin (unless one can get something for the trophy head). Altogether the 600 elephants would be earning $100,000, the 750 hippos rather less, and the 4,500 buffaloes almost a quarter of a million dollars. Some experts think a much greater proportion could be cropped, perhaps twice as many elephants, on the grounds that the cropping would stimulate the breeding rate, and an altogether more vigorous population (a less diseased one as well). And all this is without counting the hartebeest and kob and other smaller creatures.

At present the plan is still on paper. Everyone knows how cattle ranching works out, but not everyone is so sure what happens when game cropping is tried. One man knows, a Canadian advisor who tried it for three years in this very area. John Bindernagel sent meat to local hospitals and schools, much as elk meat is disposed of from cropping schemes in Wyoming. He found that the most rudimentary marketing proved adequate, and could be much expanded if a wide-scale scheme got off the ground. He did not include any elephants or hippos since his facilities could not accommodate such huge beasts, but he took nearly everything else: buffalo, hartebeest, kob, oribi, reedbuck, waterbuck, and warthogs. Just over 1,000 animals produced 290,000 pounds of good, solid meat. He had difficulty in cropping buffalo, since they are very wild creatures, and they get wilder when they are cropped. But he thinks better techniques could be worked out by nighttime shooting or by burning small patches of grass to lure buffalo into convenient areas. Over a period the buffalo might become more amenable as they get more accustomed to human beings, like those at Queen Elizabeth Park, where a researcher can pick one off while the rest of the herd stands a couple of hundred yards away and watches the carcass being dismembered. Bindernagel's trial in game-cropping produced $20,000: a fair trial. Had he taken elephants and hippos and extra buffaloes, the returns might well have been doubled.

The Murchison scheme has been drafted by stockmen, wildlife workers, economists, marketing experts, park-planners, and tourist officials. There is only one aspect they have not covered, and that is the ultimate will of the Uganda authorities. These are the authorities on which all depends, and upon which all *should* depend in an independent country. Uganda is a nation as ready as any other to go its own way, and as obliged as any other to consider such further factors as do not concern advisors, especially political interests. Uganda clearly wants to do what it can to build an expanding and prosperous nation, making for a more independent nation. Uganda is taking counsel with itself.

OSTRICHES

As the sun climbs higher, the larger animals begin to make their way toward the water hole. At the right season of the year this can be a good time to watch out for an ostrich and her eggs—or *their* eggs, for the male takes a share in the proceedings, too. During the weeks of brooding the female sits during the day, when her gray coloring provides fine camouflage, and the male, with his black plumage, takes over at night. A herd of elephants marching toward the river may make straight for the nest en route. The ostrich rises to defend her clutch with her wings spread, flapping about, doing her utmost to turn the intruders aside. Twenty elephants move off the track and step around it; so will fifty zebra or a hundred wildebeest. This is the time to spot a broody ostrich from a long way off—its antics tell a story. When a smaller intruder approaches, the ostrich stretches its neck along the ground to make itself less prominent at close range, which has given rise to stories about ostriches and their heads in the sand (though that would be very unostrich-like). Striding across the plains an ostrich looks almost ungainly. It regards you from a height of five or six feet. It looks as if it has its proportions mixed up, and its feet seem unformed—only two toes, allowing a doubtful hobble. But when it breaks into a run, grace flows from those legs and the ostrich reveals its power, surging along, built for speed. It is the largest living bird, which may be why it "forgot" how to fly; beyond a certain size a bird cannot get airborne anymore. Possibly the increasing power and bulk of ostrich ancestors made it less necessary to get out of the way of predators by taking to the air; an ostrich can run faster than any lion and keep up the pace longer than

It is not often that both male and female parents of a species join in raising the offspring. Not even the two ostriches will be sufficient to keep away hawks and eagles, hyenas and jackals. If a chick cannot keep up for a moment or two, it is probably gone for good. But if enough survive to act as male and female in turn, that is much of what the bushland balance requires.

a dozen lions. A cheetah would not want to get near those flailing legs: a single kick could be enough, and a peck as bad. In the main, only one predator bothers the ostrich and that is man. The first great onslaught occurred in the Roman arenas: it made a fresh spectacle to see 1,000 ostriches dispatched in a single afternoon. Things were not much different a couple of thousand years later when ostrich plumes became all the rage. For a while it looked as if the ostrich might become a permanent casualty of this temporary fashion. Fortunately, ostrich farming came in just before the ostrich went out. As long as the exploiters of wildlife are prospering—and want to *go on* prospering—their activities can work for the survival of the same splendid creatures that delight those who object to exploitation of any kind.

Only a few moments ago in the long African day there were ostriches in Asia. Now they are spread throughout most of Africa, much more widely than most creatures. In the northernmost areas the ostrich was easily persecuted by the Bedouin after they noticed it always ran to the same side of the wind; all they had to do was head it off. At the other end of Africa, the Bushmen learned to dress themselves in ostrich feathers and creep inside a flock, then let fly at close range.

Yet where the ostrich is not excessively preyed upon, it does not multiply in vast numbers. A world with too many ostriches would be as bad as a world with too few. There are natural regulators to maintain the balance. (This is a world where everything depends on nothing becoming everything.) Not every ostrich egg comes to a happy conclusion; in fact, often less than half. Sometimes only six or eight chicks are left to grow up. To start the process, a single ostrich scoops out a nest and lays her eggs. Another female, possibly a companion of the same male ostrich, places her eggs in the same nest. Other females follow, which makes for many more eggs than even the ample form of an

Above: Some of these chicks are two days old, one not yet two minutes. If the eggshells are prominent enough, the gray downy covering of the infant chicks makes fine camouflage against the dusty savannah soil.

Right top: Egyptian vultures are not always sure how to tackle an ostrich egg.

Right middle: The younger one brings stones from twenty yards away and drops them on the egg.

Right bottom: A dozen direct hits are needed to break open the egg, but then the adult recognizes what is happening.

Overleaf: The lionesses need
only a small patch of scrub
near the water hole to hide,
provided they stay still—
absolutely still—until the
moment one of them makes
her attack.

ostrich can cover—occasionally a hundred in one nest. A lot are thrown out, and some are preyed on by hyenas; the same hyenas may help themselves to a chick or two later on. Jackals and mongooses also take the nestlings, but they cannot do much before that stage because the eggs are too tough. Only one other creature is known to be able to deal with these strong shells, and that is an Egyptian vulture. With its beak it throws stones at the egg—even bringing stones from a good way off. Does its stone then become a "tool," and is the Egyptian vulture capable of intelligent anticipation? Doubtful; it does not store stones against a future occasion, nor does it do anything else to suggest conceptual planning beyond what is represented by an egg here and now. However one may view the vulture's stone, it makes a fine blunt instrument; half a dozen shots on target are generally enough to crack open food for many a vulture. If the vulture is chased away from the eggs by a marauder, it continues its stone-throwing from a distance even though it no longer has a target—the urge finds release through "displaced activity."

The eggs take several weeks to incubate. During the final stages the parent's body temperature rises a little, stimulating the chicks inside. A man needs a hammer to break open an ostrich egg. How does a chick manage it in that confined space? Possibly the moisture inside is absorbed, and the egg desiccates until a slight blow is enough. After a while the beak peeps forth, all chirps and struggles. Several hours later a bedraggled being crawls out and falls among the shells. It is tired and hungry and helpless. It makes its way toward any sound near at hand. If that is a safari vehicle, how is the fledgling to know? It struggles over, all innocent and hopeful, while the parent puts on a special broken-wing display a few bushes away to distract the potential predator.

Within a few days the brood is ready for a walk. They totter out into the open and strut around. Sticks in their path are a great trial, and there is many a ground-level view before they find their permanent feet.

WATER HOLE

To many animals the water hole is both the center of life and the scene of possible death. It is where great herds come to ease their thirst and where the great predators come for the chance of an ambush kill.

In most wild country few creatures venture near the water during the hours of dark. An antelope cannot see as well as a cat. Often enough there are no arrivals until well on toward mid-morning. Then the herds of wildebeest and zebra appear. They approach to within 100 yards and congregate in thirsty masses, torn between the sight and smell of the water so close and the memories of times when they have stampeded away, leaving one of the herd on the ground. They may hang around for an hour or more. A good deal of pushing and shoving goes on. The African sun gets higher and stronger. Finally they can wait no longer. They inch nearer. But the last fifty yards may take another hour. The leader of the herd advances cautiously, ears cocked, nostrils flared. He watches every shifting shadow. The others follow slowly and equally suspiciously. Every ten paces they review the situation: every reed patch is scrutinized, every grass clump is watched for a bending against the wind. They sniff the breeze, they check the area a dozen times; sometimes they wander off to another water hole anyway. But if they feel it is worth the chance they advance a few steps at a time. Stop, stare, search, step again and stop again. A bird rises from the sedge, and the herd wheels in a cloud of dust, desperate to be anywhere but there. A hundred yards away they turn around and look back. If an animal has not been brought down in that time they are safe. No lion will bother to pursue if its initial charge fails. A wildebeest needs a start of only half a dozen strides to get away. The herd looks around and assesses the situation. Reassured, they start all over again.

This tiptoe tension lasts a good while. The earlier herds have been joined by others, but the late arrivals wait their turn. Zebras are generally more nervous than wildebeest. Scarcely another creature on the plain can match the wildebeest at picking out the hunter in hiding, which is perhaps why they seem more confident—just a little. Eventually, the leading animals are a dozen yards from the water's edge. The breeze whips the scent into their nostrils. With a boldness they probably don't feel they march up to the brink. They lower their heads and their muzzles brush the water.

Now they are at their most defenseless: vision is reduced, attention fixed on the pool. But this is not the moment the hunter chooses to charge. Soon the leaders are joined by scores of followers. Their confidence soars. They wade in up to their hocks, twenty yards from the bank. The young ones frolic around. The older ones drink their fill for the day. Ten minutes later they may still be there. The first ones start to leave. The main body of the herd drifts after them. Still no attack. They leave more carelessly than they approached. The flanks in the reeds bunch together. The grasses part to release a silent blur. The nearest antelopes wheel in panic. They will make it. The others panic too and get in

Top: But before the lioness has worked up proper speed, the wildebeest herd is scattering—the prey can run faster than she can, and they reach full stride sooner than she can. But if the wildebeest get in each other's way, one may find itself balked.

Middle: (1) When the lioness is close enough to strike, she forces the prey to miss its stride. (2) It falls, and she grips it by the throat. But it struggles to its feet again. She cannot let go for a better hold, so she strangles it while it is standing. (3) Slowly the prey subsides and she pins it to the ground, (4) covering both of them in mud from the stream shore. (5) Before the wildebeest is dead, a lion arrives from a nearby thicket to seize the prey. He uses the same throat-hold to finish off the kill.

Bottom: With bellies bulging, the sated lions drink at the same pool where the wildebeest herd drank.

each other's way. One falls; it will be lucky to rise again. But the lioness has to work hard to catch one of them. Despite her speed and strength, she may need a dozen attempts before she is successful. All too many charges end with the wildebeest gathered in a ring around the hunter, snorting and tossing their heads at the lioness, hungry as ever. No matter; she retires into the reeds and waits for another herd. Those watching wander off across the plains. On the way they meet other wildebeest heading for the same water hole. They may be able to transmit some sense of apprehension but nothing further—and isn't a wildebeest always apprehensive? It is its livelihood to be so.

The new arrivals trek on toward the stream, unaware. After a pause, but encouraged that one group has already drunk there, they wade into the pool. The lioness waits for the tactical moment, then leaps from hiding. Thirty wildebeest leave one balked in the stampede. The lioness strikes at it and it staggers. She closes with it, and her forelegs reach halfway along its back. She drags it to the ground by sheer force, but she does not rip at it the way a hyena or a wild dog would—if she is hunting singly, she has to make sure of her grip. Once it is down, she seizes the prey with a throat grip or a stranglehold over the muzzle. She hangs on and just waits for the frenzy of the limbs to fade away. Even then she does not move: sure is sure. Finally she gets up, and the carcass doesn't flicker. She stands over it, panting. It may take a quarter of an hour before she is ready to do much else about it.

The technique a lioness uses to make her kill varies from time to time and place to place. Some safarists think a tap from her paw on the animal's head does the job: the prey goes

down with a crash, breaking its neck. The lioness may bite a smaller animal through the back of the neck, crushing the vertebrae. Some people say she not only throttles the animal, but bleeds it as well. There seem to be as many theories as there are patches of lion country; they could all be right. Common to most areas, however, is what happens when the lion takes over. Often enough he is lying up in a nearby thicket. As soon as he hears the noise he comes running. The lioness does not hesitate about making way for him. He seizes the prey and finishes it off. She also has to let him have first go at the results. The lion's share can be a lengthy process, and the lioness may have to sit and watch (though he allows cubs to join in, an important factor in allaying starvation during hard times). By the time he is ready to let the lioness feed, they may have been joined by the rest of the pride, a half dozen other lions, so her share is that much less again.

Lions don't like to feed in the sun, but shade is often available among the same vegetation that provided the ambush. From time to time the mass of growling lions parts to allow one to stagger away for a rest; a short shaking-down and back for more. Eventually they can hardly move. Gorged to the teeth, the pride moves off for a lie-up; a well-fed lion likes its twenty hours a day. But first it takes a drink at the pool where the wildebeest was caught. This time there is no need to approach with the same stealth.

BIRDS

There is much else to see at this concentrated scene of middle-day Africa. Waterbuck, for instance: they are not nearly as numerous as wildebeest, but they are never far from water. If a waterbuck wanders into a lion ambush, it does not make for the open plain, but turns toward the water where it leaps around with much more agility than a lioness. Many a water hole has its hippos dozing in favorite corners. Across the way there may be several buffalo; they delight in the mud and don't emerge until evening, dripping with ooze. They are not such addicts as hippos, but they take their leisure more indolently than elephants. For the unwary drinker there are those "floating logs" that drift suspiciously close to any animal at the water's edge. And here too come the vultures and the marabou storks, slaking their thirst even as had the animals they have been feeding off.

There is a further myriad of birdlife for the watcher while he waits the hour or two for the wildebeest and lioness to cross paths. In half an hour he can often glimpse twenty varieties, and in a morning he can find fifty along a lake edge. There are several places in East Africa where a single day can produce a hundred. The true enthusiast could follow it up the next day with a hundred more. The three-mile Crescent Island in Lake Naivasha has been visited by one in twenty of the earth's 8,500 sorts of birds, as many as are to be found in any major region of Europe or North America, where tracking down a couple of hundred will not take a weekend, but a year. You could even go to another lake in East Africa the following weekend and find a further hundred if you were lucky, and another hundred again at the migration season. A month's safari could produce six or seven hundred, as many as would take you a lifetime to find in temperate lands. Some of the migrants range as far as Siberia, or almost to Alaska, before they return—another insight into how East Africa represents a crossroads for the wildlife of the continent. According to Dr. R. E. Moreau, Kenya alone features three-quarters of Africa's 160 migrant species, a greater share than the whole of West Africa with four times the area. Kenya's year-round total of individual birds may rise to 1,600,000,000, five times more than Great Britain's. The number of species sighted in Kenya has topped 1,000 and grows with every season. The enthusiast who knows how to go about it could well spot a new species, which is more than he is likely to achieve in New England or California. All told, East Africa is second only to Colombia in total species recorded, and it is far ahead in the ease with which birds can be spotted in the open habitats of its wild country.

Right: Once airborne, pelicans soar on thermals of rising hot air: they may not need to flap their wings more than once in a quarter of an hour.

Below: Even at take-off a pelican does not flap its wings much more than once a second (by contrast with the hundreds of times a second needed by some of the tiny sunbirds). The pelican has an appetite that needs one-third of its body weight a day.

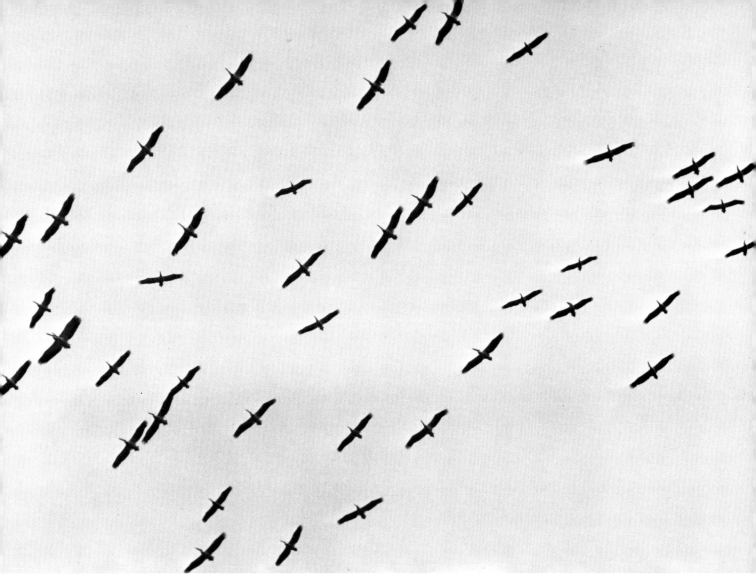

The regions to the north, west, and south each have their fairly distinct avifauna, but East Africa tends to be a meeting ground for all of them. There is such a broad range of landscapes here—another meeting ground. The main savannah zone shows 458 species, the more arid zone slightly over half as many, the lowland forest zone somewhat less, and the high-mountain forest zone a quarter as many. In between there are various subzones with their further species. An ecotone, representing the miniature transition area between two zones, offers the watcher the best of both zones: a lakeshore is an ecotone for water birds and plains birds; a forest fringe is another, where there may be nearly half as many species again as inside the forest itself with its greater range of food and shelter and protection. Miss Jean Angwin found 169 species in only two acres along a river in Nairobi Park; one in four of them was a tree-feeder, another one in four a ground-feeder, one in six a bush-feeder, one in sixteen a bush-and-tree-feeder, one in eleven an air-feeder, one in fifty an animal-feeder (or tick bird), and one in twenty an all-round feeder.

But these are all figures. It all depends on what you want. Bird enthusiasts are inclined to be either "listers" or "lookers." The watcher by the water hole can see an array that is enough for most, in spectacle alone—the more brilliantly plumed birds stealing the show. A splendid sight is a flock of pelicans. Those that come swimming past in stately formation are great white pelicans. They fish in groups, forming a semi-circle and ducking their heads under in unison. Possibly they are driving fish into a corner of the shallows where they trap them together: down goes a foot-long fish in a single gulp. The pink-backed pelican, by contrast, feeds on half-inch fish. It is not truly pink, rather a grayish-white,

Above: The African darter's chicks keep their light downy feathers until they are half-grown or more; by that time things are getting crowded in the rudimentary nest. The darter is also known as the "snake-bird," since it swims low down in the water, with only its kinky neck sticking out.

Far right: Egrets are very gregarious birds. Their pattern is similar to that of many such flocking birds: when one wheels, they all wheel. Nobody is sure how the message is communicated so instantaneously throughout the flock.

but it reveals a pink coloration as it takes off. Both are to be found on fresh-water and soda lakes. They prefer open sheets of water since they do not like to nest around confined areas, which makes the Queen Elizabeth Park–Albert Park a major breeding area. Perhaps the other areas have become congested, with human populations spreading around every watersheet, just as the hippos and crocodiles are finding themselves restricted to all but a few of their former areas. The larger pelicans nest on the ground; the pink-backed in euphorbia trees. Some of these trees in Queen Elizabeth Park are now on hard times, under the effect of pelican droppings, or possibly the sheer weight of pelicans, which causes the spongy branches to break wholesale. Apart from the euphorbias' fine appearance (what is termed an "aesthetic amenity"), they provide main shelter not only for the pelicans but for the marabou storks (which damage them in similar fashion) and a host of other birds. It may seem undue interference with the environment to plant extra trees, or to try fertilizer on those that can be rejuvenated—but what if the pelicans have nowhere to go?

An area where there has already been gross modification of the environment is Lake Nakuru, though the changes took place before the area became a park. Until 1960 there were no large fish, and so no birds such as pelicans to feed off them. Came the day when a few tilapia were introduced to attack the mosquitoes—clearly a worthy cause. A year later the lake filled up following the floods, and the soda became diluted; hence the water became less alkaline. The fish flourished. Now the lake supports not only flamingos, but pelicans by the thousand, and plenty of other waterbirds such as cormorants, darters, spoonbills, yellow-billed storks, grebes and terns. A greater variety: a greater spectacle? Most people would think so, though it is doubtful if anyone considered what reactions might ensue when they took the step of altering the environment in the first place. One might well wonder if the former "natural scene" is improved, or adulterated—or merely a different natural scene.

What is not improving the scene is a modification that is potentially far more significant. The farms around Lake Nakuru are using nitrates and chemical fertilizers in far greater quantities than before. The residue is draining into the lake. Furthermore, the lake acts as a sewage outflow for the nearby town of 50,000 people, scheduled to grow to five times as much by the end of the century. The park, which was set up a few years ago with great fanfare to safeguard the birds in all perpetuity, is unable to do anything about these problems: its border runs largely along the lake's edge, not the edge of the ecosystem. Perhaps it is not given to man (least of all to park planners) to dispose of things for immortality: one park in the United States, the Everglades, was decreed twenty years ago in such terms, and is already in chronic, not to say critical, ill health. And if the park at Lake Nakuru was set up to protect the flamingos, it took little account of the total flamingo habitat. Lake Nakuru is one soda lake out of a string along the Rift Valley. In the course of a year flamingos may range over half a dozen different areas hundreds of miles apart, none of them a park or anything like it (except Lake Manyara and Lake Hannington). Perhaps Lake Nakuru was honored with the designation because it was the one center that attracts tourists, and hence is a main money-spinner. Nothing wrong with that as long as it is not the central driving force behind conservation; there are other forces around.

At certain seasons almost 2,000,000 of East Africa's 3,000,000 flamingos (half the flamingos in the world) gather at Lake Nakuru. Less than one in fifty of them is a greater flamingo, but it is worth watching for; the male may stand six feet, or twice as tall as a lesser flamingo. Each of them gets through food equal to a tenth of its body weight a day (more than a lion, and ten times more than the onlooker). The greater flamingo weighs about 60 pounds, and the lesser rather over half as much, which means there are at least fifteen tons of blue-green algae disappearing down flamingo gullets every hour. According to a very experienced ecologist, Leslie Brown, the lake measures slightly

over twelve square miles when it is full (which it generally isn't), and must be producing eight tons of algae an acre every year for every 1,000,000 flamingos. The secret of this extremely simple ecosystem is that the shallow water (you could walk across most of the lake most of the time) allows the bird droppings (sixty to eighty tons a day) to undergo quick recycling through hard-working bacteria, which act with greater rapidity when they are closer to the surface and closer to the sunlight that is needed to make a basic ecosystem speed along with such extraordinary efficiency. Beginning with the "input" of all those nutrients from the birds, there is a speeded-up "energy transfer" from basic material to plants to birds; with this initial impulse, one can well imagine the algae doubling themselves within hours if need be, and the various fish-eaters taking 250,000 fish from the whole lake, or up to two tons per square mile every day. The 3,000 great white pelicans are taking three-quarters, while the 1,000 cormorants are taking 10,000, and the 21,000 grebes are removing at least 40,000. The lake is more like a foul soup than water, but it is producing nutritive food at a rate that rivals the best pasture land, and certainly better than the surrounding farming country that is being stimulated by fertilizers.

If the flamingo feeding grounds offer remarkable insights, their breeding grounds are likely to offer even more, whenever somebody finds out what goes on there. If all these flamingos were to breed as regularly as most other birds, there would be an enormous increase each year. Chicks are very vulnerable to marabou storks and other predators; their nests out on the open soda flats are easy to get at, in a heat, moreover, that daily soars over the hundred-degree mark. A whole breeding ground can be wiped out in no time. If they survive these early days, the flamingos are more or less safe from predators, though they often fly at night to avoid the larger birds of prey: a tawny eagle has been known to live mainly off flamingos. What then acts to restrain their numbers? Nature abhors an excess just as much as it does a vacuum. Maybe their strange breeding habits are a stabilizing force. Flamingos generally breed at different intervals, just as they generally breed in different localities. This less-than-systematic system could be the brake to keep things steady. Occasional catastrophes may help, too. During the floods of 1962, when the usual nesting centers had disappeared under water, the flamingos tried breeding at Lake Magadi, where the soda is more concentrated than in most lakes. The chicks soon found themselves with anklets of soda that stopped them from walking, let alone flying. A team of volunteers sweated for weeks to chip the shackles off chicks in the scores of thousands. They were "saved": to set up pressures in the system that would have to be relieved by further catastrophe? Nobody knew. Nobody asked. No time for population parameters in the face of such a situation. Nor was there much information available; there still isn't.

One predator the flamingos are virtually safe from is the secretary bird, an inhabitant of the grasslands. It lives off smaller prey, such as rodents, lizards, grasshoppers, other birds' eggs, and snakes—which it carries up into the air to drop on rocks. During the breeding season it carries its prey back to the nest not in its beak, but in its stomach, to be regurgitated when the fledgling pokes at the parent's breast or legs. Among the other striking birds of prey one may look out for are various eagles, notably the martial eagle, the Wahlberg's eagle, the tawny eagle, and the bateleur eagle. In the right locale, such as the Embu area investigated by Leslie Brown, there may be a pair of Wahlberg's eagles to every twelve square miles of home range; martial eagles are far less frequent, with pairs twenty miles apart. Secretary birds in Nairobi Park average two to every eight square miles of home range, though the actual area needed for hunting would be much smaller. A Wahlberg's eagle probably feeds on small mammals, lizards, or snakes, which means that the residents of a home range (two full-grown birds and one juvenile) need something like 1,500 such creatures to make up their total intake of almost 250 pounds a year. This is probably in insignificant proportion of the prey available, since in a good season there could be at least 200 to an acre. Even at twenty to an acre, the home range of twelve square miles offers a choice of over 150,000 creatures. The "kill" is therefore only one in a hundred or even a hundred times fewer again!

Martial eagles breed more slowly and probably work out at fewer than three birds to a home range. Their food can be put at 650 pounds a year. But since the prey they kill is too large to carry away, they tear a portion off and leave a lot behind—about a quarter. So each pair is killing nearly 800 pounds a year; if their range extends to sixty square miles and their prey averages two or three pounds in weight, they need almost 300 such creatures. Adding in what all the other bird predators need (estimating that all told they account for at least ten times as much as the Wahlberg's eagles), the overall diet comes to 2,700 pounds, or 1,500 small creatures a year: still a trifling part of the 150,000 for each twelve square miles. A typical small mammal might produce litters of ten or twelve young. If the hunting pressure exerted on their prey populations by all these bird predators is so slight, why don't they become much thicker on the ground (or in the air)? Apart from the social sanctions that perhaps keep them apart, they may find it so difficult to sight those small creatures hidden away in grass tangles and thickets that each pair needs plenty of hunting space.

Right and below: The crested crane—or crowned crane—ranges from East Africa south, and wherever it is found it makes quite a spectacle, whether on the ground or in the air.

Fish eagles show a similar distribution, though it varies from area to area. A common spacing works out at a pair for every 600 yards of water's edge. On Lake Naivasha, however, with its sixty-mile shoreline, there are only seventy pairs—yet at some points there is a pair every 300 yards. Lake Baringo is almost three-quarters the size of Lake Naivasha, yet it maintains only thirty-two pairs: perhaps the fish are harder to see in the lake's opaque water. What counts could be not so much the amount of food or the amount of competition or even the coloration of the water, but the number of suitable trees for nesting. Fish eagles like large trees, especially trees that are not so easy for other creatures to climb. On Lake Victoria they prefer tall, smooth fig trees, while at Queen Elizabeth Park they are partial to euphorbias. At Lake Naivasha they prefer dead trees of any kind; hence, more birds since the 1962 flood killed trees by the score.

Not long ago there were no fish eagles at all on Lake Naivasha. Nor were there any cormorants, darters, goliath herons, pelicans, ospreys, or pied kingfishers. This is a lake with 300-odd species of birds that has been adapted in somewhat cavalier fashion. Sixty years ago there were no tilapia in the lake. Forty years ago there were no black bass. Still more recently other fish have been introduced. A greater range of birds is no bad thing so long as one knows what a new species will do to the residents or to the rest of the local ecology. Most parts of the world would view Lake Naivasha as a bird wonder beyond compare. In Kenya it is a place for fishermen, power-boaters, and duck-hunters, and a sump for farmland fertilizer pesticides—all of these pressures from the human populace expanding in numbers as well as in demands. Now there is talk of introducing all kinds of other fish with little thought for what that entails beyond fishing lines. There is also talk of shooting out coots by the thousands on the ground that they interfere with the ducks that

Egrets do not follow the animals of the plain to peck ticks off their backs, but to pick up insects stirred up by their feet.

are targets for a few dozen nature-lovers who do their nature-watching down the sights of a gun. The coots here, like those in North America and Europe, have been accused of eating duck eggs and attacking their feeding grounds. But in fact coots feed on plants that are of no consequence to the ducks, which prefer seeds and detritus. The coots do not compete for nesting sites, nor are they territorially aggressive, except to other coots or cootlike intruders. The 40,000 coots do not seem to present any problem to the 15,000 ducks. Perhaps a greater problem is the man who shoots 500 ducks in a season. The tilapia may be a factor, too; in years when they are thriving they may eat more of one sort of vegetation, causing some bird or other creature to turn toward a reserve type of vegetation, passing the domino effect right down a line that not everybody knows exists, let alone traces throughout its meanderings. The duck-hunters might also look to the speedboaters that swamp nests by the hundreds. They might also look to the Russians and the marshes that they are draining in Siberia, upsetting the breeding grounds for a number of Lake Naivasha birds. So much for limited-area ecosystems!

These migrants are among the birds that travel from the farthest points in the northern hemisphere. They trek right across the deserts of northern Africa, possibly piloting by the stars—despite the fact that when these species were undergoing their earlier migrations the stars were in a different setting, passing on no useful message that could count as "experience knowledge." The enthusiast from Europe may well be looking at birds that shared his own habitat only a few weeks back. He is also looking at birds that attained their family forms, some of them by the Eocene period, almost three hours back in the long African day; other species are no older than the Pliocene, half an hour back or less. They have lived through more of the African day than most of the antelopes and other creatures you see across the savannah. They are a part of the African scene that should seem as distinguished as diverse to the watcher, provided he takes time off from the wildebeest and lions to look closely enough. If East Africa is a paradise for the man seeking big game, it is even more for the man with time to stare at birds.

ELEPHANT YOUNG

A water hole is a good place, too, to watch for a herd of elephants with young ones, even if it means staying out in the midday sun. The young elephant needs protection as much as any other infant of the plains or bushland, and it gets it. It stays with its mother for up to ten years, a protection second only to man's—as is only appropriate for what is often the second most dominant animal on earth.

At the water hole the tiny 250-pound creature needs special help. It suckles with its mouth from the first hour, but for several weeks its trunk does not develop muscles for drinking. So it has to kneel at the pool. It is watched at every move by its mother since at first it wobbles on those stubby legs. She constantly uses her trunk to care for it, clean it, protect it, reassure it. The calf itself waves its trunk around like an animated hosepipe. When it scents anything amiss it rushes under its mother's ample girth, to emerge with tiptoe spirit if not tiptoe tread, then regains confidence enough to offer a five-yard charge at a shifting shadow, or at a hulking back-end nearby.

An elephant mother has been seen carrying her dead youngster around for two days or more. Occasionally she may risk her life for her offspring. This cuts across the instinct of self-preservation, suggesting she is more than a bundle of machinelike forces over which she has no control whatever. Maybe sometime, just sometime, she can display an element of ultimate "choice" by placing the infant's needs before her own. And yet, animals cannot reason or anticipate or comprehend. A mother elephant plunging down into a flooded river to rescue her offspring is possibly not so much putting the infant's survival before her own as responding to an impulse of nature that places the survival of the species (or the local population) above the survival of the individual, a compulsion to keep the train of life going rather than a single component of it. Perhaps what the elephant mother is doing is being an elephant mother—and what that is nobody properly knows.

The newborn calf needs sustenance often. The mother elephant produces milk of a very special mixture, which is why elephant orphans rarely survive without the antibodies from their mothers' milk. They thrive for a few days, then suddenly sicken. Possibly they get pneumonia from swallowing too much air with the bottle, or perhaps they pick up enteritis. Neither is as bad as loneliness: a baby elephant should be allowed to rejoin a herd. One abandoned youngster in Queen Elizabeth Park found itself picked up by a park truck and taken off in search of a nursery group. Holding down a week-old elephant is not easy, and the elephant infant was not the only one glad to come upon a herd moving through the bushes. The baby needed no prodding to go and make overtures. Nor did the first female it approached; she was already suckling one calf, but she put forward her other leg and allowed the newcomer to join in. Few other creatures would make a stranger so welcome. A lioness just might, since she permits suckling by offspring other than her own. But a lioness is used to having more than one infant at a time; elephants hardly ever.

During the weeks that follow, the elephant mother holds down tree branches for the youngster to pluck at; she lifts it over boulders on the track. But there are some blights she cannot do much about. The young one might get hit by a fallen tree; it might even be snatched by a pack of lions or hyenas; it could fall victim to sunstroke if there is not enough shade around. In the largely treeless expanses of much of Africa's elephant country nowadays (the result of too many elephants and their appetites for trees, and more trees, together with nowhere else to go), many a baby elephant does not last out its first couple of years. In what used to be an elephant world as much as any other world, an infant elephant would have four chances out of five of growing up. In parts of Murchison Falls Park there are now only three chances in five; they are getting worse, and other places are going the same way.

Overleaf
Left: Samburu Reserve is one of the few places where elephants are not too badly congested—yet. The destruction along the riverbank is only beginning, while the hinterland is still fairly unconstricted. The watcher here can pick out more calves and juveniles at their midday bath than at places where elephant birth-control tactics, triggered by inadequate food and over-crowding, are cutting down drastically on the number of youngsters in a nursery herd.

Right top: An elephant calf spends much of its first few hours suckling, or searching around again for the right spot to have another go. It is still very wobbly; the herd waits nearby until the two are able to keep up. By evening they may all have moved only a hundred yards, and by next day only half a mile, despite their wide-ranging needs.

Right middle: Best way to deal with a charging elephant is not to meet one; or pick one without a calf, when the charge may not be for real.

Right bottom: The elephant mother protects her calf from all manner of threats, including the sun—a major factor in the habitats where many elephants now must survive, with fewer trees left for shade-seeking elephants after food-seeking elephants have devastated the environment.

It might seem a hard shift to turn away from a live infant elephant before one's eyes and start thinking about infant elephants in scores and in statistics. But this is what the middle-day spectator must do to appreciate some of the problems, and if he is to come back and see more elephant infants in thirty years' time. Elephants throughout almost all of East Africa are producing fewer offspring. After years of investigating elephants, Dr. Richard Laws and Ian Parker have worked out that a female elephant normally starts to breed around the age of ten or eleven. It takes twenty-two months for her first calf to arrive and at least another twenty-two months before she starts to produce another calf. If she produces one every four years, then during her forty or fifty fertile years—virtually her whole lifetime—she could be mother to ten or a dozen calves. Under the stresses of the modern environment, she is often unable to breed for the first time until she is somewhat older. In Tsavo, where the pressures are more recent than in other areas, the females wait only an extra two years or so. In Murchison Falls, on the north bank, they wait for four years; on the south bank, seven. More important still, the interval between calves is increasing: at Tsavo and Murchison north the gap is seven years, and at Murchison south almost nine years. This means a female from Murchison south is producing only three or four calves in her lifetime. Just what triggers the delaying mechanism is not certain. Less browse food is a likely factor. Things vary with the rains, since during particularly wet years the fertility goes up; when better rain brings better vegetation and improves the nutritional plane, there may be three times as many young elephants. Dr. K. G. McCullagh has found that elephant hydroxyproline, a substance derived from the breakdown of connective tissue, indicates how fast elephants are growing, and hence how fair a state of health they are in. During the dry season, while the vegetation is lower in protein, an elephant's growth just about comes to a halt. For a young elephant growing up, that could mean a series of stop-and-start periods before it becomes mature. Or if it is already fully grown, there are hardly any reserves left for such things as starting off another elephant (let alone feeding a suckling calf: which may be another reason why so many calves do not survive in Murchison south).

The landscape at Murchison south of the river is mainly grassland, in contrast to the northern side, where there is less congestion and where fair wooded patches are holding out. Grass does not last well in the dry season, but there is still foliage on the trees at the end of all but the harshest dry season. Yet, oddly enough, the overall growth rates for elephants in the two areas do not vary very much. Nor do the hydroxyproline results differ much. Moreover, the elephants in the Budongo Forest, on the edge of the south bank region, are also retarded. They do not reach maturity until they are twenty years of age, despite masses of varied vegetation around them. Perhaps the birth-control factors are not only a consequence of physiological state but of social status—a singularly strained status at that. The overcrowding at Murchison south may set off stresses that act in a "density-dependent" manner to slow down breeding. To get a fair idea of what goes on you would have to compare several communities to find out what makes a "normal" elephant, one without social problems. At present it is not always easy to compare two parts of an elephant community if it ranges from one country to another, as do the populations in Tsavo and Serengeti which spill over from Kenya to Tanzania, let alone compare them with other groupings elsewhere in Africa.

But this is birth control with a vengeance. Unless the environment can be somehow improved, or unless elephant numbers can be reduced to match their limited surroundings, or unless the social inhibitions can be removed, there will be fewer and fewer young elephants in the years ahead. Some people say that as the elephants cut down their numbers they will right the situation themselves. Others say that elephants are too slow in counteracting the artificial conditions they find themselves in. As long as they cannot reinforce their birth-control mechanisms by migrating elsewhere to relieve the pressure (rather than have others wandering in to make matters worse), they just can't keep up.

What goes on inside an elephant can't match what goes on outside. In Murchison south the decline started twenty-five years ago, in the north only a dozen years ago, and in Tsavo less than that. But Murchison south is a portent of things to come. Its population has already fallen by over a third from halcyon times. Considering that the decline has been speeding up rather than slowing down, and is likely to speed up still further, they may be half gone by 1975, two-thirds gone by 1985, and almost four-fifths gone by the year 2000. The visitor in an elephant area in 1972 may think there are plenty of elephants anyway. He will hear plenty of people tell him so. He will hear that there are more pressing problems. Few people tell him that elephants act so slowly in their life cycles as in their daily routines that if anything is to be done it must be started now. Elephants are not to be hurried; they need decades to be safeguarded.

This is all a long way from the infant elephant at the water hole, pink behind the ears, all wrinkles and stumbles, unsure of the world but going exploring from its first few hours. There is hardly a more attentive creature in the animal world than an elephant mother. The lengths she goes to are legion. In Kruger Park there has been an attempt to assist overgrown elephant herds by capturing calves and sending them off to areas where elephants have been shot out in the past. The only sound capture technique has proved to be drug-darting the young elephant from a helicopter—no volunteer could be found to do the job from the ground. Capturing a young elephant can take a whole day, sometimes longer. The mother spends hours trying to wake the drugged offspring with her trunk or with soft nudges from her foot. She takes no notice of the helicopter hovering a few feet overhead to scare her off, except when she is driven beyond endurance and rears up on her hind legs to try to pluck the monster from the sky with her trunk.

This is why an elephant mother is the one creature in Africa the safarist should avoid on foot. A man pursued should make sure he is heading for a good tree and that he is a good climber. The best answer is just not to meet a charging elephant. One ranger in Murchison Falls National Park had a tale to tell:

"I was riding along on my bicycle when I found myself amidst a herd of elephants. All of a sudden an elephant charged. I threw down my bike and took to my heels at a speed such as I have never attained before in my life. The elephant did not want my bike so I threw her my greatcoat. She did not want that so I threw her a shoe; but she did not want that either. I picked up a stick and the elephant got hold of the other end; so there we were on the run. I thought I was flying, but this proved untrue as I got tired very quickly. I was losing ground rapidly while the elephant was gaining at double speed. I felt her trunk almost touching me and then I fell down between her front legs. She bent her head and her tusks got stuck in the ground. I was pinned between them. I took off my coat and pushed it into the mouth of the beast. She then kicked me and rushed off."

HIPPOS

At midday the hippos are just a row of backs far out in the middle of the water hole, with a flock of egrets hopping around them. The Thames used to look like that in warmer times. Now there aren't many hippos even in a river like the Nile except for stretches near its source in Lake Victoria. Together with the hippos of the Lake Edward area on the Uganda Congo border, there may be as many here in the heart of Africa as in the rest of Africa. There used to be plenty along the Mediterranean coastlands, but the Romans accounted for them in their thousands—the first slaughter of Africa's wildlife at the hands of foreigners. Then came the Arabs, who showed themselves as capable as the Romans at wholesale slaughter, almost as efficient as those who later penetrated the continent from every other side and lost little time in converting it to their liking.

Not that every wildlife enthusiast finds there is much appealing about a hippo. Its cumbersome name is appropriate to its bulk, which makes it a candidate for the outsize "behemoth" of the Bible; and no wonder it spends all its day in the water where buoyancy relieves the strain. There is no outward sign of bone structure; it is too well covered with fat. When the hippo runs it wobbles at every stride. And it displays a repertoire of revolting habits. It blows off fountains of water. Some hippos spray themselves and their neighbors with dung, flinging it around with their tail in great gusto. A hippo is usually covered with slime and doesn't smell too sweet. Altogether, it is a creature with plenty of things except grace and charm.

But for the man who thinks as well as looks there is much more to a hippo. Why for instance would such a placid-looking member of the community be so antagonistic towards the world? Perhaps because it senses that the world is against it—with good reason, considering what the world has done to it, with digging hoe as with spear. Hippos are now being crowded into smaller and smaller areas. They are not creatures that take lightly to congestion. Even though the great schools of hippos suggest a creature that likes the closest possible contact with its companions, a hippo fights more ferociously and more frequently than most other creatures on the African scene. You wouldn't expect that pudgy frame to conceal a hair-trigger temperament, but the water erupts a dozen times a day in domestic disputes. Probably the bulls do most of the battling, since they carry more scars of titanic onslaughts than the females. When a fight breaks out, the wallow fills with sounds of combat, until a bloody victor hobbles back to its favorite spot and the vanquished withdraws—if it still can. When they can no longer hold their own, the older bulls are obliged to leave the main mud holes: no live and let live among hippos.

Although the hippo does little to encourage the outside world to share its living space at close quarters, there are a few creatures it allows to spend much of their time as close as possible. Those scars make first-rate scavenging for egrets and other delicacy-hunters, even though hippo hide shows remarkable powers of recuperation (researchers who want to recognize certain hippos try marking them with branding irons while they are in drugged docility, but the scars soon heal over). It is not unusual to see a hippo with a great patch of raw flesh, though rarely an infected wound—despite the wallow "soup" where they spend so much of the day. The egrets are joined on the hippo's back by an occasional sacred ibis, or a small brown jacana, a wader bird that pecks with such vigor that it draws blood. The hippo's thick skin may be easier to penetrate in an area such as Queen Elizabeth Park where the grazing has become so depleted that the hippos are

An egret is permitted to search wherever it wants in a hippo's hide. Generally it finds what it is looking for in scars, such as those on this hippo's shoulders. In all manner of ways it sees eye to eye with its partner, a symbiotic relationship allowing both to benefit; the bird, for example, is more alert to intruders, and its alarm warns the hippo.

deprived of the usual layers of fat under the skin and in it as well. But it is still a thick skin, almost one and a half inches on the flanks, though a slim half inch under the belly.

Throughout the long hours of the middle day the hippo feels a compulsive desire to spend its time basking in slimy serenity. It cannot stand the heat. If it is caught out of the water its skin dries until it exudes a red sort of liquid—hence stories about a hippo "sweating blood." A hippo seems to lose moisture through its skin two or three times as fast as a human—or any other large, hairless creature of this hot environment, such as an elephant or a rhino.

Midday is a good time for seeing a baby hippo. You can sometimes spot one climbing onto its mother's back, struggling up on one side and then toppling down the other. Born underwater during the rainy season when there is plenty of fresh grass for the mother, it often suckles underwater. An orphaned hippo cannot suck at a bottle; it can only take milk poured straight down its throat, which it swallows very capably. The hippo mother probably pumps milk into her offspring's mouth after the fashion of whales, since the infant cannot stay underwater all that long. Despite what it will become, an infant hippo is as pert and diminutive as a young animal should be. It weighs 100 pounds at birth, and it grows two or three pounds a day till it reaches 600 by the time it is half a year old; before long it is huge as only a hippo can be.

All kinds of creatures enjoy the sanctuary of a hippo's back. The hippo rests immobile for hours at a time—no need to stretch frequently, as must a rhino in a dust bath to relieve the weight on its legs. A hippo reclines in a kind of kneeling position, leaving buoyancy to do the rest; which is why hippos prefer water holes with gently shelving shores; they are easier for getting in and out of the pool, too.

SURVIVING IN MIDDLE-DAY AFRICA

As the sun mounts higher, Africa heats up. By late morning the plains are shimmering. For tourist and animal alike the African day becomes a bit too much. One and all make for the shade.

The safarist can feel his own body trying to maintain its regular temperature. At the point where it can no longer keep up, he finds heat flowing in from the hotter outside. A man's body can absorb only so much of this heat, and then it tries to get rid of it in other ways: it can sweat or it can pant. Either way, the evaporation keeps him cooler. For an antelope the technique more often is to give up the battle of holding its body temperature at a steady level, and to let it keep pace with the surrounding environment. Only a very well adapted animal can allow its temperature to rise much, but many of them manage it.

If the onlooker's temperature were to race up and down during the day like an oryx's, he would not see sundown. And just as the antelope's temperature varies with the temperature of the air outside, so does its respiration rate and its heartbeat. The oryx, an antelope of the semidesert, is almost as capable of coping with the midday sun as a camel. Both can withstand a fluctuation in body temperature of up to ten degrees Fahrenheit, though they do not like much above six or seven degrees. Ten degrees in a single increase would cause instant fever in a human, and it wouldn't be a fever to last long. When an oryx has heated up for the first half-dozen degrees it switches to a second method of dealing with the heat: it increases its evaporation rate, which allows it to survive Africa's midday sun easily enough.

A buffalo can tolerate a similar temperature rise even though it is not a desert animal. Its skin and thinner coat can resist less radiation from the environment. Once warmed up, a buffalo finds it difficult to get rid of the heat, since that bulk absorbs a considerable amount. Hence, it spends much longer periods of the day in a mud bath than, say, a rhino. But it can afford to spend much of its time away from feeding because it is likely to have a previous stomachful to ruminate. The black rhinoceros, on the other hand, half as heavy again as a buffalo, is capable of a temperature variation less than a buffalo's—around seven degrees. Oddly enough, it spends hours at a time dozing in a dust bowl instead of a mud wallow, often out in the blazing sun even when there is plenty of shade close by. Perhaps its thick skin, much tougher than a buffalo's, acts as insulation. An eland and a giraffe show variations of less than five degrees. Generally speaking, a larger animal has a larger problem of heat dispersal, since it has proportionately less exterior for the job of dissipating heat. A giraffe, however, achieves a ratio (pound of weight per square inch of skin) that gives it less trouble in staying undercooked than almost any other animal of similar ton weight. The watcher will have little trouble finding a giraffe at midday when most other creatures have disappeared. A hippopotamus gets by with only a couple of degrees range: its day-long wallow in the mud keeps it cool enough. On the other hand, a white rhinoceros, the same size and shape as a hippo, needs a range of at least ten degrees.

There are a number of other creatures in Africa that are watched with special care: everyone wants to know how their body systems work. They are the domestic stock that man has gathered about him. African cattle show a temperature range of about seven degrees, unusually high for creatures that usually weigh a good deal less than 500 pounds. Local breeds of sheep reveal a variation of only a couple of degrees, but they are small animals and not wool-producers. The rival claims of wild animals and domestic stock range back and forth between those who wish to show that their own preferred creatures are better adapted to hot Africa by way of producing protein. The debate, conducted with great conviction from all sides, frequently gets as heated as the atmosphere.

Can antelopes like eland produce better than livestock? And which livestock? An

During the day's main heat, an elephant flaps its ears more than usual. This is not a sign of anger. Those enormous ears help keep an enormous animal from overheating—fully spread, they more than match the elephant's height and their surface area is roughly equivalent to one-third the rest of the elephant. A network of blood vessels, particularly on the rear side of the flaps, keeps a supply of cooled blood circulating throughout the elephant's body: the total blood supply may pass through the ears every few minutes, causing a drop in blood temperature of as much as ten degrees. The larger the animal, the less its additional body surface: an elephant's outside matches that of a few hundred mice, but its inside can surpass 1,000,000 mice.

overseas breed is different from a local strain. And although cattle have not been in Africa a fraction as long as antelopes have, they have gone a long way toward making themselves tough enough to withstand the harsh environment. They have tended to develop small bodies, which are sturdy enough provided they are not confined to scrub vegetation such as is their frequent forage. In a tropical environment there is little profit to the beast—whatever its owner may want—in building up stores of fat. Bulk and more bulk may be a fine enough adaptation to colder climates where cattle and cattle-raisers benefit from whatever keeps away the chill. Not that fat-rich meat is necessarily an appropriate food for man. During the ages he spent as a hunter-gatherer—99 percent of his existence—he developed as a carnivore, utterly unacquainted with the excess of animal fats that make up his diet today. No African animal has ever developed the amount of fat a modern-day steer is supposed to generate, which may be all against the use of nature. A hippo, despite its appearance, is mainly muscle—otherwise it would never be able to carry its bulk so fast on dry land. Most wild animals of Africa produce only 5 percent fat, as opposed to seven times as much in a steer. Cattle were possibly first domesticated in regions not so warm as Africa; hence they could be bred in forms suitable for colder regimes. Why, then, urge the wildlife protagonists, should Africans have to depend for their protein on creatures that have not had millions of years to work out their adaptations in an unhelpful environment? Why not use the creatures that are found on the spot, and have been there for eons? If antelopes do not produce nearly so much surplus fat, fat is not necessarily the best thing for a malnourished African: he may benefit more from straight protein than from extra calories to go with the thousands of calories he already gets from his cereal-carbohydrate diet.

These are the factors that weigh in the balance of wildlife survival, just as much as the convictions of people who see a wild animal as a thing of beauty never to be exploited. Investigations into body-regulating mechanisms, particularly on the part of Dr. Richard Taylor and Dr. Toni Harthoorn, use miniaturized transistors and telemetric recording devices to measure deep-body temperatures. The whole range of fluctuations that the animals reveal can be monitored for two days or more. The early hours of the day set off a steady increase in body temperature. But Africa does not get really hot until well past eleven in the morning, even though the sun is approaching its zenith; nor does Africa cool down until beyond midafternoon. This is why the steep rise in an animal's temperature immediately after sunup is followed by a slower climb throughout the day that does not stop at midday but carries on until sundown. Throughout the day the atmosphere has been heating up rather more slowly than the sun, and the animal's body more slowly still. When dusk falls the earth retains its warmth longer than the air: the animal's body does the same. In some creatures the temperature even continues to rise after dark until it levels off at a peak, followed by a steady drop throughout the rest of the night. The animal doesn't get really cool until sometime near dawn, and its temperature may even continue to drop for a short while after the sun has appeared again.

The first temperature rise for an antelope is enough to keep things tolerable. But for creatures like an eland or a hartebeest, the real blaze of noontime brings a sudden rise in the respiration rate from ten breaths a minute to as many as seventy. The extra water vapor dissipated through the breath, causing greater evaporation and cooling, continues only as long as the extreme heat, after which it falls off equally rapidly. Apart from panting, there is no other outward sign of distress. The shade does not help much, because enough residual radiation still reaches a sheltered spot. But having allowed its body temperature to climb and having offset part of the heat strain by panting, the antelope is less dependent on other cooling mechanisms. Certainly it does not undergo as much loss of body water as do livestock, which survive through sweating more: moisture is far too precious for an African antelope to dissipate.

The contrast has been further emphasized by experiments by Dr. Taylor and Dr. C. P.

Top: When an oryx is standing around doing nothing, plenty is going on inside of it. It can slow down its metabolism at midday to reduce the heat burden, and it can adjust its breathing at night to cut down water loss in the respiratory tract. For resisting arid conditions, it can deploy tactics more efficient than a camel's.

Bottom left: An eland can feed off parched bushy plants, and thrive. It can possibly live permanently off little grass and no water, revealing a capacity for adapting to an unfavorable environment that is being exploited by Rhodesians and Russians.

Bottom right: The Grant's gazelle is found far into Kenya's desert country, though it is also found in country with over fifty inches of rain. It lies out in the midday sun oblivious to shady patches nearby, employing a method of keeping a cool head that is among the most refined anywhere—a network of mini-arteries in the nasal passages.

Lyman with an eland and a Hereford bull. Putting on weight means getting through a large amount of food, and the process of metabolism produces extra heat. A Hereford is one of the most efficient meat-producing animals in the world, but it is still an outsider in Africa, and Africa is not always kind to aliens. The more efficient animal at producing protein from a limited quantity of food turns out to be the Hereford, partly because it can derive nutriment from a reduced diet by recycling nitrogen through its system. But the eland can cope much better with a reduced water supply, partly because it is not so wasteful. Out in the wild the eland spends up to six hours a day standing in the shade to cut down loss of body moisture: but it has to take in a greater amount of food than a Hereford, making for a higher rate of metabolism—and an eland is a large animal to start with. It is able to cope with these burdens only by extra panting, which helps it to avoid sweating so much, which in turn means less moisture loss again. In the face of extreme changes it can even allow its body temperature to soar by a good twenty-five degrees! While it would not survive so well in good grasslands as a Hereford, it would prosper beyond belief in more arid areas—and these, rather than lush meadowlands, are the sort of savannah areas that make up three-quarters of East Africa.

But if an eland survives amid scanty vegetation by wandering far and wide and by being less than prolific, these factors could raise problems for those people who want to use wild eland as a ready source of meat: eland often average only one herd of ten to every ten square miles. They are timid beasts, difficult to approach in the wild. They would not be easy to "harvest"—if one is to use a term of utilitarian efficiency. The cropper would have to work in difficult terrain. There would be problems of preserving meat at high temperatures. There might be a long distance to market. Arguments in favor of game cropping never carry much clout as long as they focus only on how resourceful wild creatures are at flourishing in a harsh environment, and do not take into account the moment of truth when a customer walks out of a shop with his supper steak in his hand. All else is futile; worse, the theorizing is seized upon by the beef barons as evidence that pie-in-the-sky talk is not the same as meat on the table.

But the prospects are tempting. Some of these antelopes show an astonishing capacity for extracting every ounce of advantage from an unpromising habitat. Dr. Taylor has found that an eland needs almost a gallon of water a day for every 250 pounds or more of body weight, or four and a half gallons for an average 1,200-pound animal. In arid conditions, such as usually face an eland, that thirst needs six and a half gallons, which is a lot of water. Practically all of it can be derived from the acacia leaves the eland eats. These leaves are over half moisture, even during the most severe droughts; this means an eland can ignore drinking water, if need be, year in and year out. A cow in the same situation would die rather than eat leaves off any tree. A goat would prosper off those same leaves, but it would almost certainly be encouraged by its owner to keep company with scores of other goats. The result could soon be no leaves at all, and no trees.

Even better adapted than an eland is an oryx. It can get by on little over half the moisture an eland needs. It does not eat leaves but lives off grass and shrubs. During the daytime the plants of the semidesert regions where it thrives are so dry that they fall apart as soon as you touch them. When night comes, these same plants reveal a trick or two of their own on how to survive in a desert environment. There may be no dew, but the nighttime drop in temperature causes the humidity to rise. Moisture condenses, allowing the parched plants to make up as much as 30 percent of their content with water, after the mere 1 percent during the day. An oryx does most of its feeding at night, taking in the best part of the gallon of water it needs in desert conditions for its 400-pound weight.

Nor does the oryx seem to mind the daytime sun. An eland, by contrast, must spend long periods in the shade of the same acacia trees that provide it with leaves. It can put up with an enormous heat burden until the cooler times of darkness when it gets rid of the excess. If the eland were to get rid of this heat load as fast as it was "stored" in its body, the animal would have to pant far faster than usual—very fast indeed to dissipate enough heat through evaporation—and the water lost in this process could amount to well over another gallon. An oryx, on the other hand, seems to be indifferent to the desert sun: it just stands there. Its coat is not so dark as an eland's and helps to reflect some of the heat. The farther you go into the desert, the lighter the oryxes become. But an oryx can also allow its temperature to soar, even to the point where it actually remains *hotter* than the outside air. This means the internal heat generated by metabolism is allowed to stream out of the oryx's body into an atmosphere that would be considered sweltering if it were not so parched that a sodden handkerchief dries in a quarter of an hour. An oryx can stand in the open sun at a steady temperature of 113 degrees Fahrenheit, hour after hour: no problem.

If, as seems likely, an oryx can go for a lifetime without drinking water, then it is even in a class ahead of a camel. A camel can tolerate a fair thirst and can lose over a quarter of its body weight in evaporation and other processes, but sooner or later it must have water to drink. In the desert a man would need at least twenty-five pints a day to make up for what he loses through sweat and breath vapor—but he might not last long enough to lose that much, or to find himself weighing a good twenty pounds less at the end of the day: he might die in a spasm of suffocation when his motor nerves gave out, and his brain became so overtaxed with heat that it ceased to function. How, then, does an oryx avoid going mad? Nobody has watched an oryx closely enough, but a Grant's gazelle shows how to protect the brain. The area inside its skull stays substantially cooler than the rest of its body. The blood supply to the brain flows along the carotid artery, passing on the way through the "cavernous sinus" region made up of hundreds of tiny parallel arteries. Coursing through the sinus area from the other direction is venous blood on its way back to the heart after passing through the nasal passages, where it has been cooled by evaporation in the respiratory tracts. The arterial blood of the carotid then flows on to the brain a good six degrees cooler than when it was pumped out of the heart.

All of this proves a lot, but does not prove everything. How would an oryx get by if it had to be confined to a paddock at night to be safe from marauders? How would cattle fare if they could feed right around the clock and take advantage of the moisture-collecting grasses during darkness? Cattle cannot do that unless the rancher goes to the trouble of shooting off all the lions and leopards and hyenas on his farm, and makes sure others do not creep in afterward. But there is little need to keep an oryx penned up, since it can look after itself well enough in the world of lions. Not that there is much point in talking about oryx farms. To exploit an oryx's extraordinary physiological capacities you have to use a tremendously wide stretch of country, and who is going to set up a ranch of hundreds of square miles in a semidesert? Nor is an oryx as tractable as an eland, anyway. You can domesticate an eland without much trouble, but an oryx is a wilder wild animal, and it has rapier-sharp horns to make its point.

But you could try ranching eland in the same manner as livestock, putting eland between the fences instead of cows—or gazelles instead of sheep: take on wildebeest, hartebeest, impala, giraffe, warthog, whatever thrives—and that means practically all of Africa's herbivorous animals. Get the best out of them by using a range of country where they can roam far and wide to exploit the full spectrum of the environment in their own integrated manner. A minimum would be 20,000 acres, according to David Hopcraft, who has been investigating the idea on a ranch outside Nairobi. His is not an entirely new idea. Eland have been run alongside cattle in Rhodesia for years, though the British colonialists in East Africa were never too enthusiastic about setting up experimental projects. In the Ukraine there has been an eland farm for decades, with a herd of hundreds bred to produce the most suitable characteristics. These elands put on weight at a pound a day or more and produce up to two gallons of very fine milk. Eland milk contains

Another resident of the deserts is the ground squirrel. It meets the problem of the noonday sun by staying underground. It probably needs water every day, but it can survive off the brackish water—often all that is available—by straining it through kidneys that could almost live off seawater.

more fat and albumen than ordinary milk, twice as much mineral material, including calcium and phosphorus, and has a protein value far higher than cow's milk. As might be expected in an animal from a hot environment, the milk contains organisms that keep it fresh longer; it also proves especially suitable for invalids, especially those with gastric ulcers.

This is what can be achieved by game farming, a concept different from game cropping. Cropping means going into an area devoid of any detailed management and shooting off what you think is a fair proportion of the animals there. Little attempt is made to influence breeding by selective cropping, since the animals are too wild. A game farm must be large enough to allow the same extensive basis to your plans, but there is scope for intensive direction of what goes on between the fences. You can examine the animals much more closely as they become accustomed to your presence, that is, as they become semidomesticated. You can find out which ones put on weight more quickly and how fast; then you harvest them when they stop increasing at their most rapid rate, generally after the first year; there is no point in letting them continue to eat good grass another two or three years, or even ten or twelve, as happens in game-cropping country.

David Hopcraft's center near Nairobi is the only place in savannah Africa that attempts precise measurements of antelope productivity, assessing just how much vegetation is turned into how much eland or wildebeest or gazelle.

This is the aim of David Hopcraft. He has spent years measuring just what happens when food is taken into an animal, how much of it is really thoroughly used. His findings emphasize how conservation of moisture is central to the whole system. Cattle lose much moisture through their droppings, which are copious and damp, whereas a gazelle limits itself to small dry pellets—much more efficient. Furthermore, a gazelle can give birth twice a year, which means a productivity rate of 180 percent or three times as great as cattle; and a gazelle skin is worth more than any cowhide. Oddly enough, the fundamental principles behind Hopcraft's work have been described by scientists for a dozen years or more. Scientists, however, rarely raise their voices, most of their material being written in a careful dry style where one is nothing if not objective; hence any enthusiasm for new ideas is taboo, any urgency is fatal: indeed, "it can be stressed that a due sense of circumspect caution is not inappropriate before accepting the tentative thesis that a scientist follows few commitments beyond minding his own business. . . ."

When people talk of the potential for using wildlife as protein, one sometimes hears that this is an idea that nobody knows much about, which means one is talking not to empty minds but to closed minds. There is no land on earth without its experts who insist that no idea is so good that it should be tried for the first time, though this would not be the first time. The exploitation of wildlife along these lines is no longer a theory; it is established practice, even if there is no center in the whole of Africa except Hopcraft's outside Nairobi where an attempt is underway to determine the exact levels of productivity on which to base precise methods for running a game ranch. Nor is wildlife as food limited to Africa. In Wyoming thousands of elk are shot each year and used as meat. Britain imports venison from New Zealand; perhaps one day it will import antelope meat from Kenya—if there is any to spare after the local market has been satisfied. When it does, the gourmet's delight will be a consequence of those same researchers who put their radios on eland's necks and a thermometer on an oryx wherever they can get a reading.

Of all the hours of the long African day, there have been few with so many shadows for wildlife as the present time. This is still a world where people linger who prefer the old conservationist approach. Africa is now "lightest Africa" as never before, except when it comes to deciding whether the animals to be used for supporting man shall be those half-dozen domesticated elsewhere and domesticated thousands of years ago, or whether one or two others are worth looking at with more than a tourist's eye.

RHINOS

The rhinoceros, like many other animals (and in a sense, the reader), originally came out of the swamp. Ever since, there is no greater ecstasy for a rhino than to get back into it. By early afternoon it is off to its mud bath. This is a daily event that is not only highly enjoyable but hygienic as well. It helps to get rid of the ticks that burrow into that not-too-thick hide. The rhino wallows blissfully for half an hour, then rolls over to give the sides a plastering. Sometimes the bulk gets a bit too much at the top of the roll and the feet wave around in the air.

One cannot really say rhinos are the second biggest land animal or the third biggest since the hippopotamus comes in between the white rhino and the black. Only the black rhino gets aggressive, but it is more than aggressive when it is suspicious or annoyed. It charges with great thoroughness and speed: sometimes because it catches a movement in the bushes, sometimes because it gets a whiff of something strange, sometimes just because it is a rhino. For all its bulk it can accelerate with a tremendous surge and can turn on a dime. Its takeoff is fast enough to beat any safari truck to the fifty-yard mark, and it could certainly take on an Olympic sprinter if there were a right-angled bend in the track: a rhino corners with feet spread out, cat-fashion. But it is not good tactics, let alone fair play, to try your chances from a safari truck. Sometimes the rhino charges with great display, but only as an exploratory gambit. It stops short at close range and turns aside. Do not listen too much to the expert who tells you it is probably a put-on show: he knows the rhino probably doesn't mean it, and you know the rhino probably doesn't mean it, but does the rhino know? One group of tourists came across a rhino "sulking" in the bush, unwilling to come out and be photographed. They thought this was rather un-rhinoceroslike behavior, so they persuaded it with whatever came to hand. The rhino emerged. It drove its horn through the side of the vehicle, lunging up through the roof. It had been nursing a rhino-sized grudge from a spear wound in its side.

Since a rhino's horn grows again after coming off, it could be "farmed" at intervals for the benefit of decrepit Asiatics. A dozen years back this might have been a preferable solution for the locality near Nairobi where over 1,000 rhinos were shot out to make way for a settlement scheme at a time when there was a scare about whether rhinos would survive at all. A hunter renowned in local circles was engaged to eliminate the rhinos. If he really found over 1,000 rhinos in those mere seventy-seven miles of marginal country, then there must have been five times as many rhinos to a square mile as in similar country elsewhere. Perhaps he thought one or two more from surrounding areas might not be amiss. This settlement could only support the most meager forms of subsistence agriculture, but $1,000,000 was spent in bush clearance and water supplies, followed by loans and grants. The new tenants then moved in and decided they didn't like it.

Apart from the snorts it makes as it is heading for you, a rhino has a fair repertoire of sounds. The mother produces a strange mewing sound when calling to her offspring, and vice versa. It is a sound not difficult to imitate, which makes it one way for the researcher to get a rhinoceros out of thick bush when he wants to have a look at it. An infant rhino in danger makes a screaming groan. A rhino about to attack another rhino, or ready to engage in mating procedure—often regarded as the same thing by the female—gives out a hoarse bellow. But these sounds are not what a rhino uses to keep in touch with its fellows over a distance. Often enough there aren't any it wishes to keep in touch with, except those it wants to get in violent touch with. Rather, it communicates with its nose. If a rhino's hearing is splendid its sense of smell is much better. It can pick up a scent at half a mile when the wind is right. It probably chooses the plants it wants by smelling them out, since the eyes at the sides of its head would not help for focusing on much at the end of its snout; and why bother when there is a nose as keen as that? It retraces its steps from water holes by sniffing its way back along the trail. But in the main it does not need to find its way back, since it never goes anywhere. One rhino in Amboseli did not roam beyond its quarter of a square mile for years on end. It knew when it got to the borders of its own particular patch by the rhinocerine method of building dung piles at various points on the home range. After making a deposit, a rhino kicks out with its back legs, which helps it to leave a scent trail as it moves about, rather like a lion covering its back legs with urine. But these dung sites are not always markers for the boundaries of the

Left: A rhino likes to make a thoroughgoing job of its mud bath. But there are still patches along the ridge of its back that miss their plastering, and this is where insects seem to prove especially bother-some.

Middle: This rhino used to go to the same mud hole at the same time every day—fine for safarists, since they always knew where a particularly presentable rhino was to be found. It was fine too for another observer: all he had to do was wait behind a bush when the rhino was coming for its daily mud-soak, then do the job with a single spear thrust.

rhino's range, since some of them occur well within the limits. They probably help the rhino to find its way around inside as much as to indicate to other rhinos when they are off limits. Two rhinos living together can locate each other even from a considerable distance by following each other's scent. A calf separated from its mother can find its way back over as much as six miles by next morning. If a sample of droppings is collected in a net and dragged behind a vehicle, the scent leads the rhino along the path, no matter how many zigzags.

Not that this means a rhino exerts territorial rights over its area and defends them against others of the local community which enter the range. Sometimes one rhino overlaps with a neighbor, a situation that does not necessarily give rise to friction. Only when a real foreigner appears does the resident rhino assert itself. Two rhinos meeting start off their overtures with a complicated greeting procedure. If it is a male meeting a female, then both sound out the situation with puffing snorts. The male makes cautious overtures in short, stiff-legged steps, sometimes weaving his head from side to side, low down, using his horn for "scything." When the female approaches, often with extreme slowness or equally with extreme speed, the male gallops away in a small circle, then starts all over again. This procedure may last for several hours. Generally it ends with one of the pair merely walking off. It is much the same when two females come across each other. They approach with similar caution and may rub the sides of their faces together. But the encounter usually ends in indifference, and one of the two continues on its way. It is when two males meet that there is combat, sharp if not very short. Generally the stranger goes back the way he came, often faster, too.

When two or more full-sized rhinos are seen together sharing the same home range rather than just occupying two overlapping patches, there is not so likely to be a "ménage à deux" as a combination of mother and almost-adult offspring. A young rhino stays with its mother for as long as it can, but when a new calf comes along it is dismissed from the area. It immediately sets about trying to join up with a rhino in a different area. Surprisingly often it does not need long to get itself accepted. But the new arrangement

Right: A rhino enjoys its dust bath for hours on end, even though it lies out in the direct sun. Every short while it has to shift positions and stretch its legs, or it may find a radial nerve getting crushed, leaving it paralyzed. This causes a problem for rhino-rescuers: how to insure that his drugged charge will endure an hours-long trip without arriving still breathing but paralyzed. And sometimes the rhino arrives scarcely breathing, since lying slumped leaves its lungs compressed, bringing a risk of rapid pneumonia.

The rhino has little to fear from any creature of its environment, apart from the single unnatural and unbalanced factor of the environment anywhere. This rhino was born without ears and half a tail; one of its offspring arrived earless too.

may be short-lived. A grown-up rhino is generally a rhino living alone, a habit that leads to the dispersal of a highly conservative species, and probably helps to meet the evolutionary need for a good "mix-up" in the population as a precaution against inbreeding. Something akin to the recessive tendencies of inbreeding was once thought to be at work among the rhinos of East Africa: either the birthrate had fallen off, or more calves were dying for whatever reason—or, most likely of all, more adults were falling to the single unnatural and unbalanced nature of the environment.

Only a few years ago it was said that the rhinos in Kenya amounted to 2,500, out of not more than 13,000 in the whole of Africa. Now it seems there may be as many as 7,000 in Tsavo Park alone, instead of the 500 or 600 previously estimated. A finding of this kind, as surprising as it is significant, is the result of three years of work by Dr. John Goddard. The research center at Tsavo presents a strange spectacle, with over 200 skulls laid out in neat rows. From this morbid scene you can work out how many rhinos live for how long. By examining the teeth and their wear and checking which new ones have appeared, you can assess how many rhinos are reaching maturity, how many are lasting out to old age, how many are surviving from either sex—the whole story. Rhino skulls grow too tough for hyenas to break up, which helps a lot. One skull lasted eleven years in a swamp, still intact enough for Goddard to read its history. Similar techniques can be used for elephants, since their skulls are even tougher. But with creatures such as wildebeest, with more fragile bone formations, there are problems. Fortunately, wildebeest are not only much more numerous but much easier to see on the open plains, so one arrives at similar insights by different routes. Rhinos are few and far between, and even several thousand of them in the 8,000 square miles of Tsavo bush country are not easy to track down, still less easy to observe.

In Ngorongoro Crater Goddard found about 100 rhinos. They seem to be in good shape, since over a quarter of the females have calves at any one time. Not that they are calves at heel, they are calves out in front (only the white rhino calf follows on behind). The gestation period for a black rhinoceros is sixteen months, and after giving birth the mother might not immediately breed again without further ado. More than likely she produces a calf every twenty-seven months or so. In Ngorongoro the rhinos are giving birth every four years, a good way off their maximum. But that may be as many as there is room for. Allowing for four calves out of five reaching adulthood, there are signs that the rhinos are limiting their breeding rates. Self-regulatory mechanisms for reducing fertility often come into play whenever animal populations reach a stand-off level in relation to their area and the amount of food available or the amount of congestion. These factors matter when you are trying to keep rhinos on the earth, just as much as looking after some abandoned infant with its endearing traits. More male rhinos are born than females, which is only common for many wild creatures. It allows for a fall-off (or fall-out) when males indulge in fighting. And males tend to grow larger, hence faster, with greater demands on nutrition resources (even if this is not as much of a factor among rhinos as among most other creatures), so they become more vulnerable to hard times in their youth; females are more susceptible to starvation later on, when they are gestating or suckling a calf.

Overall the status of rhinos at Ngorongoro gives grounds for hope, rather more so than in areas where they are in severe straits because of the one threat against which they cannot adapt: the arrow that flieth by noonday. Rhinos do not seem to be as prone to disease as the more proliferant species like wildebeest. Rhino numbers are so small, even when there are "lots," that there may not be the ecological need for disease to rank as a factor in reducing their numbers from time to time as there is among wildebeest. Too many wildebeest become subject to epidemics of contagious ailments that run right through their overlarge herds; the excess numbers furthermore create a food shortage that in turn makes them weaker and more susceptible to more diseases. This sort of blight would not apply to dispersed creatures like rhinos, even though they run up against things like famines from time to time—a consequence of too little rain or too many elephants,

The start of a fig tree and the end of a thorn tree. The fig's creepers get a hold on the host tree and send long loops down into the ground to form aerial roots. Slowly the whole plant consolidates until the original tree is swallowed up.

rather than too many rhinos. The Tsavo rhinos that died in 1962 revealed a large number of lesions, which gave people pause. But rhinos with lesions have been found elsewhere while in perfectly good health. Some possibly die from tick typhus or tuberculosis. At one stage it was thought that an occasional one could actually die from sunburn, especially in places like Tsavo, where much of the shade cover was disappearing in the wake of the elephant destruction. Rhinos were found with great dark patches across their hides. At first it was thought these marks were just dried blood from insect bites, especially since two rhinos in Ngorongoro had died from flies during an earlier plague. Then it was thought that since elephants, especially the young ones, are susceptible to heatstroke, rhinos might be, too. But then it was found that rhinos make little effort to get out of the sun even when there is shade enough close by. Moreover, rhinos with "sunburn" have been found in places where there is so much thick bush that it is difficult for them to get out of the shade! Now it is thought that the patches may be caused by insects after all, since they are grouped along the ridge of the rhino's back where there is no mud pack after the daily wallow. Only recently have such riddles come to light. This is a time not only for seeking the right answers but for asking the right questions.

If the black rhino now appears to be in a much healthier state as a species, there are still only thousands where there used to be scores of thousands. A while ago there were rhinos across 90 percent of Kenya, but now they survive in only half that, and the area is falling with every tick of the clock—just as there used to be rhinos roaming across two-thirds of Africa south of the Sahara that now must make do with less than a quarter of the region. There are only a little over 1,000 left in the whole of Rhodesia, a portent of what is to happen as more of Africa becomes more developed. For some time there was a plan to pick as many as possible out of areas where they are under major threat and release them into sanctuaries. Only a few of them normally live in parks and reserves, since rhinos tend to scatter themselves right across the landscape. Modern techniques were brought to bear, ultramodern devices to aid the 70,000,000-year-old-rhino. Few people have not heard how Dr. John King pioneered drug-darting.

This rescue method has accounted for around sixty rhinos in Kenya to date. All fine and successful. But it is an operation that costs hundreds of dollars each time, hence the need for more cash than East Africa can muster. The scheme received support from conservation bodies around the world: such last-ditch protection, exerting its own obvious impact, is just the thing to draw in support from overseas. But how many rhinos can be released into a place like Nairobi Park before it reaches saturation? When the rescues started there were only a dozen or so in the park. It could certainly hold many more. What happens when the residents are met by fresh arrivals? Do the newcomers find a slot for themselves? If the males try to drive out other males, it might be better to capture more females (good for breeding purposes anyway). But you cannot always tell from a helicopter whether a rhino is a male or a female. The newly imported rhinos of Nairobi Park are proving a tremendous tourist attraction, no doubt about that. Twenty-two have been released, and Dr. King and Patrick Hamilton believe that most of them have found a range of their own in the park. This has more than justified the rescue operations, even if that were not the only motivating factor.

Something of the same approach has been tried elsewhere. Six captives were released in the environs of a new hotel in Tsavo Park to attract visitors. (There may be plenty of rhinos in Tsavo, but they do not always show themselves where the guests look for them.) The six rhinos promptly showed they had other ideas. They all wandered off, some of them twenty miles in the first week. Two invaded villages outside the park and brought the operation back to the starting line: it was for just such misdemeanors that they had been plucked out of their original stamping grounds. They may have been harried by the same resident rhinos that did not see fit to appear for visitors.

And by now there is less urgent need to carry on rescuing individual rhinos. While funds are being spent on rescues, there is a shortage of cash to start off research projects in areas where little is known about rhinos at all, not even how many there are. To which one might respond, and with some point, that research programs are not the sort of things to induce people to contribute money to wildlife, not as compared with the panache and instant results of rescue operations. Rhino-darting from helicopters brings in support for wildlife to assist projects beyond the rescue of rhinos. This is perhaps not the way things should be, and certainly not the way things were ever planned to be; but that is the way things turn out. Who can guess what the spin-off benefits will be? One cannot emphasize too heavily, even though it is reiterated ad nauseam, that saving wildlife depends on people, and many people in many places. The alternative is continued slaughter of wildlife, ad nauseam and beyond.

More to the point, there are now people looking at specific areas and trying to find out how many rhinos make enough for that particular spot. In the harsher parts of Tsavo a rhino may need five square miles; in the better parts it needs only a tenth as much. All depends on the vegetation. In the open woodland around Treetops a square mile of country can support a dozen rhino. In the Lerai Forest of Ngorongoro Crater thirty are crowded into little over a square mile, sharing their habitat with about twenty elephants. In Nairobi Park there is a tiny patch of forest that may support as many rhinos as all the open stretches of plains ten times its size. In one area, outside Tsavo Park to the west, there used to be between 200 and 300 rhinos in the 200 square miles. This salient was an extension of Tsavo in ecological terms if not in political fact. It was also a block of land projected for "development." The planners were all in favor of wild animals, of course, but when it came to people they had to choose. There were too many rhinos to be rescued; the expense would have been horrific. The best of a bad choice might have been to have them eliminated by researchers. There is a constant need for information, which these rhinos could have provided in abundance. When research is undertaken on elephants or hippos, it is not too desperate to shoot a few and find out what goes on inside. It produces immediate data not to be gained from observation for a very long time. Yet it would hardly have been fitting in this day and age for rhinos to be shot, not when funds were being raked up for rescue schemes. What if word had got out that researchers were actually slaying the rhinos? Again: wildlife conservation nowadays depends on people, and many people in many places.

PLANTS

While many of the animals are resting out of sight during the midday hours, there is still plenty to look at. Trees and grass, for instance. They are as much a part of the African scene as the wildlife; they are "wild life" too, and they have had their own long African day.

The plainest stretch of plain has a tale to tell. If it is covered with grass, it is covered with one of the more recent plant forms to appear on earth, and one of the more successful. The safarist is often struck by how the merest shower of rain causes Africa to flourish. Where there was nothing, there is plenty. The red-oat grass that covers the plains can grow an inch in the first couple of days. Thereafter it can be eaten away, dried up, burned off, but still it comes back. A resilient, adaptable material, this grass. It has had plenty of time to learn how to make its way in the world. It first appeared in the early parts of the Miocene, about one hour back on the African clock. How it arrived is not clear. At one time there was no grass; at a later stage there was so much of it that grasslands covered two-fifths of the earth. Nowadays fire has a lot to do with the way grass thrives in Africa. At some stage, around 25,000,000 years ago, there may have been an outburst of volcanic activity that burned off whole patches of forests, especially at a time when unusual dryness

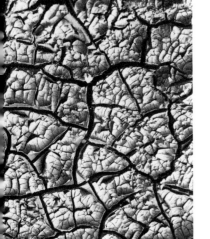

This, too, is Africa. It won't stay that way: it will either desiccate further to become dust, or it will be encroached on by plants that specialize in colonizing such lifeless-looking zones.

was causing the forests to shrink. After the forests disappeared in smoke, the soil was left exposed until it also largely disappeared over wide areas. Trees with their long roots could not come back to reclaim what had been theirs. So plants that could get by with much shallower soil moved in.

Or one can shift the angle of approach slightly and come at the mystery from another side. At some stage the plains became covered with lava. Outpourings from volcanoes like Kilimanjaro and Mount Kenya spread layer after layer of molten material over the landscape; or lava welled up out of fissures in the plains. Great sheets of rock overlaid the face of Africa. No place again for deep-rooted trees, until the eons of weathering and erosion had produced more than a thin scattering of soil. In the meantime fire-resistant plants with short roots moved in to claim the new regime. After a few millennia of experimentation, the grasses emerged in all their proliferant vigor.

All this marked one of the great upheavals in earth's history, a peaceful and productive one. Grasses changed the way of things with revolutionary speed. One might say that they went to the root of things; there was new plant growth that could resist whatever went on above ground better than tall-standing trees, vulnerable trees. The grasses developed small masses of fibrous roots that safeguarded the energy of life whether fire or herds of grass-eating antelope were sweeping across the landscape. The grasses also concentrated their areas of growth at the bottom of their leaves, not at the top as had been usual for trees. Ground-level was where the action was to be.

There followed an outburst of evolutionary creativity that was in its own way as miraculous an appearance as grass itself. Creatures evolved to take advantage of the phenomenon, primarily antelopes. There was a similar spurt of development among the horses, which had already moved a good way from their origins. Now they grew more horselike. They eventually produced the modern zebra, though at what stage the striped splendor emerged is not apparent: fossils tell what went on inside an animal, not much about its outside. But primarily it was the whole new family of bovids that made the difference, thriving on new plants that had greater nutriment packed in than before. You can follow the story by the bovids' teeth. It is fortunate that when a skeleton survives, the teeth—being the toughest part—survive better than the rest. The teeth of these bovidae show how the molars took on a new look. They became longer, and just as important, some kept growing so that hard wear did not leave the owner toothless after chewing on tough silica-supplied grass. As these new plants became exposed to the full impact of the tropical sun with no forests to protect them, they had to develop tougher forms with more fiber. To keep up, the antelope teeth evolved new grinding surfaces. And as they set about getting the best nutriment out of the grass, the new grass-eaters evolved larger bodies to accommodate the rechewing and fermenting processes. They developed longer legs so that they could move longer distances to seek fresh growths. Long legs also meant they could avoid the fleeter predators that were evolving in these open, cover-sparse plains. The long legs likewise lost their soft feet, developing hooves more suitable for the hard surfaces of the grasslands, which were dried out far more than any forest floors. To withstand the hardening hooves of the grazers, the grasses grew tougher still. Stronger hooves demanded tougher teeth; tougher teeth, stronger hooves. Africa was moving steadily toward modern Africa. In fact, one might say it was at its most "modern" something over 1,000,000 years ago, three or four minutes back in Africa's long day. It was a heyday for the mammals, a golden age of extraordinary diversity. What happened to cause many of them to disappear is not certain. Among other things, there was one particular species that grew to a stage where it became dominant as no other had ever been, not even the greatest of the dinosaurs. This was a species that proliferated and waxed strong and made its two-legged presence felt wherever it went. It was a revolutionary appearance on an evolutionary scene, so momentous that it made the appearance of the grasses look a trifle.

And this, too, is Africa, a few miles outside Nairobi on the lower slopes of the Aberdare range, a landscape of frosty nights followed by misty mornings—though only half an hour's drive from the sun-scorched savannahs. The flat-topped thorn tree—a shape suitable for more arid areas—marks the transition from one world to another; at higher altitudes the foliage-thick wattle trees are at home.

Plants, animals, rainfall, fire, grazers, plants again: this is a unity in which cause and effect get jumbled up. You can only roughly follow the relationship in all their interlacing intricacy. In the temperate zones things are simpler; you can sometimes think of animal ecology without plant ecology as well—impossible in Africa. You can gain a fair insight into this interdependency on the plains of the eastern Serengeti, as Dr. Lee Talbot has described. The grasslands stretch over toward Ngorongoro, some of them outside Serengeti Park. The savannah inside the park is grazed by wildebeest and a range of other grass-eaters. The sections outside the park are grazed by man's livestock as well. Grasslands that escape the attentions of excess cattle may feature as many as thirty kinds of grass, which are fed on by wildebeest, wildebeest in their hundreds of thousands, together with zebras and gazelles. This grazing pressure induces the grass to grow, constantly held back at its more vigorous and nutritive stages. Season after season the wild grazers exert their biotic impact: they help the grasses to flourish. Over the border, outside the park, there is a different story; there the lopsided pressures of Masai cattle, concentrating on only a few of the plants, can cause the thirty species to fall to ten or less inside a mere half dozen years. The total ground surface that is covered by vegetation declines to a fifth of what it was, causing the earth to dry out. Erosion sets in; soon there are patches devoid of any life at all.

A similar decline, though not so rapid, is set off even where there are no Masai. If there are no wildebeest or other grazers, and no fire either, the environment is again out of balance. When a fire-induced grassland like the Serengeti is deprived of both grazers and fire, the predominant red-oat grass falls off. Large bunch grasses prosper, gathering in clumps whose centers are so overgrown that they are practically lifeless. The number of different grasses can fall by a half, and the basal cover likewise falls off rapidly. Once again erosion creeps in. Slowly there is less plant life and less animal life; the same story.

On the other hand, an area with too many wild animals can decline as swiftly as one with too many cattle. This happens all too often in African parks of the present day when there are pressures from the borderlands outside. Animals crowd in to avoid the poachers or cultivators. Within the park the animals find a sanctuary where they are relieved of human predation, however limited it may have been, pretty much for the first time since before man has been man. It is not always realistic protection, and it can often be artificial overprotection, especially for the largest animals with the largest appetites, which are usually too big for any other creature to kill except man. The better vegetation shows signs of early decline. As described in Alan Savory's graphic accounts, perennial grasses are replaced by annuals as the expanding system is thrown into reverse gear. Small shrubs appear, to thrive briefly before they, too, are thinned out. The grazing antelopes are now in a decline; their herds "crash," while browsers such as impala or eland enjoy a short upsurge before they, too, start to starve in the face of a debilitated environment. A habitat overloaded quickly becomes a habitat undernourished: the process generates its own momentum. Erosion gathers force to carry away the topsoil by the ton, silting up the rivers; the Tana River in Kenya is removing 12 million tons from its 2,000 square mile catchment area a year, while other areas are occasionally losing ten times as much. Water runs off useless, making for flash floods followed by abnormally dry periods. The more palatable bushes disappear, just as good grass is replaced by bad (bad, that is, for the overall community, since there are not enough specialist feeders to balance the unregulated fluctuations in the vegetation mosaics). Browse lines become more apparent; trees are damaged wholesale; only one thing is on the spread, and that is bare earth. There are no more dry seasons, only droughts. The vicious circle becomes a vortex to suck down every living thing, animal and plant alike. The scene is soon deserted.

Many of these stages can be picked out by the discerning safarist. No park of East Africa is in the final stages yet, though it has happened elsewhere. At Queen Elizabeth Park you can look out on a variety of scenes, though not the full spread of the wild spectrum (no park has as many as one could include in a theoretical scenario). Except towards its southern end, the park is primarily a place for hippos, elephants, and buffalo. Why there are not more antelopes is difficult to say, though the area was only freed of human habitation following a tsetse outbreak fifty years ago, which is not long enough for the full array to reestablish itself. Not only is there plenty of rain, but it is spread more evenly around the year, allowing for a steadier growing season. Meanwhile, the hippos of Queen Elizabeth have overgrazed their habitat at several points; there is a fine opportunity to compare one stage with another. Dr. W. G. Swank and Dr. G. A. Petrides have revealed how, in a lightly grazed area, the red-oat grass makes up well over two-fifths of the grass cover, but in a moderately overgrazed area it is down to almost nothing. Woody plants flourish in the modified parts, up to one-seventh of the vegetation, while nongrassy herbs account for a third, and less popular grasses a fifth. As long as the process is limited and the disastrous stages are controlled (by cropping the hippos instead of random poaching), the disruption does not spread too far. But the park must be managed if it is to manage itself.

The decline proceeds from one stage to another through a "succession." In a succession the opposite way round, the environment renews itself as the life forms grow more diverse. In this direction the different stages are harder to pick out. As the process gets

Below: A plant that generally grows six inches: a groundsel. At 15,000 feet on the upper slopes of Mount Kenya the intense radiation and perhaps the volcanic soils cause it to sprout six feet or more.

Right: Above 10,000 feet on the Ruwenzoris astride the Uganda–Congo border, heather forests flourish higher than a row of houses. They grow on Africa's continental divide, where winds from the Atlantic surge right across the Congo two-thirds of the way to the Indian Ocean before dropping their moisture on the Mountains of the Moon. Here the atmosphere is never less than soaking, and the plants never less than grotesque in their vigor.

more powerful, it gets more gradual: it advances to a higher state of things up a steady slope with none of the jerky steps to be found on the downward path. If the factors that make for growth can be recreated, the process starts off with a patch of bare ground being colonized by annual plants. They are soon followed by a greater variety of grasses, notably perennials. A while later again there are shrubs and forbs. More sturdy growths follow, especially bushes. The entire vegetation grows thicker and taller, then gradually much thicker and much taller. Eventually there emerges a forest with a spreading cover thirty feet high or more, until the canopy closes in and the sun shines no more. Light and warmth filter through as best they can. But this is not the end. The layers of growth go on multiplying. Plants that are independent and self-sustaining reveal more plants growing on them, or from them, enclosing them. Ultimately, pretty well every niche that can be occupied is occupied. A state emerges where the parts are so interdependent that their relationships are themselves a factor of the habitat: an organism greater than the sum of its parts. All of which is a long way from the bare ground where it all started. The earliest stages leap after each other from one season to the next. Bush takes over from grassland in half a dozen years. Then comes stages that last half a century, and the final stages take several centuries.

East Africa is a powerhouse for plants. It is a hothouse, and a hothouse of many varieties: hot and damp, hot and dry, hot and in between. It has far more of the world's 375,000 plant species than the region's size would suggest. It does not feature nearly such large a share of the 1,000,000 animal species—mammals, birds, insects, and the rest— though again it includes a greater proportion than any other part of Africa. And the person who looks closely will see how plants in some senses are more versatile than animals: they have to be, since they cannot run off elsewhere to avoid every threat that appears. They have to adapt themselves as thoroughly as they can to wherever they happen to be growing. Some seeds in the world survive cold two or three times more frigid than the iciest spot on Kilimanjaro's crater. In fact, plants have thrived at one time or another in worlds where few of the present animal forms could have existed. When the first glimmerings of life began to stir in the oceans, there was little oxygen around the

Below: Zebras spend long periods in the middle of the day standing around like this, possibly because they feel well disposed towards each other, or because they want to know what is going on behind as well as in front.

Right: The lion has learned to live with its environment: when it is lying quite still it cannot be picked out by a zebra. And a zebra standing quite still cannot be picked out by a lion. But a zebra keeps on the move much more, since it must feed most of the time—which means it could end up feeding the lion.

Overleaf: Those stripes: when there is a milling mob, especially at the moment a lion strikes, the pattern makes it difficult to tell where one zebra ends and another begins. At such times it does not matter whether the stripes merge with trees and bushes, or whether they are black-on-white or white-on-black.

earth. Invertebrate creatures were the first to appear, with one or two rudimentary plants like seaweed to go with them, 600,000,000 years ago—two and a half times as far back as the start of the long African day. While this early life was evolving in the primordial seas, the planet's oxygen gradually increased to about 1 percent of the earth's atmosphere. When life forms crawled out of the oceans to spread over the land, it was the plants that pioneered the way. Their photosynthesis helped to raise the oxygen to 10 percent, and by the time Africa was emerging as a continent in its own right, there was nearer the present-day 21 percent oxygen.

For all that Africa has a remarkable spread of plants, there are one or two oddities. In this land that is often parched there are no cacti. There are euphorbias instead, with similar spiny, succulent arms to store water. Africa puts a premium on water-storers. The fig tree has roots that are sometimes eight inches thick ninety feet away from the trunk, ready to pump up every available drop of moisture. But for any plant it is not total rainfall that matters, it is how hard it rains and when. Looking over the Rift Valley escarpment, one might see storms dotting the floor half a mile below. Some patches are getting a lot, some too much to soak in all at once. Most of it runs off, while a mile away there are patches left dry. Next day, the valley looks mottled across its plains. Again, a shower can fall so lightly that it evaporates before it reaches the ground (and on the equator the potential evaporation can far exceed the rain throughout the year). Or again, the rain falls so hard that it manages to reach the ground all right, but brings with it a drop in temperature of ten or fifteen degrees. The storm finishes and the sun comes out to draw the temperature back up again just as fast. The result is evaporation even more rapid. Moreover, landscapes with a good "average" rainfall over the years may receive hardly anything one year in four, a factor that counts more than any average. And having reached the ground without steaming off, the rain might not always do as much as it could. Plenty of vegetation helps it to penetrate, just as it helps plenty of vegetation to become yet more vegetation. Rain falling onto bare ground hardly seeps through the first inch, whereas on grassland it penetrates up to three inches. Furthermore, as Dr. P. E. Glover has noticed, some of the taller plants assist by collecting rainwater in their leaves, allowing it to drip, drip, onto the ground at a regular rate for hours after the shower: the moisture may penetrate two or three times deeper if there are tussock-like plants or trees to spread the impact. Tussocks are not suitable food for many herbivores, but they insure that more water is held in the ground to benefit other grasses. The watcher taking a look at a tree a few hours after rain might notice how the patch of ground under the branches is still moist long after areas roundabout have dried up. The protected patch also features a different kind of vegetation. A good scattering of umbrella trees, such as are often to be seen dotted about the plains, does not mean less food for the grass-eaters; it could mean more, though of different types.

All of which can be of as much direct significance to the workings of a wild community as the great mammal populations and their spectacular spasms in numbers. If the vegetation of Africa presents a face as variegated as the wildlife, it is no less unique and irreplaceable. Plants become extinct just as much as animals. They have a history just as distinguished; and in some places they are just as endangered, these creatures less able to scramble away from the dreadnought approach of modern man. Kenya has become one of the first lands anywhere to establish a reserve for the protection of plants.

ZEBRAS

You can see zebras all day long. They do not often go into thick bush areas to escape the heat—they might not come out again. But they are affected by the noonday sun all the same. A languor comes over them, and even grazing seems too much of an effort.

All appearances apart, this zebra is not defending a territory. Unlike wildebeest and others, it does not take its stand on a particular patch of ground. The piece of country that other zebra stallions must avoid is wherever the defending male and his harem happen to be during the day.

And a zebra is one of the most handsome and conspicuous creatures to watch on the plains, even if, at a distance, its stripes merge with the heat shimmer. No two zebras have stripes exactly the same. They can be similar, but they are like fingerprints. Sometimes there is a faint dark line between the black stripes, and sometimes they run together along the back to form beautiful mottled patterns. Possibly the coloring breaks up the animal's outline rather than conceals it, as would be appropriate on the open plains where there are not many bushes or trees to merge with. If a lion does not have proper color vision, but rather sees its prey in neutral tones, this might help a hartebeest or a gazelle, but would not prove much use to a black-and-white zebra. Evolution must have had some reason for producing a pattern like this, since it would hardly allow an animal to develop whose coloring put it at a distinct—however distinguished—disadvantage. Perhaps the pattern has something to do with heat regulation: the black stripes absorb five degrees more heat, while the white ones reflect it, helping things to keep in right proportions.

Sometimes particular colorations arise for a subspecies in response to local conditions. Around Lake Magadi in Kenya, as Dr. Malcolm Coe has pointed out, there are unusually light-colored zebras and wildebeest. This is a barren area, much of it soda flats or sparse scrub. The zebras retain the brown stripes from early days right into adulthood, while the wildebeest often show a sandy color. The heat haze in this, one of the hottest places in East Africa, makes the light shades more difficult to pick out than a more striking coloration. The characteristic may have originally arisen from the high mineral content of the habitat, a metabolic factor to reduce pigmentation. If the coloring made for better camouflage, then the predators would steadily eliminate the more conspicuous strains. The survivors would concentrate the softer coloration to produce a new race on local lines.

A zebra is always fat and contented looking. Even the zebras that starved in the 1962 drought seemed well fed, though their population of 1,350 in Nairobi Park fell by a third, indicating how dependent they are on water and how much they need tolerable grazing. A few years later their number had dropped almost another third; the breeding cycles had been thrown out of rhythm by the disaster. On top of that, their year-round movements were being disrupted south of the park, where a local meat-packing factory had extended its holding grounds. Like other plains animals, the zebras need this corridor for their short, wet-weather migrations. Masai tribesmen are also closing in with increasing herds of cattle. Perhaps the zebras migrate out of the park and just don't want to return through such difficult country.

Zebras are generally placid creatures; the wary wild animal emerges as the herd approaches a water hole. Their senses are good enough, but the problems of staying alive for a zebra have been, are, and always will be. It has learned to live with its environment; otherwise it would no longer be here. It probably makes use of the sharper senses of the wildebeest and the enlarged vision of the ostrich or the giraffe. But every day it has to go down to drink, and the lions know that: they, too, have learned to live with their environment. Not that a lion finds it all that easy to get within true striking range. An occasional zebra sporting a foot-square patch of hide hanging down its rump tells its own story.

Like most plains animals, the zebra has eyes at the sides of its head. It has to keep watch on a broad sweep of the environment, rather than focus on a particular small part of it as predators do. When it is fleeing it tends to run along a curve or follow a zigzag, so that it can see how things are behind. On the whole, however, it prefers to follow a leader; then it just runs blindly ahead.

Most zebras live in a herd community. You rarely see a zebra on its own, not as you will see a male wildebeest with its territorial system. The social unit for zebras is a wandering group that a stallion maintains for years on end. He defends his harem rather than any territory. Other gregarious animals, such as buffalo, allow several males to run with the herd, though they are usually dominated by one or two overlord bulls who make sure the rest recognize what goes on. Dr. Richard Estes has pointed out how the zebra approach to social organization seems to be somewhere between the wildebeest at one end and the buffalo at the other. It is a unique arrangement. Various other members of the equid family have their own solutions: among wild horses there is something of both the harem approach and the territorial system, while herds of wild ponies usually stick to small areas and do not wander more than a mile or two, which suggests a territorial pattern. Wild asses of Mongolia roam in huge troops of hundreds, but within these throngs there are smaller units, each with a leader stallion. By contrast, the herds of Nubian wild asses are reputed to be led by females and are only joined by males for a short period of the year— somewhat after the manner of elephants. The Grevy's zebra sometimes maintains a territory a mile wide, though there are also breeding herds with more than one male.

A zebra stallion has little trouble keeping his herd of females intact. They even help by staying close together when he is separated from them during a running fight or when the plain's community is thrown into confusion by a lion attack. A couple of dozen zebra may mingle with a couple of hundred at a water hole, but they sort themselves out again. Dr. Hans Klingel, watching zebras in Ngorongoro Crater for over two years, has seen only nine herds lose one of their females, and of these only two were abducted; the rest just disappeared, probably down lions' throats or hyenas'. What bothers a stallion is not trouble within but trouble without. He is constantly under pressure to defend his herd against all comers, and that is a lot: a busy life. Eventually he falls, though not until after as much as a dozen years and hundreds of fights. Old age gets him, or a lion. Or another stallion hustles him off the scene. The herd notices the leader is gone and they straightaway accept the new regime.

ZEBRAS FIGHTING

Zebra stallions fight frequently, and they fight vigorously. But, as with most animals, a fight is not intended to leave one of the antagonists bloody and battered: the aim is to establish a hierarchy or confirm it. Enough is achieved when one of the contestants dominates the other to the point where both sense what is what. There may not even be need for a battle, if a threatening display gets the message across; and if there is to be a struggle it does not have to be an all-out affair: more often than not a standardized ritual is enough. The armament of many creatures is devised to lend itself to threats and gestures rather than direct combat.

Since zebras have no territories to defend, a scuffle can break out wherever they roam during the daily round. Often enough a fight erupts as the herds gather at a water hole. A group of bachelors turns up, and one of them approaches the herd leader too closely. Teeth are bared in challenge, with much circling and prancing. The usurper gets pushed away, he pushes back, and the dust swirls. But much of this is aggressive show, mere bravado. The antagonists toss their heads, they paw the ground, they gallop around and maneuver for position. If suddenly one escalates with a lunge or a vicious bite or a kick, then the fight is on for real. Rearing up, they push against each other, looking for a mouthful of neck or chest. When they come to earth again they reach for a grip underneath. If one can knock the other's legs away, there is a good chance of attacking the rump. A zebra cannot really tear another—it just gets a good grip and pulls. Up again and off they go racing around, until they may end up a mile away from where they started.

Eventually one of them withdraws. But occasionally the defeated zebra makes no attempt to run away. He can't, with torn leg muscles. The winner vents his heated-up temper as long as he feels like it, biting and ripping at random. Finally a sorry-looking loser staggers off. No doubt he gets over it soon enough; it is not too desperate as long as the damage is on the outside. But an injury within is a more serious affair. Unless the zebra recovers by nightfall and can gallop away as readily and rapidly as ever, he might find himself in a struggle where the outcome would be final indeed.

TERMITES

Many safarists notice pillar-like mounds of earth by the roadside and see nothing more. But whatever has constructed an edifice twenty feet high must be a formidable being: it is one of the very few creatures that saw the dawning of the long African day.

The mound is a termite nest. Termites are sometimes called white ants, though they are neither ants nor generally white. They are one of the most widespread forms of life in Africa, ranging from forests to semideserts. They are also one of the most tiny, but their effect on a forest can be as great as an elephant's. Yet termites seem singularly ill-equipped for survival. In all their 200,000,000 years—five times longer than the ants' or the bees'—they have developed nothing better than a thin skin, nothing like the tough covering of a true ant; moreover, they are weak and blind, with nothing like the physique of a bee. They cannot bear heat or cold, only something in between, and exactly in between: On days when the outside walls of the mound are too hot to touch, the interior stays around 85 degrees Fahrenheit. In addition, they need a damp atmosphere all the time. Yet their tunnels conserve enough moisture for them to build in places where there is drought for months on end, even years. Evaporation keeps the colony near the saturation point, even though the atmosphere outside may be parched.

These are among the most indestructible creatures on earth. They survive not because of what the individual is, but because of what the community is. Society is sublimated over the individual far beyond the most extreme notions of the watcher's world. In a termite universe the individual is an abstraction. Their colonies run up to 3,000,000 strong. Some mounds are three feet across at the base, some fifteen feet high, while the wall of a big termitarium is a foot thick, built of a mixture of earth and saliva and special secretions. Many have a high central chimney (which can be closed off with great speed in an emergency), usually to assist with ventilation: air circulates around the living quarters at the foot, then rises in shafts almost to the top where it passes down other channels just inside the surface of the outer wall, allowing the honeycomb structure to absorb oxygen steadily while carbon dioxide is filtered out. The process further helps to keep the temperature constant, though this air conditioning is largely the function of fungus gardens. Termites live off wood material, which they cannot use just as it is. Some of them modify it with microscopic protozoa in their digestive systems, then excrete it so that it can be used in more suitable form by other termites. Or they have the cellulose converted into digestible material by their fungus farms within the colony, which produce tiny white modules of food. In addition, the fungus farms regulate the warmth and act as a store for moisture when things get too damp. The whole complex structure of the inner termitarium makes for a climate so delicately balanced that it could never be found so constant outside.

Termites flourish more in forests than in arid areas since they need steady supplies of wood food. They remove tons of debris from the forest floor as fast as it is deposited by all the agencies of the forest environment put together, elephants included. There is less "surplus" vegetation in an East African forest than in a North American woodland. Moreover, as they convert the fallen timber into further organic material, the termites use it for more than food; the process acts as a social stabilizing factor of some force. Each time wood passes through a termite it is only partly digested, to be passed on to another termite. As it is eaten time after time, it picks up "social hormones" on the way, which circulate as regulators throughout the entire colony, causing some of the termites to remain permanent adolescents. The system is reinforced by a waxy secretion produced by certain termites, which becomes food for other termites. Especially important are the substances ingested from the bodies of the king and queen by constant licking. Possibly this is what prevents the workers from ever becoming mature.

The queen termite grows as thick as a man's thumb when she is distended with eggs. She is quite motionless except when the caressing of termite palps causes her abdomen to ripple. Together with her consort, she will have founded the colony at some earlier stage, when they settle down to a lifetime of producing termites. The queen can lay 10,000 eggs in a single day—or two or three times that many if need be—and up to 500,000,000 in a lifetime.

The queen lies deep within the center of the mound. She spends her life in the six-inch royal chamber, and the entire colony consists of nothing but her offspring. Of all this gathering only the queen and her consort are fertile. The rest find their life's role in working, or protecting the colony, with no part in reproduction. So the king and queen alone act as agencies for survival and natural selection. But producing more termites depends on the success of the whole society. The two progenitors are induced to produce efficient workers, workers that will build up a smoothly functioning colony and allow full protection for the king and queen, who produce more of the most capable strains of workers; and so on, for all the millions. The community is constantly taking counsel with itself in some fashion, presumably through the hormones, to decide what new roles are to be allotted by the colony at that time.

Just occasionally termites emerge; this can be the basis for a new community. A king-and queen-to-be fly off to seek a site for a nest, often during the rainy season when the soil is soft. When they come to the end of their wedding flight the wings break off. Without a pause they set to their task. Each offspring will be small and weak, helpless in itself, yet in concert with others it becomes an engineer, an architect, a farmer, a guardian of the royal personage, or a defender of the realm. All goes to make up a society beside which the social systems of elephants or wildebeest or lions look as if they have only just arrived on earth. And in a sense, they have: elephants and their forebears have been here only a fifth as long as termites, wildebeest and lion only a hundredth as long. Termites have been capable enough to come through all the vicissitudes of Africa's long day. It looks as if they will be here for a long time to come. Whatever happens to other wildlife, termites will survive.

Below: Whether adult or infant, a giraffe is all curiosity and confidence. It just stares at you, ten minutes at a time, as if you were like nothing else on earth.

Right: Not only are these reticulated giraffes different from other sorts, but one giraffe is different from every other: the individual patterns are like "fingerprints." The herd shown here proved a haphazard gathering; since, although the giraffes remained in much the same area for months on end, they were hardly ever seen together again.

GIRAFFES

Some of the most interesting animals are almost as active at noon as they are in the morning or the evening. And if they are not as active, they are still as visible. A giraffe spends up to three-quarters of its day feeding, so it is likely to be out and about almost any time. Even when it is resting or chewing its cud, as it often does during the middle of the day, it stands out in the open, ignoring such shade as may be close by. Perhaps that inch-thick hide protects it from the heat.

An especially fine sight is a herd of giraffes at a gallop. Nobody has been able to describe a horse's gallop adequately, much less a giraffe's. A walking giraffe moves both legs on one side at once; then when it breaks into a gallop it has to change to lifting both forelegs together, then both hind legs together—quite a feat of gear-shifting. Fifteen feet at a stride, the giraffe appears to waft across the plain as if it barely touches the ground at all. Its name, originally Arabic, means "the one who is graceful." According to African legend, the giraffe was created when God had finished constructing the other creatures, using leftovers from the antelope, the camel, and the leopard to produce *Giraffa camelopardalis.*

At a gallop the giraffe makes contact with each foot in turn. The first one in the cycle to reach the ground must take quite a shock with all that giraffe behind it. Not that a giraffe likes galloping. It always slows down as soon as it can (to the chagrin of the onlooker). If a giraffe is chased too far it develops a giraffe kind of water-on-the-knee. It does not really walk at all, which would mean moving forelimbs and hind limbs alternately on opposite sides, as most animals do (including the reader). A giraffe, with its legs placed so close together under its body, would trip over such a gait, so it paces, moving both limbs on one side at once. Camels and bears do the same; the reader might see how he makes out. Whether moving fast or slowly, the giraffe uses its neck to counterbalance the tremendous shift in weight at each stride. The giraffe's forelegs provide the main power stroke, not the hind quarters as in the horse or various other animals that can cover ground at a fair pace. At the same time the neck moves forward following the line of thrust, to shift the body weight off the back legs and move the center of gravity forward. When the front hooves meet the ground again the neck swings back to reduce the momentum; otherwise the giraffe would fall on its face. Back hooves move forward again, to start the stride all over again. When the giraffe paces, much the same happens except that there are two phases, not one. The legs on each side move in unison, over two cycles, with the neck moving twice for each complete movement. Marvelous to watch—and marvelous to consider what forces worked at this problem for an eon or two until such synchronization was achieved.

The neck is similarly used after the giraffe has been lying down and wants to get up again. With closely grouped limbs and a great weight to lift, yet only a cramped leverage, the giraffe has to time things carefully. It throws its neck sharply backward, producing enough impetus to get its foreknees braced against the ground. Then a swing forward to roll the weight over the pivot and get the rear-end weight off the hind legs, enough to stretch them out and take a stance; followed by another vigorous backswing of the neck to take the weight off the front end enough to change the kneeling position to a standing one. Success! And this all takes about a second and a half, which can mean the affair is not a success at all if there is a lion about. That is why the watcher rarely sees a giraffe lying down, and never unless there are other giraffes nearby. Occasionally one lies down for a quick five minutes and goes into a deep sleep, the head curled round on the rump; altogether a giraffe may spend half an hour out of the twenty-four in this way. Sometimes a snoozing giraffe is woken up by the little ox-pecker searching in its hide for food. Giraffes are bothered a good deal by ticks, and they relieve themselves in any way they can, such as by rubbing their stomachs on six-foot bushes or reversing in and out of tall-grown thickets.

The powerful beat from the giraffe's two-foot heart is powerful enough to drive the blood all the way up that neck to the head. (For all its length, the giraffe's neck has only seven vertebrae, the same as most animals', including the reader's.) But there are special valves in the blood vessels to stop the blood rushing to the giraffe's head when it bends down to drink. The heart beats 150 strokes a minute, in contrast to what one might expect—generally, the larger the animal the lower its heart rate: a cow's is slower than a man's; a lion's is around forty; an elephant's comes right down to twenty-five. But the rate might also be determined by the unusual demands that are put on the animal from time to time. A lion needs plenty of reserve to allow for sudden immense efforts; human long-distance runners have lower heartbeats for a similar reason. A giraffe's flat-out heart rate does not go beyond 170, a trifling increase above normal when a human can reach 170 as well. Perhaps it is geared for the job of keeping that huge body functioning under more tranquil conditions. There is little normal need for the giraffe to break into a gallop, since it is rarely troubled by predators.

The oxygen required for all that bulk demands twice as many red-blood corpuscles as in man, about the same as for a camel. And as in the blood of most ruminants, the corpuscles are smaller than a man's. Like their number, this makes for a greater surface area of oxygenation. The air that a giraffe breathes is drawn down in the direction of a pair of huge lungs, but much of it never gets all the way down the windpipe. Which bears

on the theory that a giraffe has no voice: the air has too far to travel from the "bellows" before raising much of a blast from the voice box. A giraffe can raise some kind of a snort, which is enough to warn others of trouble. Not that a giraffe usually needs to make noises to keep in touch; it can see the rest of the herd well enough.

If a giraffe hardly ever needs to go to a water hole, it rarely misses an opportunity of going to a salt lick. At either place, it maneuvers down to business level by splaying its feet in a series of jumps nobody could call jerky. The whole affair is risky, because it puts the giraffe at a complete disadvantage. So it experiments first with a series of "bobs" to try out the situation. Sometimes it bends its front knees instead of splaying its feet, but no matter what the method, it is plain enough how the giraffe's neck, far from being all that long, it is not really long enough! One might think, in theory, that together with the foreshortened backbone and the massive structure of the shoulders, the giraffe amounts to a series of compromises that don't really work out. But there are few things to bother a giraffe. Occasionally its gets its head stuck in the fork of a tree. Only one creature can really cause it much trouble, greater trouble than all the other hazards put together—several times over. Giraffe skin is rated highly for buckets. They are killed in their hundreds every year for this purpose alone. They are killed in their further hundreds for an even less reputable purpose. There is a growing demand among tourists for giraffe-tail bracelets, since its tail hairs are so much better than an elephant's.

Sometimes a giraffe at a salt lick bends its knees, sometimes it splays its legs. Zebras are often seen with giraffes: but do they really sense that giraffes provide an early-warning system against lions? Hardly any animal manages the rudiments of "reasoning" about the here-and-now, let alone about the what-might-be-sometime. Or do some zebras associate with giraffes for some other reason, and survive better through these incidental factors?

For those who have seen a giraffe close up and looked into its gaze beneath those out-rageous eyelashes, it is easy to understand how the hunter might pause as he sights along his arrow. The creature is so gentle and inquisitive that it is by no means difficult to approach on foot: the hunter lets fly at close range and just waits for the poison to work. But many a giraffe carcass is found with only the tail missing.

Unlike many savannah animals, the giraffe does not usually go in for well-defined herds. A haphazard group of only a few is more likely. In fact, it is difficult to tell where a group stops and becomes a random collection of however many giraffes happen to be in that place at once. Individuals join and leave as they feel like it; while a single giraffe does not need many pairs of eyes for survival. Even calves do not stay with the mother long. Not that the mother shows an undue amount of maternal instinct; at an early stage she refuses to let the young one suckle. A safarist once saw a giraffe mother clear a farm fence in the elegant manner that giraffes are capable of, but which her infant could not copy because it was too small. She seemed puzzled. For some time the pair wandered up and down, each on its own side of the fence. Finally the mother wandered off, leaving the youngster to its own devices. But if giraffes follow a social pattern markedly different from many savannah creatures, they may have little need of the gregarious instincts of wildebeest or zebras, which have to migrate and find fresh grass or recent rain. Giraffes do not need water, and they feed at trees instead of grass, which makes them less driven to search for new supplies during the dry season—tree foliage does not give out nearly so fast as grass. A large group of forty giraffe beyond the Ngong Hills near Nairobi does not seem to have shifted much for years. On the other hand, some of the Nairobi Park giraffes have been found to wander away for fifty miles, only to come back another season. Of course, different giraffes have different habits. The Nairobi Park males seem to prefer the wooded areas, while the females stay out on the plains where they may find greater protection in the open spaces for their offspring. But then, females do not give overmuch attention to their calves; and the woodlands must afford a greater range of food.

Oddly enough, giraffes do not feed only at the trees that are easiest for them to reach. They take in a fair amount of low-growing vegetation such as shrubs. John Wyatt has even seen them taking the trouble of bending over small bushes when perfectly good tall trees are nearby, often of the same sort. Their favorite material is thorn bushes, or trees whose branches they can "comb" with their mouths. The saliva, thick as rubber solution, helps with the chewing and protects the lining of the mouth against spikes. In some areas the giraffes feed so heavily on trees that there is a distinct browse-line, nothing much below about seventeen feet and plenty above. This is a danger signal apparent at various points in East Africa. There is plenty of evidence in the Mara country, where giraffes have been safe for the past forty years from such limited poaching as used to go on. Deprived of a minimum of human predation, the giraffe has little else to hold its numbers in check. The herds have flourished, until now a blight is setting in.

The Nairobi Park on the other hand reveals a different kind of warning sign. Some of the trees are browsed to an hourglass shape. Again, there may be too many giraffes; or simply those that are there cannot move onto new pasture/treelands when they need to. Nearly a hundred giraffes live in the forty-four square miles of park, which may be too high a density for the good of either. Or there may be something awry with the makeup of the population: there are many more females than males, which quickly leads to extra giraffes. Perhaps the "surplus" females, which prefer a plains existence, cannot get out onto the Athi Plains hinterland as easily as they once could. In Amboseli the male calves seem to outnumber females by three to two, as in zoos. This is a "disproportion" not uncommon among wild animals, a safety valve to compensate for the fighting among males later on, or to counterbalance the more solitary lives of males that make them more vulnerable to predators.

FISH

The East African coast, like the eastern coast of any continent, is fed by warm ocean currents. This is what counts for wildlife—or fishlife. The western shores are barren by comparison. On the east there are tropical fish ranging around coral reefs in the hundreds of species. Looking down into a sheltered pool you are looking into a world like no other, whether in a temperate-zone sea or anywhere on land. And there is no need to stand and watch at one remove; you can go and join the fish in their own environment.

As you dive down, you enter a realm even more remarkable because it is silent—silent in a way you never know on the surface. A few hundred yards away the ocean rollers are roaring on the reef, but down there you hardly know they exist at all. Nothing causes a ripple on your serene seclusion. The best time to wander and wonder is neither too early in the day nor too late, but rather when the vertical light illuminates the scene best.

Among the coral growths are plenty of small fish that make these gardens their home. They swim around among meadows of sea grass and sea flowers, which wave in the breeze of the tide as it surges along the valleys of the coral canyons and around the hill-tops. In this secret world live communities of fish far more variegated, not to say colorful, than any groups of antelopes on the savannah. In an hour you can see more different sorts than you would manage with birds in a day, or with mammals in a week. You might think by the end of your month-long safari that you have come across more species of insects than anything else, but the fish are much more diverse in shape and size than insects. Most fish within the reef are small, an inch or two long, while a few are a foot, and a very few in the deeper pools are several feet. These are by far the oldest of the earth's vertebrates. They appeared close to 100,000,000 years before the insects; the backboned fishes themselves were preceded by the primitive sea-dwelling vertebrates 100,000,000 years before that, or 600,000,000 years ago. This all took place two or three times further back than the earliest stages of the long African day. While all the ancient

The butterfly fish sports a false eye in its tail to distract a predator. The young one retains a second spot for a short while.

land forms were drifting and dividing, before the continents emerged in recognizable form, there may have been fishes swimming around their shifting coasts not much different from those the onlooker sees today off the shores of Kenya and Tanzania.

The skin diver sees fish so tiny he can scarcely spot them; he also sees some a good deal larger than himself. All an outsized fish has to do is lie and wait for whatever small food forms drift its way (though the skin diver is too big). The grouper, for instance, spends its day opening and closing its mouth; it is harmless—not like some of the denizens of the deep. Inside the tropical reef there are none of the ocean monsters, since they cannot get through the gaps. Beyond the sanctuary live whale sharks up to fifty feet long and armed with 300 sets of teeth. Yet they are harmless, too, since they filter small fry through their membranes and leave aside anything big enough to choke them, such as a human swimmer. The smaller fish are multicolored enough to make the swimmer rub his goggles and look and look: red, green, orange, black-spotted, blue-and-white striped, in all shapes and shades, the most subtle colors, luminous and lovely. They dart around the swimmer, even nibbling at him. It is a world that shouts with color as much as it is silent in seclusion. There are bardel eels and catfish, zebra fish and gaterin, red snappers, parrot fish, surgeons, moorish idols, wrasse, scorpion fish, damsel fish, trumpet fish, and sergeant majors. There is a little pilot fish, half an inch long, an electric-blue wriggle that likes to ride on the pressure wave in front of the swimmer's mask and stay there for an hour at a time.

However many different kinds you see in your exploration, there are hundreds of others. In fact, there are about 800 others, counting those just over the reef, ten times as much diversity as on the seaboards of western Africa. And these fish seem to sense they will not be harmed by the human intruder. They come right up close to peer at you, a fish bowl the other way round. The waters of these East African parks are slowly building up their populations after the former destruction and disruption. Banning the harpoon not only keeps the fish alive, it keeps them there. They don't swim off scared to where the skin diver can't follow. In and out of the groves you can wander in silence, just you and the fish.

But then you find it is not all that silent. Some of the fish are squeaking to each other, and there is a regular bedlam of sounds going on. Above all, there are constant scratching noises. These are the coral-eaters. The surgeon fish are the main browsers, but the butterfly fish, with their elongated mouths and teeth at the tips, can work over all but the hardest material: they nip off the tops of the limestone towers where the coral animals are hiding. The parrot fish have even stronger front teeth; they chew off coral and crush it up with their back teeth, like grinding mills. The trigger fish also bite off lumps of coral, but they swallow them whole; the polyp inside is digested while the rock is merely ingested, to be thrown out again as white coral sand.

Just as they vary in color, the fish vary in their habits and needs. The stripes on some act as a form of camouflage or disruptive coloring. The spots on others gather into large blobs at the back where they form a "false eye," designed to deceive an attacker. The real eye at the other end is part of another stripe that disguises the vulnerable front parts, except when the fish turns its eye to look at you, when the stripe becomes a zigzag. The swimmer may wonder how far the fish are concealed by all these colors, as bold as they are brilliant. The corals on the seabed are variously colored, but hardly with such sumptuousness. Perhaps the main aim is to confuse. The younger fish are often less brightly colored than the older ones—yet this is the age when they most need to hide. Or

Far left: The sea world derives much of its marvel from its mystery. When you look at the animals of the plain, you are at one with their environment, or roughly so; you share a common descent with them, and when you breathe, you live as they do. But when you plunge into the sea, you realize how far you are from being a creature for underwater worlds, however much you can glide along with fish in front, behind, and all around.

Bottom left: There are several species of scorpionfish, all equally attractive and all equally to be kept from coming too close: their poison is very persistent.

Bottom right: In the coral gardens of the Indian Ocean reef, it does not take long to come across one of the more common fish, the moorish idol, though it may take a while to look away from it.

possibly the colors act more as a warning than as a disguise; many of these tropical fish are highly territorial, and the vivid patterns help to keep off trespassers. Or perhaps the coloring acts as a means for a fish to recognize another of its own kind. If it is an aid to courtship, then this is some sex appeal! How far can fish see colors anyway? Or do they, like most creatures with eyes, manage not much beyond black and white and shades of gray? In which case, the stripe designs are what matter.

East Africa's coast has long attracted people from outside. The Phoenicians were here centuries before Christ, together with the ancient Egyptians. If man ever succeeds, as some think he might, in developing a technological process—or a surgical one?—that allows him to devise "gills" and return to the sea on more equal terms, the coral gardens will still be there with their residents, not much changed from those far-gone times. The marine parks have been set up at just the right time. Meanwhile, nobody should say he has seen African wildlife until he has seen the fish. Visitors come to see the marvels of Africa, but largely to tour the wilderness areas that start at some point just beyond the Indian Ocean beaches. On the other side of those palm-tree fringes there are herds of elephant. But there is not much to see in the savannahs and the torrid bushlands that compares with the lagoons of the Indian Ocean. Besides, it is much more comfortable here: you just laze in the superheated water and look.

Bottom left: The batfish is camouflaged by the stripe through its eye: when it turns to look at you, the stripe turns into a zigzag.

Bottom middle: Less attractive, and even more to be avoided, is the stonefish; a sting proves as painful as anything inside the reef.

Bottom right: The "flotsam fish" hangs upside down (well halfway) in the water, looking like a piece of seaweed.

Top left: Inhabitants of many a coral garden: the acanthurus on the left, another form of butterfly fish above, and one of the variations of surgeon-fish at right.

HARTEBEEST

By the middle of the afternoon antelopes begin to dot the plain again. As they emerge from their midday shade patches, one that strikes you as among the more grotesque-looking is the hartebeest. It seems to have got its proportions all mixed up, with fore-quarters and shoulders sloping away to a ridiculous rear end, and puny hind legs trying to power that bulk. It moves with a rocking gait that makes it look more incongruous still. The nature of the animal, a mixture of muddled curiosity and nervousness, bears out its strange aura when it stands and stares at you. With a fearful snort at nothing, it wheels around and bounces away.

And yet this just shows how one wants to interpret a hartebeest in terms of one's own experience. Is the response to anything fresh so jaded that one no longer recognizes it for what it is? Is one's routine so fixed that a departure from it is to be classed as only a variation which would revert to "normal" if it got the chance? Will the time come when we can no longer be stimulated except by things of our fabrication—an extension of what was there before, is now familiar, and will be so for evermore? Some people feel comfortable in a world of their own stereotype, where they feel secure and certain. For those who don't, there is more stability in a world that is constantly changing. So long as it is in flux, it *is*. All other experience is hardly living; it is only moderately existing.

The hartebeest cannot be other than a manifestation of its functional efficiency. To some people, this is what makes it beautiful. To which one might retort that this beauty must be partly in the eye of the beholder: back to the human prison again! And yet, unless you have seen a hartebeest in a place where it can be a hartebeest in its own manner on the African plains, then you cannot get away from the zoo viewpoint. You can say, as has been said many times, that a hartebeest stands such-and-such a height, has horns of a particular shape, weighs so many pounds, has teeth of so-and-so formation, all of which qualify it for its own Latin label. This is the approach that has persisted for years in the world of naturalist "experts," and beyond which the enthusiastic game watcher cannot always get much help. Perhaps that is why people look at a hartebeest and say that

it is just not right, or just not interesting. If the viewer could look at a hartebeest with the eyes the hartebeest uses to view its environment—or another hartebeest—he might see not only an animal but an animal in its own living space; then he would see something alive, and get an impression that is equally alive.

A hartebeest is not like a wildebeest, though its outline looks much the same (except for the horns). In its feeding patterns it is somewhere between the wildebeest and the topi. It can accommodate long parched grass, though whether out of strict preference over short green grass is not certain. It does not seem to go for the really withered stuff the topi prospers on. Grass does not reach its dried-out stage until toward the end of the dry season, so for much of the year the hartebeest has no major advantage over the other grass-eaters. But this may be why it is subject to less catastrophic declines when things get desperate. This may also be why it does not build up to such large numbers as the wildebeest during good times; its forte seems to be surviving in the worse times rather than flourishing in the better periods.

In Nairobi Park there were once around 1,000 hartebeest, half as many as the wildebeest and still a good way below the zebra. This was in 1961, when a drought was gathering force. The herds began to die off, and the hartebeest lost a third of their number, the wildebeest plunged by well over a half, and the zebra by more again. By 1966 the wildebeest had dropped to only 250. They used to make up half the diet of the park's two dozen lions, a factor which may have helped their decline until such time as the remaining few learned how to avoid the lions. Now they only account for a quarter of the lions' food. These two dozen lions need at least 400 full-grown prey creatures a year, probably more. Two thousand wildebeest could well sustain a loss of 200 a year, but

Left: While the fetal membrane is still sticking to it, the wildebeest is ready to get to its feet; learning to walk takes less than ten minutes. A hartebeest calf is not born in the open savannah where the only defense is in moving to a fresh spot on the plain—fast. It is scarcely on its feet by the time the wildebeest calf is ready to make for the horizon.

Below: With its first moments of life the gazelle calf knows to lie still when danger threatens. You can even touch it and it won't move. The gazelle mother tries to distract the threat from a hundred yards away, and even if she wanders off half a mile she can still find the calf.

when they fell under 1,000, things became difficult; under 700, they were catastrophic; under 300, beyond enduring. Fortunately, the lions shifted their attention to other prey such as eland and warthog and hartebeest, creatures that either did not suffer from the drought or were able to recover their numbers afterward. The hartebeest have in fact fared better in terms of numbers since the drought. Five years later they had returned to their former totals of just over 1,000, and there they have remained. One wonders why they do not expand beyond their old levels, now that the other grass-eaters have been decimated. Possibly more hartebeest have been appearing but more of them have been disappearing as well, now that they are the number-one species on the lions' menu. If the wildebeest partially recover their numbers so that the lions shift their preference back again, will the hartebeest proliferate? Or will the greater competition for grazing limit them once again?

A hartebeest with its calf illustrates just how distinct they are from other plains creatures, and just how influenced they are at every stage of life by all those other creatures around them. Dr. M. R. Gosling has found in Nairobi Park that most of the hartebeest births take place in scrubland or places with a modicum of cover: the opposite of wildebeest, which choose the most open spot they can find. Wildebeest are very dependent all the year round on keeping together with other wildebeest, not just because they are sociably inclined, but because they cannot go without fresh grazing, and a whole herd of wildebeest has more chance of finding it than isolated animals. Around this factor has grown up a nexus of wildebeest mores that helps to determine even the place where they will give birth. A hartebeest, by contrast, is never as dependent for its very survival on being close to other hartebeest. When the time for birth arrives it actually prefers to avoid others. It goes off to a place of hiding in the bushes. While a wildebeest calf needs to follow its mother as soon as it is a half hour old—and follow it at a steady pace—a newborn hartebeest may not be able to stand properly by that time. Instead of hugging its mother's shadow, as a wildebeest calf must, the hartebeest infant even makes moves to get away from her. Unless danger is directly threatening, the mother makes no attempt to dissuade it. This is a protective arrangement somewhat like the gazelle mother's leaving her calf crouching in a grass clump while she goes away to distract attention from the spot. Gazelles, too, have little pressing need to stay with a herd. The young one can best defend itself by keeping motionless with its head on the ground, especially in dried-up clumps of grass that match the brown color of hartebeest and gazelle coats. A wildebeest calf is rufous-fawn at first, becoming black later on. This early coloring could be a throwback to times when it was not differentiated from hartebeest as much as it is now; hence the same defense device.

The hartebeest mother leaves her offspring for long periods, only returning when it wants to feed. She is careful to eliminate all traces when the calf relieves itself, so that the smells will not attract predators to the hiding place. A gazelle mother does the same. Frequently a wildebeest calf is born early in the morning: since it is a creature that depends on running to survive, it is essential to have as much of the day as possible to get used to the world before nightfall. A hartebeest derives little benefit from one time of day to another; yet even though what matters is concealment, a hartebeest cannot get by in thick bush country. For one thing, it needs plenty of grass. For another, the males are often strongly territorial during the breeding season. Possibly the males in certain areas have been induced to adopt a territorial system to insure a proper distribution of their talents, given that the hartebeest is a creature of the grassland plains. Preference or compulsion? The territory may now amount only to a tenth of a square mile in Nairobi Park after the population has built up in recent years, causing high competition among the males. This territorial system is a factor central to much that determines hartebeest society, and the whole park's society as well.

If Nairobi Park were to be enclosed along its one open boundary and more KEEP OUT

Little milk can be left for the hartebeest calf so long after birth. Soon another calf will be on the way, if it is not already. But suckling is perhaps an important way of maintaining the mother-calf bond, since the youngster spends much of its first months lying concealed in the grass, well away from its mother.

sign boards were added—addressed to humans and animals alike—then the migratory wildebeest could disappear altogether. The lions would be more tied to the fortunes of the hartebeest than they are already; so would the cheetah, hyenas, jackals, vultures— a whole range of creatures. The hartebeest could be the only creatures to prevent the park from degenerating into a zoo, with artificial food supplies for the lions. Could they withstand such pressures? And if the hartebeest were to exploit more of the vacated grassland, with more hartebeest appearing overall, could the males endure even smaller territories? The park managers could consider a bit of help, by clearing away more bushes to allow more grazing lands and the space the males need to set up their breeding grounds. Or they could encourage more bushes for the hartebeest mothers-to-be. Hard to do both at once. Yet on such a dull and gauche-looking creature may depend the future of those far better-looking lions, not to say the zebras, and the rest. Even the rhinos and the giraffes might be involved. If the bush growth were cut away, they could be as hard hit as any. On the other hand, more bushes might mean greater stalking cover for the lions, with greater prospects for kills.

HYRAXES

There is nothing like an elephant—not until one takes a look at its anatomy, and notices an unlikely resemblance to a hyrax. There is something about the toe arrangement, especially the flattened nails, that makes it akin to no other creature except one. And the hyrax has upper incisors something like tusks-that-never-made-it. So the two are more related to each other than to any other creature. Fossils found in Egypt show that the ancestors of modern elephants were much smaller, while hyraxes in the early part of the Miocene, 25,000,000 years ago, were frequently much larger, some as big as a donkey, though others hardly a match for a rat. At this stage, an hour and a quarter ago in the long African day, the hyrax ancestors were still showing similarities to the fore-runners of elephants, though not so much as when they both started out in the Eocene, six hours ago in Africa's long day, when the elephant was a two-foot-high midget.

The hyrax is round and furry, scurrying about full of life and curiosity. It is easy to find during the middle parts of the day in the Serengeti, in and around the rock outcrops. These are rock hyraxes. There are also tree hyraxes, shyer beings that live deep in the forests, but they are much less prone to moving about during the middle of the day. Their hair is grayer and longer, and they live on the fruits and leaves of forest trees fifty feet above the ground.

Rock hyraxes live in colonies of dozens. Rare is the hyrax that ventures off on an independent track to see what is over the top of a rock. During the day they like to sit out in the sun, a whole tribe of them, but they spread themselves around in groups of threes and fours so that they can watch every part of their surroundings. There might be leopards coming around some rock corner or a hawk dropping out of the sky. They leave their feeding largely to the early morning and the later afternoon, and spend the rest of the day basking, according to the findings of Dr. John Sale during his lengthy research into hyraxes.

In the Bible they were called conies. Now the visitor might call them a lot of other things, since there are few creatures that look so appealing. He might also think again if he heard one calling, a screech that rises to a crescendo as if the creature were being parted from its skin. Wildlife may look lively and it may even look appealing, but it is still wild, and wild in a sense you remember after the "attractive" features begin to fade: but that does not make it any the less memorable. If you watch a hyrax while it is nibbling you get a glimpse of its teeth; you might think it must be a rodent. It is not. The upper incisors are used only for fighting. It has to use its molars for biting off food, which means it turns its head sideways. It has a keen sense of smell, and keeps in touch with others by giving off a scent from a naked patch in the middle of its back. Hyraxes let urine run down rock faces near their refuges; the smell may make them more adept at making a dash for a hole. They live in dry environments and can sometimes limit the amount of moisture disposed of in their urine, which then becomes viscous, less likely to run straight off the rock face—and more likely to smell strongly!

Wild animals have plenty of chances to throw off subspecies when they run up against an environment different from the "normal." Over the years individuals emerge that are better able to handle the local situation than others. They pass on their genetic characteristics until there is a concentration of these traits in a group that differs from the rest of the species. In East Africa this has happened to the hyraxes on Mount Kenya, as Dr. Malcolm Coe has described. Within the last 50,000 years the earth's climate has warmed up. When the ice caps of Europe and North America retreated for the last time, the extended glaciers of Mount Kenya withdrew from around 10,000 feet to the present patches at 15,000 feet and above. The climber on Mount Kenya finds the forests end very abruptly at about the 10,000-foot level. One minute he is sweating among trees, the next he emerges onto open moorlands—all within a few hundred yards. This marks where the ice once reached. The giant groundsels and other freakish growths that are found above this line have followed the retreating ice: at one time there were probably groundsel forests along the hills and valleys that are now the maize plantations of Kikuyuland.

At this stage, a bare quarter-minute ago in the long African day, there were plenty of hyraxes living around Mount Kenya. There were tree hyraxes in the forests and rock

The hyrax spends much time in dark holes among the rocks, which may partly account for its long, catlike whiskers. Its elephant-like toes, with a claw on each back foot to help, are adept at hanging onto steep rocky faces.

Two sorts of zebra overlap beneath Mount Kenya, the narrow-striped Grevy's from the north and the broader-striped Burchell's from the south. On the mountain there are two sorts of hyrax, but their needs and life styles are so different that their ecological separation leads to geographic separation as well, with hardly any overlapping: the rock hyrax ranges from the upper massif down to the moorlands, while the tree hyrax clings to the forest belt at the foot.

hyraxes lower down on the plains. The ones that established themselves among the mountain peaks were not the ones that were nearest. An area on the northern side of the mountain receives less rainfall, leaving a gap in the forest belt. The rock hyraxes squeezed through this opening and out onto the moorlands. For a while both hyraxes may have tried to make a go of it, but the one that was accustomed to the open habitats of the plains below seems to have been more successful up high where it found open, treeless countryside. The modern-day climber on Mount Kenya finds hundreds of rock hyraxes scuttling about the boulders of the moraines. On the other hand, in the peak areas of the Ruwenzoris the more successful hyrax has proved to be the tree hyrax. But then, the mountain massif of the Ruwenzoris is covered with forest-type vegetation; fine for the tree hyrax, while the rock hyrax remains below.

Living at a height of three miles on Mount Kenya within sight of the equator has left this particular race of hyrax with an unusual habitat. The ground freezes every night, while during the day the air grows warm enough for a climber to walk around in shirt and shorts. This means the area passes through a temperature change each day that takes a whole year on the Rockies or the Alps. To meet these extremes, the Mount Kenya hyrax has produced a fur that grows thicker and longer. Its young appear at the opposite time of the year from those of the lowlands, since it has had to adjust its breeding times to the periods when the mountain vegetation is likely to be lushest. The youngster has to learn to perch on its mother's back for the first few months so that it won't get crushed by other members of the colony all crowding together in a burrow for warmth. Only one infant is born instead of the usual two (or up to six) of the lowlands. This single offspring has a far better chance of surviving. There is less competition for food and protection and all the other things a young hyrax requires from its mother. But up on the mountaintops, where there are fewer creatures to snatch up a hyrax, only an occasional leopard or eagle, there is not the same need for a lot of young ones. In fact, the only being it is likely to see sometimes is a human climber. One infant at a time is sufficient to have kept this specialized breed of hyrax going during its lengthy/brief period of the African clock, where a tick is a thousand years.

CHEETAH AND CUBS

During the heaviest heat there is small chance of seeing lion cubs; they are far inside their thickets. Leopard cubs may be around, but they will be way up at the tops of trees catching the breeze. Only cheetah cubs are likely to be visible, and then only if the mother is out on the prowl. A cheetah likes to do its hunting by midmorning, but an unsuccessful cheetah may feel more hungry than hot.

During the early stages of a hunt the cubs keep by their mother. It would be dangerous for her to leave them in a patch of long grass, as a lioness can when she goes hunting. The same lioness might find the cheetah cubs and that would be the end of that. So the cubs trot along behind until the prey is sighted; then they crouch down in any small patch of cover. It is hard for the human eye to make them out even at a few strides because their fluffy smoke-gray hair blends so well with the surroundings.

Cheetah cubs, like all cubs, chase each other around; they tumble and roll about; they scamper over logs. Every conceivable game is played in helter-skelter succession. Like lion cubs, they especially like "ambush," yet whatever their innate sense for this sort of tactic, they will hardly ever use it when they grow up and prey is no longer play. The bushes might still act as temporary cover, but only until the prey comes within a few score yards—not the final dozen that a lioness waits for. Perhaps the cheetah cubs are acting out an impulse that harks back to the times when they and lions were all archetypal cats together.

While the cubs are small their claws are sharp, allowing them to clamber up tree trunks much more than they do when they are grown up and those nonretractable claws get worn away. A cheetah on the hunt uses an occasional tree as a lookout, but it must be a tree with low branches; the cheetah does not have the powerful limbs that make a leopard at home in a tree. A cheetah is built for action on the ground.

When a cub is nearly full grown it might join a group, possibly with its brothers and sisters, though sooner or later the males go farther afield. Yet the cheetahs that go around in twos or threes do not often hunt that way. The group instinct is not nearly so developed as in lions. Lions are large animals, which means lumbering animals, as compared with the lithe strength of a lighter-built animal. A single lion makes heavy going of it trying to trap a gazelle. Better to go after something not so agile, something large and likewise lumbering in its own way, especially a buffalo or a giraffe. That takes more than one lion, but there is less likelihood of dispute if more than one lion wants to feed at the result. And so on: communal living; larger prey creatures to keep the whole group going; frequent hunts; coordinated patterns emerging in their rudimentary form; further adaptations evolving to maintain the social system; caring for the young shared all round—a whole system develops that makes a lion more of a lion and less of a catlike

Overleaf
While the mother cheetah makes ready to go off after the prey she has spotted, the cubs crouch down in clumps of grass. She later calls them over to the kill with a strange chirruping sound. The cubs must get their meat at the carcass, since the mother, like lions, leopards or hyenas, though unlike jackals and wild dogs, cannot regurgitate food for her offspring.

Top right: Occasionally a cheetah in the wild produces eight cubs. Rare, zoo-born litters average well under three. Either way, not more than one or two are likely to survive. In some savannah areas there are signs that the cubs are born during the heavy rains of April and May, so that the stage when they are learning to hunt coincides with the time when antelopes are concentrated in dry-season localities.

Bottom right: In the Serengeti more female cheetah cubs survive than males. This should be a hopeful sign, allowing for more and more cheetahs—but things do not seem to work out that way, despite the excellent hunting terrain and plenty of prey.

creature such as a cheetah or a leopard. A leopard is the least sociable of the lot: it has no need to be sociable. A leopard can get by even with one paw missing, through deploying the full feline hunting skills refined to their ultimate leopard-style degree; or by supplementing its diet through scavenging. A cheetah with a single toe missing is in immediate trouble, possibly final trouble.

Before that far-off day when it will try to exist in a grown-up world, a cheetah cub has a lot to learn, though not as much as a young lion. A great deal is known about rearing lions and releasing them in the wild. Everyone has heard of the problems that arise. No need to wonder how a nine-month leopard would fare; almost certainly it would get by from the first moment. That is what makes it a leopard. Ron McLaughlin has seen a mother cheetah catch a gazelle fawn and bring it back alive for her cubs to play with. When they let it scamper off, she brings it back for another try. They have another go, knock it around, do everything but what they should. They bowl it over a score of times before one of them finally gets the idea; then learning is very quick. Which makes one suspect that cheetah cannot be "rehabilitated" so easily. Some people think a cheetah has less intelligence (by man's standards) than a lion or a leopard, though it makes a pet of sorts. Cheetah have been widely used as hunting aids, like falcons; they were first recruited for this work by the ancient Egyptians 3,500 years ago. Nor is the look in a cheetah's eyes that of a "loner" like a leopard; hence it is perhaps more predictable, though those eyes reveal a wild peace not like any other creature's.

Often five or six cubs are born at a time. Only two or three of them are likely to survive. They are completely helpless for a while, blind, weak, and prone to rickets. In some cases more females last out than males, though what the ratio is at birth nobody knows. Cheetah are not common anywhere in their range of country, and it has been suspected at one time or another that they were going under to some disease. A survey in East Africa found them still holding out in a wide variety of areas, wherever there is plenty of game and not too many humans. Their range is roughly that of lions, which means only a fraction that of leopards. The survey estimated there were at least 2,000 cheetah in East Africa, possibly many more. It is difficult to count cheetah. Those that were sighted seemed to be producing more cheetah well enough, and there was no sign of disease— so all was well. At which one pauses: how many is enough? Does a species have to be down to its last few hundred before it is time to start thoroughgoing protection? If the cheetah is subject to other dangers—as is obvious from the furriers and the demands of their foreign environment—then at what point does it become "endangered"? Do you wait until it is in bad straits, or while it is under early threat? Or will there never be all that many cheetah anyway? In the 6,000-square-mile Serengeti, with perhaps 500,000 gazelles (the cheetah's favorite food), and plenty of good open country for hunting in, there may be as few as 150 cheetah. Which, as George Schaller has pointed out, means that the skins imported into the United States alone in a recent two-year period would account for as many cheetah as you would find in almost 100,000 square miles of typical country, a far bigger area than Uganda, and as big as Colorado or thirty Yellowstones.

With its lean and lanky body, and its "tear-streaked" face, a cheetah does not look much like a leopard at all. But it is close enough to satisfy too many people. That golden coat has become its blight. Though hardly velvety, it does something for those who want a handbag made of it, or want to wear several skins on their back, or have bathroom slippers made of it or have an executive chair covered with it. If this creature has developed special adaptations to its world over the stages of its long African day, until it has differentiated itself from other hunters in its wild domains, and become the fastest creature on land (it can accelerate to forty miles per hour in a couple of strides and cover a hundred yards in three seconds), it has still neglected to make itself fast enough to outspeed an arrow or a bullet. As leopard skins become more scarce—and hence more expensive, hence more sought after, hence scarcer again—the pressure is transferred to

A cheetah does not like heat, and a mother out on the hunt cannot do much about it. Meanwhile, the cub finds otherwise.

the cheetah. Yet people thousands of miles away from cheetah country say with absolute conviction that the cheetah is still "all right."

All that is certain is that the cheetah is not plentiful at the best of times. Kruger Park has only 250 cheetah in all its 7,000 square miles, as compared with twice as many leopards and four to five times as many lions. But the Kruger cheetah are subject to more than one threat. If they have to cope with the poacher, there is a danger yet more insidious. Until 1960 there was the idea that predators should be shot on sight, as a safeguard for the antelope herds. Hundreds of cheetah, as well as lions and others, were dispatched before the people who were so sure of what they were doing decided they were not so sure after all. With all those carnivores gone, the impala and other antelopes proliferated. The grass became overgrazed, fire was banned anyway, the bush moved in. Bushland is not good hunting country for cheetah. Now they are on a decline. Stopping poachers, even when there are the salons of Paris to spur them on, may be easier than pushing back the bush again. A number of cheetah cubs are found emaciated, possibly abandoned when the mother finds it impossible to kill enough to support herself and the family. These cubs are fostered at a special center, to be released from time to time—and when that day arrives it will *really* matter whether they can rehabilitate themselves to the wild or not.

Even if they manage to hunt for themselves, that may still not be the whole story. There is more to a predator's survival than being able to hunt; there is the matter of finding a place to hunt in. Cheetah do not seem to be territorial the way lions are, but, within whatever system of social sanctions cheetah operate, will the residents in Kruger make the interlopers unwelcome? And if the males are more territorial, as with lions, or the females, as with tigers and possibly leopards, perhaps more should be released of the "right" sex than the other. There are rarely signs of cheetah fighting among themselves, and cheetah of either sex seem to roam around while they are hunting, apparently overlapping with each other's areas. Cheetah constantly urinate on bushes and other landmarks, as Randall Eaton has noticed, while at the same time sniffing their way across the countryside, moving from one "marker" to another. When one group of cheetah comes across a sign that they are encroaching on country where another group has passed within twenty-four hours, they may move off in a fresh direction. There could be a "time-plan" to replace the usual territorial system, with the same effect of spacing out the animals and reducing conflict among a species that can afford injury less than most predators and can afford to lose members less than almost any (perhaps half the cubs are already falling to lions or leopards or hyenas). This is a system used among domestic cats, also mountain lions in North America—cougars, like cheetah, may never have been prolific enough to need to limit their numbers through stringent space regulation, but they would still need to cut down on aggression among themselves.

Evolutionary efficiency is a complex process, but it is something the safarist can wonder about as he watches for signs in the savannah. The savannah itself is not always a very stable affair, not like a rainforest, since it has a tendency to revert—or advance—toward bushland. The cheetah in Kruger are on bad times, since their open country is disappearing; and while a leopard might like the environment closing in about its ears, a cheetah doesn't. Not that anyone properly knows how much cheetah country in Kruger is already apportioned out among those already there, if indeed it is "shared out" to capacity. There may be less favorable areas not yet occupied—but they may be too unfavorable for any cheetah. If the newcomers have to fight all along the way for such territories as they establish, that might not leave many more survivors than before. One wonders what has happened to the hunting niches vacated by the cheetah that have not survived in the face of the encroaching bush. They could have been partially taken over by additional leopards or even lions, though no leopard or lion can hunt like a cheetah. Habitat is not altogether a geographical entity, just as environment isn't; niche much less so. It is one thing to say where an animal lives, another to say what it does there—and how it affects its surroundings, until more can adopt the habitat, more then adapt it, and so on.

Something of this kind is going on in Ngorongoro Crater, where there is a marked absence of cheetah despite all that splendid open space to hunt in, and all those gazelles. Some people believe there were more cheetah before 1961. Following the fly epidemic and the decline of the lions, the hyenas probably took over part of the lion niche, with suitable adaptations in hunting style. More hyenas—hunting hyenas—could have led to conflict with the cheetah. Cheetah can escape lions merely by running a little faster and a little farther; to avoid hyenas they would have to run a lot faster and a great deal farther. Perhaps things become too crowded at some stage, and if lions are now making a comeback in the Crater, leaving the hyenas to look out more for themselves, will that mean less competition against returning cheetah—or more? The Crater is ideal for these hunters that need space for long pursuits; fine for hyenas, fine for cheetah, fine for wild dogs. A wild dog pack, too, prospered there for several years before disappearing. If wild dogs cannot make out in packs of a dozen, how much less can solitary cheetah, or groups of merely two or three?

Only one thing is certain in the whole tale of cheetah survival, and that is that as a species they are not so massively successful, not like other cats; but successful enough for their own purposes. It is when they conflict with the purposes of far-off furriers that they run into difficulties they cannot handle. The world **may be** getting rich enough to do without cheetah.

HOMO TOURISTICUS

In the lull before the burst of late-day activity, there is still one creature worth watching, and it is likely to be stirring again by this time. It is one of the most diverse and fascinating species, unpredictable in a way like no other. It comes in all shapes and sizes and defies classification. It would be a topic worthy of many a researcher. It is visible only by day, and it is a creature exerting an increasing effect on the environment: the tourist.

Strange man in a strange land, he drives around in his safari truck looking for something to look at. The African ranger picks out an anthill that is not an anthill but a rhinoceros asleep. They drive over. The visitor gazes out of the roof-hatch at the rhinoceros, or rather gazes through his viewfinder at the subject matter. He clicks a few times, then a few more to make sure. He decides that despite his encouraging noises the rhino is not going to "do something." He shuttles off to another rhino, or lion, whatever else bears promise of "doing something." Out of the two or three hours spent on a game run, well over half may be taken up in traveling hopefully, just as well over half a month's safari may be spent in a breathless dash from one "must" area to another. If this is the tourist's first park and he has not yet seen a lion, he is interested in little else: after all, lions are what make Africa Africa. But by the time he gets to Ngorongoro, he is likely to have seen lions in Nairobi Park and more lions in Mara and lions by the score in the Serengeti. One wonders why he does not wait for a while and watch what the rhino does —and give the lions a rest. A rhino cannot lie too long, or its legs become cramped. It must go off to chew at a thorn bush, or set out for a mud wallow. A whole hour spent with a rhino is not an hour wasted. But a rhino, with its ambling disposition, is not to be hurried.

Nor is the African day. The visitor comes to get away from the rush of his appointment schedule. A little less time commuting from one bunch of animals to another might show him more of what makes up Africa. So might leaving his camera behind—heresy to most wildlife watchers, but worth trying, for a single day at any rate. The tourist might then

see what he has come to see. Some people use their camera to show what they have seen, some use it to show what they haven't seen, some use it to show they haven't seen much at all. Wildlife is more than just an "attraction" to record on film, as if animals were inanimate objects like ancient buildings or national shrines. They are less than what they might be when they are transfixed in statuesque photographs. Some people use their cameras to collect species: find one, tick it off the list, on to the next one. The view through the camera lens is much the same as through the glass of a museum showcase. Some people want to isolate the creature, "capture" it on film; not much different from those who want to hang its head on the wall (but at any rate their approach isn't as final).

Of course, the visitor can't spend days and weeks waiting and watching, even if he is so inclined. But with a little anticipation and less frenetic ambition, he could spend half a dozen hours a day watching wild creatures just a few yards in front of him. He could watch and wonder, in depth and in peace: after all, isn't this what he has come thousands of miles for? He might even see a wild animal going its way free and un-disturbed, rather than a creature to be pulled to pieces—as if he were using a scalpel in a laboratory—with incessant questions of "what does it do?" What it does best is *be*. To see wild animals as they really are, you have to enter their wild world on their terms; they will accept you in good time, and not before. As long as you don't chop your day into schedule-sized chunks, they will give you an experience complete and sufficient.

Treetops, the lookout lodge built fifty feet up in the trees, uses an artificial water hole and scatterings of salt to get the animals to match their seasonal shifts to the year-round influx of visitors. There are now scores of rhinos and hundreds of elephants and buffaloes making a speedy impression on the narrow forest strip where Treetops stands. Unless the wildlife migrations, as well as those of the visitors, are allowed to follow a more varied pattern, there could be little long-term future for Treetops.

Wild animals have an integrity of their own: they cannot give poor value, they must reveal a being entire and at one—except when their normal rhythms are interrupted by a safari truck that drives up in a hurry in a cloud of dust. The seasoned safari escorts, those who have been at it for forty years, hardly ever travel at more than walking pace. Or they sit for ages looking at the world through binoculars. They stop at an empty baobab tree and show you ants, dragonflies, hornbills, wood-borers, all part of a teeming world that most visitors do not see because they never think to look.

A further way to get the full treatment in Africa, the experience for real, is to leave the vehicle behind, too. This is beyond most visitors, who have only a limited time to see a wide range of areas (apart from other limitations). But the car acts as an insulation between the spectator and what is outside. Precisely its purpose, some would say: the African outside can be a dangerous outside as well as a hot outside. Yet if Africa is sun and glare and dust, would one be any the worse for experiencing the lot for a short while? It would be a new experience, not the canned product you get from inside a steel cocoon. This is a foreign environment: all right, then, let it be foreign—it just might be something different and worthwhile. From the back of your safari car you can't very well respond to it unless you can find something to *do* with it: perhaps that is why there is such avid clicking of cameras, or why there are such efforts to stop the sleeping lion from sleeping—you have to get involved, and if the only convenient way is by throwing something at the lion, then it is the lion's fault for not conforming to the "real" image. If you were outside, the lion would be fascinating enough whether dozing or not. But Africa is to be subjected to the same ethic as the suburb, where the environment is shut out except when it can be safely wrapped. Being in Africa should be a bit like walking in the rain: it is not what you want to do every day, but it makes a change. Some people would not mind if they never felt rain for fifty years, just as others do not always want an umbrella. At East Africa's altitude the sun won't give you sunstroke even if you walk around in it all day; but it can give you something deeper and more lasting than a tan.

All the more heartening, then, that Kenya and Tanzania are setting aside areas for visitors on foot (who first sign a suitably emphatic waiver against the possible wreckage). In a northern sector of Tsavo Park you can wander about with the African earth beneath your feet. It is the most remote and inaccessible part, but just what some people want. Also in Kenya there are places where you can go, and only go, on horseback or camel hump. You go with a guide and with your own resources (and you find out before you get back just what they amount to). But the usual reaction to this sort of idea is that the average visitor does not want it. Possibly not; what about the visitor who is not a statistic?

Of course, travel like this is not much good for photography: you spend all day getting to the place you could reach by car in half an hour, and if you see an animal you can't get very near. But if you have the luck to eye a fully grown lion at thirty yards, albeit fully fed, you know more about a lion than you do when you view it at a quarter of the distance from a car window. If you come across a herd of buffalo at close quarters you learn quickly enough what you need to know about buffalo powers of smell and hearing and sight. When you are invited by young Masai warriors to play a game of placing a pebble in turn on a sleeping rhino's back, you get a precise impression of what makes a rhino. All you could learn about the same rhino from behind an auto door is much the same as from a textbook: a certain size, a certain color, a certain species— halfway to an abstraction. When you are auto-bound, a rhino asleep looks like a rhino useless: what can it tell you about itself? Moreover, any safari on foot gives you a feel for Africa through the sole of your boot, irregularities and all, a sense that is lost when you feel it only through the bounces of your car—after all, the auto firm claims you are safeguarded from most such experiences. This is the museum approach again, except that you are in the glass case looking out, an experience dead instead of dynamic.

Besides, travel by vehicle makes the place small, and Africa is never small. A day's trip 100 miles long would take you a week on foot: by so much is the park's expanse reduced. While the colors of a car-taken transparency might fade in time, the experience on foot would never lose its vividness. You would have known Africa, just as Africa would have known you. Africa can be a dangerous place, and you might not come back the same as you went.

And yet, and yet. For the person who must go by safari truck because he hasn't enough time to go by any other means, or because he no longer knows how to go by any other means, there is much to be said for seeing your wild animals this way. When you are a few feet from a group of cheetah, you know what it is like to stare into a cheetah's depths, something you do not get from less than point-blank range. On foot many animals wouldn't allow you to get much nearer than the horizon, unless you were very careful and had as much time as they have. African creatures survive mostly by spotting the stranger before he is in their midst. They would have their world and you would have yours: they would make it clear that you are the one reject of the animal world. Yet when you get close in a safari truck, you occupy the same patch of country as they do, and you are in some way shielded from the awful sense of being a stranger in their land. They live in it; you are tolerated. Driving right in among the herds is a simple experience and an absolute one.

Not until the last few years have people been able to approach wild animals in Africa in this manner. If there has never been a time when people could roam the earth in instant travel, there has never been a time when they could go to a distant land and take off in a safari vehicle along tolerable tracks deep into the ancient country, or leave the tracks altogether to follow something special. Perhaps, after a few years' time, they will never be able to do it again in this unrestricted manner. They will be limited to paved roads, and they won't be able to drive over to the lions and get right on top of them; or if they are still allowed to approach at close quarters, they might be rationed to two minutes (groups of ten viewers or more, three minutes), then move on again—and sharply at that. But having come five thousand miles, isn't a hundred yards as good as fifty feet? It all depends on what you want. If you want to view African wildlife with the same perspective as at the zoo, and you do not bother about the African environment (which after all makes these African animals what they are), then you have to be in a position to see the lion's tonsils, and not just see them but have them fill your viewfinder.

How can Africa cater to this kind of tourist? He looks out across the face of Africa. The harsher aspects might have limited appeal; he likes natural beauty, but he can do without the hair-shirt stuff (a long way from the day when travel was associated with "travail"; the modern traveler likes raw Africa without becoming raw himself). Each to his own taste; Africa should be big enough to accommodate them all. The animals exert an attraction, though just exactly what is hard to say. There are all kinds of reasons for this new interest in anything that is wild and moves. Perhaps it is the mood of an age of potential destruction; whatever lives is to be saved. Perhaps it is a reflection of an age of gross national product in some of its grosser forms. The unmechanical has its attraction as long as it is not man-made; perhaps wildlife is the current curiosity, a two-headed freak in fresh form (until the three-headed version comes along). A visitor watches an Egyptian vulture picking up a stone and carrying it a fair distance to break open an ostrich egg, without always realizing what a phenomenon he is witnessing—a creature using a tool, if not manufacturing one. Like the discoveries of the wild chimpanzees, this might be a breakthrough in our view of animal habits and their entire relationship to man, including tourist man, with his evolutionary past. Yet the visitor asks for the tenth time where the lions are, and away he goes.

Possibly he would be more interested in the workings of wild creatures if he knew what to look for. He sits in the sun and is left in the dark. If he goes to the Serengeti in June, he sees lion cubs as only lion cubs should be, full of food and fun; two months later when the wildebeest and zebra herds have migrated away and the lioness with her cubs cannot follow, these youngsters are skin and bone, surviving at best from day to day. The onlooker does not have the background knowledge; he complains that the parks should do something about the cubs. The park does—though the warden agonizes whether he interferes more by disposing of a zebra or two or by disposing of a cub or two. With a modicum of information, the visitor might see that he is viewing a situation that over the years, over the millennia, has helped to make the African lion what it is.

Yet knowledge should not be presented as an end in itself. Nothing is more lethal to an appreciation of wildlife than a collection of facts. Where does one end and the other begin? People arrive with a passion for learning everything, and leave knowing little new. The wildlife watcher looks at a wildebeest: would he call it any less of a clown if he knew how efficient it is at turning grass into protein? Would 50,000 wildebeest on a trek be any more impressive if he were told the whys and wherefores of migrations? If he comes across a tropical rainforest, does he sense what an awesome place it is if he is told the names of some of the plants—or would he then fail to see the forest for the specified trees? Africa is sometimes a land not so much to analyze as to wonder at: it is a whole, not so many bits that happen to be in one place. There is so much of it, it is so utterly integral, it cannot but be a single impulse—yet if the proliferant diversity is stunning, how many times a day can you be stunned? To be conscious only of superlative after superlative is to be no longer conscious of any superlative. Might it be better to examine one or two along the way and leave the rest to be themselves? The Rift Valley is something wonderful every time you see it, no matter how it first became the Rift Valley, and a savannah sunset is a sunset, not just a combination of climatic factors.

In the absence of more information the visitor fills in the gaps as best he can. Animals are not animals, they are repositories of whatever human characteristics he wishes to attribute. A creature is regal or stately or charming or fierce or foolish; it is even cute. The more an animal is a caricature of the human condition, the more it deserves approval. If, like a crocodile or a snake, it presents no features to reflect the onlooker's, then it is all the more repellent. Of course, many people are able to accept (not just put up with) the creature for what it is. If a crocodile is uniquely capable of surviving in its own domain, then that is all that makes it worthy—and nothing can make it less so. Some people like animals because they are not demanding or critical; these may be people who get on with animals because they do not get on with humans: the animals are a safe refuge—and they cannot answer back. Some people are attracted to wild animals in a manner that is said to express a kinship with man's evolutionary past: they "revert to type" for a while. Yet the entire approach is not far removed from those visitors who come to Africa and want to feel at home. There are not too many such people when they arrive, and perhaps they are fewer when they take off, supposing they have known Africa enough for some of it to have rubbed off on them. They may even have become a little African themselves. When they get back, home will be a little less of a routine-filled place. If it is less like home, is that any loss? Africa and its horizons enables people to see things differently, to see them more steadily—even to see them whole.

And not every visitor wants the scenery and animals projected against humdrum ways of reacting to a new situation—or not reacting at all because he has seen it before (while seeing next to nothing). Some people suggest that man is a creature with such a passion for investigation (another throwback to his early days) that he has prospered through being an opportunist, able to turn his hand to anything. By specializing in being unspecialized, he has grown up the supreme explorer, forever wanting to see how he can satisfy not only a demanding stomach but a demanding mind. Just as there are few places with such diversity of environment where wild nature still holds sway, Africa is rarely more wild Africa than in East Africa. Whatever your insistence on cutting the sights of Africa down to the familiar, safe dimensions, you have to work hard to with-stand the splendid assaults on your senses. You may hardly be aware of what is happen-ing, and you may not mind the process, apart from the memory to take back home. While you are in Africa you can hardly avoid *being*—with more of your being than you manage in secure suburbia. You can try to avoid exposing yourself to too much of Africa, but you will come back knowing you have been somewhere else. Only those who are so bored they no longer know the difference between being bored and not being bored will fail to sense where they are. Not an antenna of the perceptions but is animated. You

watch the scene and Africa ignores you, but there is something to make you feel more than just a watcher. If you feel satisfied, you will never feel satisfied in the same way again. Africa is variety and it is contrast. It does not do anything much, it does not construct anything or devise anything. It is just there and you are there. You are sur-rounded by it, especially the sky; perhaps more than in areas where there is spectacular scenery but little wildlife, you know, however fleetingly, what it is to be at one with your surroundings. You are in a land of living creatures on every side, thousands of them, like yourself and not like yourself. But you have to bring more with you than your suntan lotion and dark glasses.

The visitor drives off across the sunlit savannah. However inscrutable the workings of this creature, one aspect is certain: more of his species are coming, 250,000 a year already, 1,000,000 before the 1970s are out. Of course, a single part of the United States receives many times as many during each summer month. Perhaps East Africa will never have to experience invasions of that kind. Yet visitors are what keep the wildlife going. Kenya now earns more of its precious foreign currency from tourists than from coffee. No other slice of the national pie is growing so rapidly as tourism. If at present it con-tributes only a fiftieth, it could soon be producing one-tenth, which would place Kenya among the vacation countries of the world, even ahead of such established tourist-traps as Switzerland.

Regrettably, the tourist does not always help the man who most needs to know what

Left: This is not the usual way to get a close-up shot. But in the places where it is now per-mitted, you get a powerful sense of what an elephant is, much more than through a thousand shots taken from an auto.

Rather than a tourist lodge, with a wall running around "to keep the world out," a safari tent is the best way to get the true African experi-ence. The wild creatures will come close, and by morning you may find tracks not only of elephants but lions, rhinos, and hippos within a few yards: but none of them comes too close.

wild animals can do for him, the man who lives on the edge of the wildlife sanctuaries. He is the one who suffers the most from the depredations of wild creatures; he is the one who finds it all too easy to go out at night with a line of snares; he is the one who lights fires to burn off the old grass in his community's pastures and does not care if the fires no more recognize the park boundaries than the animals going the other way. Talk to him about the national economy and how visitors stimulate it, and he finds it hard to be all that comprehending, any more than any man in any country when it comes to growth-rates and money-flow systems. Talk to him about how he has to pay fewer taxes because of what the country derives from all those visitors, and he smiles, though it is becoming a pretty poor joke in some areas. He is the man who *must* find extra cash in his pocket because of the tourists, cash to take to the local market and buy something specific such as a shirt or a saucepan.

To say that tourism helps everybody and therefore will save the wildlife is a simplistic story told by somebody who has not been out in the bush and talked with the man who counts. Not that many conservationists ever talk to him; they are a species more inclined to sit in comfortable offices and look at uncomfortable figures than go out and spend a few hours sweating in the African sun with the man who spends his whole life sweating in the African sun. Unless tourism can dispense its largess more equitably, it might even have the effect of embittering the man in the savannah, who is in the best position to sabotage the future. If the tourist tycoons grow rich off wild animals, why shouldn't he as well? They have their spear-emblazoned safari cars, and he has his spear. The Masai watches all those tourists dashing around spreading clouds of dust, and he has to listen to talk of actually extending the game reserves within his own region: just how has he benefited?

Properly managed, tourism can be a massive shot in the arm for any country, especially a developing country. Tourism does not supplant other activities, it supplements them. It can be exploited indefinitely. It is a plant of tender growth, given to blight from international incidents a thousand miles away, but not as subject to threats of synthetic substitutes as coffee. But nobody should talk about wildlife and its splendid array without acquainting himself with rather less-than-splendid facts. These are facts of life. In the long run public opinion is what counts, the same public opinion that raises other queries: how far does a country want to have groups of foreigners running around its territory? Judging by the way some visitors react to their host country, with hardly a glance at their hosts, one can understand why some nations decide they can do without tourists. But if the guests are understanding and sympathetic, this can be a way for an emergent land to show itself to the world and get itself on the map. Visitors on their way home are ambassadors to beat all, frank and hopefully friendly. But these visitors must also—first—give the impression that they have come to see more than wild creatures. Nothing slights a new nation more than the feeling that its achievements and aspirations are not worth a moment's notice from any visitor. A few safari organizers in Nairobi are now arranging for visits to nearby Kikuyu villages for their clients to see Africa as emergent as it can be, side by side with Africa ancient and abiding, with insights into a history the foreigner does not know much about largely because he doesn't know it exists. There are traditional ceremonies to be watched, side by side with frantic modernity, and they are all closer to Nairobi than most wildlife areas. All the more credit to the safari firms, mostly African-run, that now give the tourist an opportunity to see self-help schools, miracle rice schemes, and women's development clubs.

The month-old cheetah cubs stick close to their mother. Their smoke-gray fur matches the withered grass well enough when she has to leave them temporarily in a clump to finish off a hunt, but cheetah cubs cannot seek refuge in trees like leopard cubs, nor receive protection from a "baby-sitter" as lion cubs often can; so they are much more vulnerable to hyenas, or a lion or leopard.

Left: A leopard is smooth and sinuous in all it does, but never more so than when it comes down a tree, hugging the trunk with body, tail, and everything that makes it a leopard.

Above: An Amboseli pride returns from their night's foray beneath Kilimanjaro's dome to find their lying-up spot during the day's heat.

Right: Lion cubs enjoy a better view from up in a tree—though one of them is not sure there is room for two in the fork.

Below: In country of withered grass and thorn trees, gerenuks look sleek and well-fed.

Bottom: There are few social activities as cohesive for vervets as grooming, when one cleans and smooths another's fur—ostensibly a most pleasant experience.

Right: Elephants often prefer the forest fringe for their foraging, where they can find the more succulent material of the thick-grown tangles where the forest is regenerating itself. But when too many elephants are at work, this protective barrier around the forest is eaten away, leaving the trees themselves open to attack from those outsize appetites.

Below: Elephants enjoy the late-day warmth under Kilimanjaro—and under a tree they have earlier killed by tearing off its bark.
Top right: A sacred ibis joins two egrets on a hippo's back, where they occasionally find morsels stirred up from the marsh (just as much as in the hippo's hide). They do their share of the symbiotic relationship by alerting the hippo to slighter intrusions than it would notice while submerged in the best patch of swamp it knows.
Bottom right: The hippos of Queen Elizabeth Park in Uganda have ravaged the grasslands, allowing the bush growths to flourish beyond the elephant's capacities to keep them browsed back; in any case, elephants seem to be very selective feeders and often abandon the bushes for the forage of the marshes—as well as the coolness they find there.

Above: Two of these rhinos are not fully grown, but it is unusual for an offspring to remain with the parent so long and even more unusual to find so many rhinos together.

Right: Soon these hippos will leave their daytime habitat and make for their night-time feeding grounds, the grassland nearby, but sometimes not so nearby: over-grazing by excess hippos can mean they have to wander as much as five miles to find fuel enough for all that hulk.

Above: Although they can browse at juicy bush vegetation, rhinos seem to need to drink more days than not. In the arid regions they sometimes frequent, such as Tsavo, they may travel a dozen miles to find water, then a dozen miles back to the home range. But the Tsavo rhinos that died in the 1961 drought were short of forage rather than water: many of them died in pools.

Right: No giraffe needs to drink very often, and reticulated giraffes are accustomed to the more arid environments they frequent. When they do risk the riverside and its ambush sites, they do not drink together: perhaps one is keeping watch.

Overleaf
Top left: Waterbuck never range far from water, which makes them a favorite prey of crocodiles in areas where any crocodiles are left (very few now). Impala, by contrast, are probably flourishing as rarely before in Africa, since they are often a reflection of deteriorating habitats in which grasslands are taken over by a more scrubby growth.

Middle left: To see a Thomson's gazelle is to understand why the antelopes of Africa are considered such a striking spectacle; and to see a gazelle streaking across the plain is to understand still more.

Bottom left: One never sees a thin-looking oryx, despite the harsh countryside they inhabit.

Right: A Thomson's gazelle has a broad dark stripe down its flank, which twitches when an intruder is spotted. It may act as a warning to other gazelles nearby with heads too close to ground level to notice everything that turns up—but may catch the flickering of that black patch.

Far left: The side of many a pool in Africa features Egyptian geese; perhaps more than ever now, since they favor short-grass areas, and the environs of many water holes are being increasingly overgrazed by too many animals crowding into the parks to escape the pressures of people outside.

Near left: Hour after hour the yellow-billed stork rakes the water with long scything sweeps, searching for its food in the mud.

Bottom left: The buffalo enjoys its hours-long soak, allowing the Egyptian geese to take their rest un-disturbed, too.

Below: Lesser flamingos find the blue-green algae they need in highly saline lakes like Magadi or Natron, or in fairly freshwater pools like this one at Ngorongoro.

Top right: This is a sight to watch for on the fringe of many a lake from the equator southward: blacksmith plovers do not care whether the water is fresh or brackish.

Middle right: The saddle-billed stork does not probe the water constantly for food it cannot see; rather, it waits until it spots something, then, rapier-swift, snaps it up.

Bottom right: The ground hornbill's long tail may help it when it is maneuvering at speed on the ground, where much of its foraging has to be done.

Overleaf: When flamingos take off, a watcher does not really care how many he is watching of the 2,000,000 sometimes gathered together: a few hundred make a sight enough.

Above: The dark of a thunderstorm
gathers over Ngorongoro, chasing patches
of sunlight across the crater floor.
Right: Lucky the zebras that can drink
like this: no deep water to slow down a
stampede to safety, no poolside vegetation
to conceal another creature wanting to
meet the needs of its stomach.
Overleaf
Darkness sweeps across the
long African day; but it is not
long before the storm clears
and the sun breaks through
again.

LATE DAY

The day draws on. By midafternoon the sun's heat shows the first signs of easing. Things are less harsh; above all, less heavy. The snows of Kilimanjaro lose their glitter as they take on a softer light. The plains no longer hover in the haze. The trees have moved out of the little pools of their own shadows, and the creatures under them respond to the new time of day.

It is the smaller animals that make the first move. Perhaps they can better appreciate the first slight changes, whereas the larger creatures, the elephants and rhinos, the buffaloes and hippos, have bigger heating problems, and wait until the main cool of evening sets in. The bat-eared foxes soon emerge from their burrows and lie out in the pleasant air. The jackals set about their wanderings, snooping after oddments from the morning's kills. They sniff every passing breeze. The hyenas doze half in and half out of their dens while the young ones frolic around until the next break for sustenance, which is every few minutes. The birds start sounding again. On every side there are shadows stirring. An impala buck strides out into the open. Life in its numerous forms at ground-level sets up a rustling and a scurrying around the thickets.

All of a sudden an antelope snorts. Every muzzle leaves off feeding and stares. A clump of bushes is disgorging lions. A lioness is first to emerge. She stretches herself and strides a yard or two before slumping down as if that short distance were an effort. She is followed by another lioness, maybe two or three. A line of cubs comes prancing behind, hardly a yard without pulling one another's tail. The group settles itself in the open, nuzzling each other several times over. Then the bushes part again: a male stands framed in the thicket,

A lion cub is not as big, nor as bothered by the afternoon sun, as the older lions, and it has little trouble scrambling up into a tree.

What is remarkable about the bushbaby's eyes is not only that they are so big, but that they are both at the front of the face: a sign of the primates, though the bush-baby is such a primitive primate it is really a prosimian. Yet, like apes and monkeys and man, it has five fingers and toes, each with a "nail." When it emerges late in the day you are seeing something that has changed very little since its beginnings more than 25,000,000 years ago.

gazing around. He yawns as if to show what he makes of the world, then marches a couple of steps before rolling over, inert.

The animals roundabout acknowledge the change in the scene. They may not do much about it—they just watch and snort a bit—but they hardly move away. They carry on feeding, although not quite so serenely as before. There is a tension about their movements, and not all heads go down to graze for quite so long. The plains have now changed more than when all the hundreds of other animals were resuming their activities.

A little later a group of smudges appears on the far side of the plain, moving slowly about. They are too deliberate to be anything but elephants. Ponderous and purposeful, they pluck a casual trunkful from this bush and that, taking a dust shower now and again. Near the swamp a rhinoceros snoozes deep in a dust bath, only its horn visible to mark the spot. A flock of egrets is swaying around above the swamp, riding along on a herd of buffaloes, which still prefer the protective coolness of the marsh.

The softer the light of evening, the more the wildlife of Africa reveals another aspect. Even the most unlikely animals look fine at this time. East Africa is the sheen on a wildebeest's coat and the sun though its patriarch's beard, just as it is the splendor of a crested crane. The landscape is alive with gazelles, all their tails going. A baboon troop wanders across the grassland; the vervet monkeys wander through the treetops. And the birds look more resplendent than at midday. See a single African starling, and you know something about birds you did not know before. If you see them on every side, you see them in every hue. The lesser known antelopes, like the dik-dik or the reedbuck or the klipspringer, emerge too, but they are still very cautious. Spotting a bushbuck is an accomplishment and an occasion.

In the morning Africa was getting over the restless activity of the night. By evening it has rested. It is ready for more. But if much of the scene is reviving, the sun is dying.

Sometimes it is not always
sunny Africa. A thunderstorm
may gather in the late afternoon, suddenly breaking with
proper African vigor. Then
soon and suddenly the sun is
shining down again, while
damp Africa smells of renewal
for soil and safarist alike.

Where it took an age to shift from the sky overhead, it covers the last arc in a swiftening plunge. The watcher will catch only a fraction of what is going on. This is a time of tranquility, too. Until dark the predators are not anxious to do much about their next kill. The plain is placid. A giraffe sways along, as unhurried as ever. The hyenas set out from their dens, but they move around haphazardly for a while. Wildebeest nearby hardly stir. It is not till the sun is nearer the horizon that they raise their heads. And when it is beyond the horizon they keep them raised.

Not keeping an eye on each other, but on the onlooker.

ELEPHANTS

As the sun loses its first fierceness the elephants emerge from the shade trees. They start eating. Whenever elephants leave off anything to start something new, it is generally eating. They are stately and leisured in all they do; for all their bulk, a scene of elephants feeding is one of splendid repose.

The safarist will have noticed earlier in the day how energetic elephants are in their feeding: when it comes to bush clearing they can be more capable than the best machinery. He will also have noticed how they are wrecking their habitat, and he may have heard how they are trying to adapt to straitened circumstances. Both are massive efforts, and both likely to end in disaster. If there are fewer elephants at the end of the century—and at the present rate of decline there will be far fewer—people will ask what was done when they first reached their particular form of endangered status. Elephants are a long way from disappearing, but one wonders about the great concentrations of elephants still to be found in Tsavo and slowly dwindling away, the last of this order on earth. Some people say that the 35,000 elephants in the Tsavo area are more than any tourist can ever see unless he stays a year. Most people stay a day, and think they have seen enough if they see a hundred or two. The park is ostensibly aiming at a greater range of wild environments. If the elephants alter the vegetation so radically that it supports fewer elephants but more grass-eaters like buffalo and zebra and other plains animals   a variety such as the safarist can see in Nairobi Park and Amboseli and Mara and Serengeti and many another place— then that is considered an advance. After all, variety is what the visitor supposedly wants.

A hundred years ago there may have been as many as 10,000,000 elephants in Africa. Today there are probably 5,000,000, a fair enough number still, but their range has decreased enormously and is decreasing even more rapidly. Elephants need at least one square mile each of average habitat. As the herdsmen and cultivators crowd in on all sides, elephants are running up against one feature of the modern world that elephants do not take kindly to: congestion. There are still over 1,000,000 in East Africa. Half Kenya's elephants, the largest group in existence, are concentrated in the Tsavo region. Yet at 8,000 square miles, two and a half times the size of Yellowstone, Tsavo Park is far too small. In fact, it is only a segment of what could be called an "elephant ecological block" at least twice as large as the park. It has taken a long time to decide how many elephants there are in the park. At first they were put at 5,000, then at 8,000, more recently at 15,000; the latest figure is 23,000, while the whole ecological area runs to 35,000. In the view of Dr. Richard Laws and Ian Parker, who have produced as much research information as all other observers put together, this means there are about twice as many elephants in Tsavo country as it can probably support; and they are trapped in a place that is ostensibly trying to protect them.

There are signs that there used to be elephant migrations decades long—times when there were elephants in Tsavo and times when there weren't. Each part of their route would undergo a period of ecological adaption while they used it, then become adjusted further after they had gone. An area would start off as bush, with much of what is thought to be preferred habitat for elephants; then it would be browsed down until the grass increased and attracted a grassland community. Under the aegis of savannah fires, the grass would be steadily burned away. Eventually the landscape would revert to bush, if it were one of Africa's drier areas, and the elephants would return. This could be a cycle extending over several elephant generations, a natural progression of rejuvenation and replenishment. Some people think the elephants might have vacated one such area for as much as fifty years, possibly a hundred.

In its present state, Tsavo is at just such an adaptive stage of its cycle—though telescoped out of all proportion by human encroachment on the environs. Eighty years ago there was hardly an elephant in Tsavo—the foreign explorers did not notice them, and there were graves left by Galla tribesmen who presumably found grasslands to graze their cattle at that time. As is the way with many African cattlemen, they may have over-burned the area until they had to move on. The grass disappeared; the land was given over to bush. This would be what attracted the elephants back to Tsavo at a later stage of their "migration." Now they are still there; but now much of the bush has disappeared. The whole ecological spectrum has shifted, and it wants to shift again. The elephants have nowhere to go. Some observers maintain that the ecological change has already taken place, because a grassland habitat is largely taking over. Perhaps things should be allowed to right themselves. If a number of elephants are to die, it is better that they do so in the normal manner than by a warden's bullets. After all, they are doing a great deal to regulate the situation themselves. And yet: in such a long-lived species, there is an inevitable time-lag for birth-control tactics to operate, or for other factors to come to bear, such as a greater number of calves dying in an impoverished environment. The 1970–71 drought accounted for at least 3,000 of them, but it probably did not remove enough, particularly of the breeding cows, to restore the habitat's "camping capacity." The herds may take twenty years to reach stability, perhaps they may take twice as long: there are signs they may reach stability only by becoming virtually extinct in the area.

This kind of thinking clearly did not count for much with those who drafted the park boundaries in the late 1940s. Their approach perhaps did not match the grand manner of elephants. The park is now a monument to the map-marking method of wildlife conservation. It was initially formed from such land as was left over after man had taken his share, plus whatever might be regarded as an extra share in the future. Nor did those old-time park-planners have much concept of the role played by fire. Elephants on their own do not tell the whole tale. There are few more heated questions in East Africa than this one of elephants and fire. Elephants strip the bark off trees, letting in bacteria, wood-borers, and diverse other afflictions that lower the trunk's resistance to scorching by the next fire. If the tree had to cope with elephants alone, it could recover from losing even nine-tenths of its bark; if it had to cope with fire alone, it could withstand all but the most intense conflagration (though some trees have thinner bark than others). To make matters worse, many of the Tsavo trees are light-stemmed, more susceptible to destruction after an initial weakening. Too many elephants soon leave lots of smashed-down trees across the landscape. Along come further fires to burn the deadwood fuel in "hot burns." Even the thickest-growing and sturdiest patches are not immune. The blaze penetrates at the edge and lets in sunlight, which stimulates more grass next season, which brings fire farther into the woody tangles. The thickets are beaten back. The elephants can work their way farther in to take a greater proportion of the remaining bush growths. Another conflagration, another encroachment by grass. And so on. Which gives the initial push and which maintains the momentum, the fire or the elephants? In parts of Africa it is suggested that fire alone can devastate an area over a series of seasons. In other parts there is clear evidence that elephants can "push" a forest, such as the Budongo Forest bordering Murchison Falls Park, in one direction, while on the other side fire is unable to resist the trend, let alone push the forest back the way it came. If fire were the main culprit, one would expect fewer trees and bushes at the very edge of the park (since most fires spread from human habitations ringing the park boundary), and thicker bush toward the center. It does not take the onlooker long to see that things work out the other way round, particularly where there are the most elephants: in some areas, the elephant heartlands, there is hardly a tree left alive, while in parts avoided by elephants, only one tree in fifty is dead. Perhaps it is the elephants that trigger off the original stages, with fires giving a helping hand. Then fires play a greater role, while the elephants accelerate the change. Eventually the elephants are only contributing to what has become primarily the work of fire.

Running along the borders of much of Tsavo Park is a natural firebreak, the Nairobi road on its way to Mombasa. This helps to keep out fires which start away from the park. But there is one threat which brings fires right into the heart of the park and this is not fire-lighting poachers or honey gatherers—they can be sent back the way they came or marched off to jail—but the Nairobi-Mombasa railroad, which also runs through the park, and a train is not an intruder to be sent back the way it came. Sparks fly off, flames shoot up, smoke clouds gather over the park. The railroad runs right alongside the auto road. The one causes fire, the other stops it. But for a good stretch the railroad runs on the park side of the auto road. Huge areas of park are burned black, while huge areas of country outside the park remain untouched. On such trifles depend the last great concentrations of elephants on earth.

The park, which appears so misshapen on the map, if not misbegotten in its origin, survived well enough for a time. The areas outside were not yet limited, and the elephants inside were finding themselves limited enough. The park verges onto country inhabited by the Waliangulu, the finest hunters in East Africa. For ages they have lived off "poaching," using the meat rather than selling the ivory. It has been their way of life and a stable one—until a few years ago, when they took to hunting for more than meat. They began to kill as often as they could, lured on by the white man's urge for ivory. At first their new activities coincided with the steady confinement of too many elephants in Tsavo. The poaching pressures relieved other pressures developing in the park. So great was the poaching that the elephants reacted by stepping up their birthrate. The present herds show an unusually high proportion of young, well beyond the usual 30 percent. But in 1957 poaching came to a sudden stop. It was considered against all proper ideas of wildlife, even though man had been killing elephants for thousands of years without wreaking massive slaughter until the arrow was replaced by the bullet. Still, the poachers

Below: Especially during the dry season, elephants gouge the baobabs to pieces in Tsavo, and at Ruaha, and similar places, though those at Lake Manyara are spared—so far—for some reason nobody has tracked down yet. An unusually large baobab, like this one, could be as old as the oldest redwood, and there are probably fewer really ancient, outsize baobabs left in Africa than there are redwoods in the United States.

Right: As elephants start on their late-day feeding, they take to their dust baths again: they may take several a day.

of Tsavo were not killing for meat, they were killing for cash. It was even thought they were taking off 2,000 a year from a total that was said to be somewhere around 10,000. Nobody had any real idea. But that was a time when you could find 1,280 carcasses within twenty square miles: that did it. In a blitz operation the poaching was crushed, and the Waliangulu way of life with it. Poachers went off to jail by the hundreds. Success.

The elephants were now at liberty to multiply in peace. Their emergency breeding methods scarcely faltered. Elephants are not creatures of rush and scramble. Man might constrict their environment with all the instant energy of a new nation getting on its feet, with speed enough to bring the elephants to their knees. It is taking several years for the most sensitive of them to react to the changes.

By 1959 the warden was already noticing the devastation. By 1961 he accepted the situation as serious. By 1963 everybody believed something would have to be done about the elephants; they would have to be reduced. But a year later there were signs of cold feet. The warden felt it would be difficult for him to march poachers off to jail one year, then allow white men to come in and shoot the elephants another year. In any case, it was growing too late to stop much of the habitat "trend," no matter how many elephants were removed. Grassland means fiercer fires still. Any tendencies for bush to make a comeback now go up in smoke. What counts is whether the grassland can hold its own, or whether there is too much momentum in the ecological shift toward more arid conditions —a semidesert regime? Some experts suggest that grassland allows more rainfall to percolate into the soil than bushland (since there are more stalk openings), and point to the fresh springs that were appearing in the late 1960s. But additional watercourses may not tell a true tale in themselves. At the Luangwa Valley in Zambia, an area with at least twice as much rainfall as Tsavo, the environment has been undergoing steady deterioration for decades under the impact of too many elephants. In one major sector of the reserve, the gulley erosion has increased six times in fifteen years—which means one can read no sure sign of stability if the number of watercourses is on the increase, since more water could be running off useless instead of soaking in. Much depends too on the basic structure of the whole system, the soil (a dull subject, but no better foundation): the easily compactable soil of the Luangwa Valley is especially vulnerable to those elephant feet and to the forty-two pounds pressure per square inch a three-ton elephant exerts every time it takes a stride.

By the 1970s in Tsavo, with the return of drier conditions, the story has changed again from the hopeful signs of the late 1960s—or perhaps one should say the scene has resumed its usual tale. Trying to find what makes up the long-term trends of Africa's wilderness, and having five minutes to do it in, is no simple project, especially when there are experts on every side insisting the whole affair could turn out to be no bad thing, or is inevitable anyway, or should be watched longer. But nobody seems to produce much evidence, except those who assert we have waited ten years too long—and they seem to have the elephants on their side, together with the rhinos, the baobabs, and various other prime features of this unique area.

Some observers believe there is already a decline in diversity: some tree species and some rodents may be on their way out, together with the occasional reptile or bird. Shooting some of the elephants would not bring back the trees for many a year, possibly decades. But it might at least allow the grassland to survive in the meantime. There are no sure signs that the changes in the habitat have come to an end. Perhaps they are not only

Below: Poaching is almost always cruel. But unless something replaces the predation pressures that man has exerted for centuries (or unless elephants are allowed more room to disperse in), every community of elephants in Africa could become as endangered as those in parts of Murchison Falls National Park, where they will have birth-controlled themselves into extinction around the end of the century. Scientific cropping would regulate elephant numbers in terms of the total environment, and would satisfy the poacher's craving for meat— as well as prove far less cruel.

Right: When an infant elephant can no longer walk under its mother, it is reckoned over one year old. It will not be very old before it starts the outpourings of "musth" from the gland behind the eye, long before it is sexually mature; so presumably the secretion has nothing to do with mating moodiness.

continuing but speeding up. Even though the elephants are adapting themselves to what they find is a debilitating environment (whether through too little food or too much crowding—probably both), they will need the best part of twenty years, judging by Murchison Falls, before they really get to grips with the crisis. By that time the crisis could be catastrophe.

The solution at present seems to be some degree of forcible reduction. But one can't just go into Tsavo and shoot the nearest 5,000 elephants. The situation needs the most careful scrutiny. The herds show a lot of variation within a single region. Tsavo's elephants are divided into ten more or less distinct groupings with a variety of birthrates. The most prolific are those around the edge of the park or centered along the main watercourses, where they were subjected to the heaviest poaching—and hence they have proved the ones most inclined to replenish their numbers fastest. The elephants to be reduced should clearly be those most reluctant to adjust. Or perhaps one might try taking out some of the younger cows, which would slow the population increase for some time to come—but would it stabilize it soon enough? In any case, it is very difficult to eliminate certain elephants from a herd without the others roaming far and wide to pass on the message. The most practical approach is to eliminate a whole herd at one stroke, which further avoids any prospect of upsetting the intricate social structures within elephant communities, while achieving a proper cross section for research purposes. And elephant communities seem to be more social than most.

Generally there are nursery herds of females and young, and bachelor groups of bulls. There are also bulls that lead a solitary existence for much of the time. If the difference between these isolated individuals and the bachelor groupings is primarily some social

The 35,000 elephants of the Tsavo eco-unit are, according to the findings of Dr. Laws, split up into distinct populations, each with its own tract of country. Moreover, the social structures of these communities vary greatly, as do the breeding rates: the herds still producing the largest numbers of calves are centered along the boundaries of the park and astride the main watercourses, where they were subject to most poaching prior to the 1957 purge. If the elephants are to be reduced in numbers, the cropping should fall more heavily on the herds most out of equilibrium with their environment.

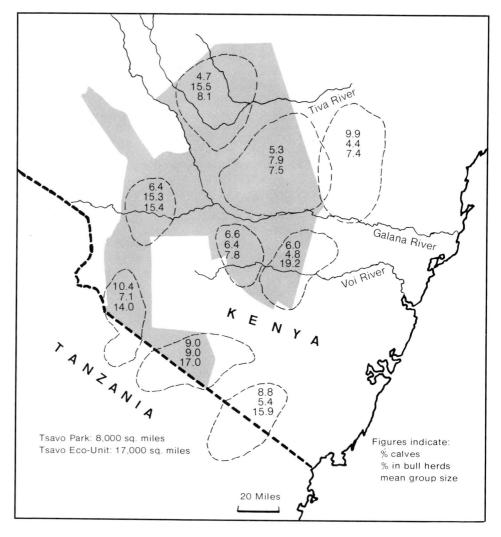

Tsavo Park: 8,000 sq. miles
Tsavo Eco-Unit: 17,000 sq. miles

Figures indicate:
% calves
% in bull herds
mean group size

20 Miles

sanction at work, such structuring of the community could be of foremost importance in regulating the breeding hierarchy. Insofar as a female breeds only once every four years at the most, are three-quarters of the bulls superfluous? Or, more than that, is breeding somehow limited to only a few of the more dominant bulls? Nobody knows, and in a range of elephant localities, there is nobody even looking to find out.

The nursery herds are made up of basic family units. A family averages six members: a leading female with her daughters and her daughters' daughters, plus perhaps a young male who has not yet reached breeding age. Such a herd can include more than one family unit; the numbers show some tendency to center around six, twelve, eighteen, and so on. This family unit is very cohesive, and may still be retaining its integrity after forty years. The bull groups by contrast are much looser associations, with members joining and members leaving all the time; sometimes they seem to be more fixed in one locality than the nursery herds, suggesting some element of territorial urge among certain males (again, a prime factor if it could be tracked down; but a factor not likely to be tracked down for some years). Over and above the herd structures there are "clan" groupings within the overall population congregations. What is their function? Are they anywhere near as stable as the family assemblages, and are they led in matriarchal fashion by some elderly cow?

The Laws and Parker team has managed to establish how family units are held together by strong social ties. They have noticed that some elephants, one in four at Murchison Falls, feature one toe nail fewer than normal. It is a genetic quirk that helps to show who belongs where; nine out of ten such elephants are to be found in herds together. The same applies to tusks: some are short and stubby, some are long and slender, some are straight, some curved—another genetic pattern with the same signs for family stability (though it is not accurate to assert that the genetic strains producing outsize tusks are being shot out by overambitious sporting hunters; if there are hardly any tusks over thirty-five pounds to be seen in Uganda now, it is because there are hardly any males over twenty years old to be seen after decades of oversportive hunting).

Whatever changes of the environment swirl around them, the family sticks together—all the more so, as the greater strains of the surroundings are inflicted on them. When elephants are subjected to stress, they tend to do as hippos do (or wildebeest, or humans), and crowd together into larger groups for security. The elephants around the edges of Murchison Falls Park, where they encounter most of the pushing and shoving from outside, reveal aggregations much larger than usual. The normal way of life there is to associate in huge bunched-up phalanxes. But within these groupings, the basic family unit still asserts itself; and if a throng is temporarily disturbed, a dividing-up process reveals the fundamental components. The number constituting these basic units varies from place to place. In Queen Elizabeth Park a mean figure is only six, possibly a reflection of the more peaceful conditions they enjoy—now. In Murchison Falls Park it is twelve or more, and in Tsavo, more again; in Kruger it is seventeen, and in Serengeti, where the elephants have perhaps been in a greater state of tension than elsewhere, there is hardly a herd under twenty and several groups of fifty or more.

Beyond all this, the tract of country comprising an elephant eco-unit may be split up among several different populations. On the north bank at Murchison Falls there are only four elephants to a square mile, but twice as many on the south bank. Moreover, those to the south reveal different parameters within their various subpopulations. Two-thirds of the area constitutes a central zone where there are just under six elephants a square mile, while in the outer zone there are over ten. Yet there are large sections of this "crowded" border region where there is less than a single elephant to a square mile. And across the subarea there are further segregations still, with the more favorable sections apparently occupied by herds led by the oldest females, the real matriarchs, while the

The research center at Tsavo Park features charnel-house scenes of elephant jawbones collected from investigation cropping or picked up in the savannah from elephants that have died of natural causes. A random cross section indicates how many elephants are surviving to what age; hence the condition of the herds.

younger groups have to be content with patches on the fringe. Supposing a cropping program were to remove the dominant groupings? Would this upset the social system that seems to order the rankings? And would it lead to less breeding for a time? Working on a straight density basis, one should conclude that those to be heavily reduced are those on the outside: the Laws, Parker, and Johnstone research findings suggest this high density area should be brought down from ten to a square mile to about half as many, while the inner zone should be reduced from something over five a square mile to four. That would mean taking out 3,700 elephants—and, all other considerations apart, the scheme would produce well over $1,000,000 for park funds. It is always possible, of course, that other factors are leading to elephant concentrations: perhaps the more intense throngs are a prelude to breeding procedures, when the elephants gather in their "heartlands." What if they could somehow be prevented from coming together for the mating season? One elephant is not easy to stop from doing what it wants, let alone a thousand. Some people have suggested—in all seriousness—that with the new immobilizing techniques available there could be a prospect for fitting elephants with contraceptive devices.

In the old days on the Galana River to the east of Tsavo Park, Ian Parker conducted his experimental cropping by going out on foot along an elephant trail. He might find his target, and it might be a long way from camp; or he might not find one at all. Now he goes out by light aircraft. A herd of anything up to twenty is all right. He lands at a bush airstrip or a dried-up riverbed, after using his aircraft to shoo the elephants toward an open space. Once down, he and an associate approach the scene. If the elephants are not yet in position, he directs them by judicious whiffs of his scent. Then the two of them open up. There is a short space of gunfire and screams; then silence. It is usually over in less than a minute. They are back at camp in time for breakfast, while the rest of the team moves in. Each man is scrubbed from head to toe. Every few minutes he douses himself and his implements in drums of disinfectant. Dressing an elephant carcass in the African bush could pick up a good bit of Africa as well, if chunks coming off the carcass did not go straight into hygienic bins. All very surgical and sterile, all very organized and efficient.

It might sound too ghoulish to visualize as an exercise for saving wild creatures, but one should think of the Murchison Falls elephants, and how their numbers have slumped in the past twenty-five years, and how they could slump in another twenty-five. Many more are likely to die (or just not be born) unless a fraction are treated in this fashion first. To talk of crop yields and such cold terms seems a long way from the warm-blooded wonder standing there swinging its trunk under a tree. But this is Africa. Every year a large number of elephants are cropped anyway to protect plantations, like those shot "on control" around the Murchison Falls borders (at least as many as would be entailed in scientific cropping), or the 2,000 eliminated in southern Tanzania alone, many in an area where the elephant is a totem animal. But if some Tanzanians will not eat elephant meat, there are plenty of others farther away who will. When it turns out those others are too far away, as much elephant meat is left to the vultures as would keep Dar es Salaam going for weeks on end. The Dar es Salaam area has some of the worst protein hunger and infant mortality in Africa, so relief food is brought in from thousands of miles away while good meat goes to waste a few hundred miles away. Nothing comes of the idea of feeding a few of the excess elephants into a few of the excess Africans, because there are too many people who have not heard of the Ian Parker approach—or don't want to hear.

Meanwhile, the elephants get into worse straits. Apart from a fall-off in breeding and in body size, and apart from the prospect of elephants under stress indulging in aberrant behavior (those in the Serengeti seem to smash down more trees than they eat: a delinquent elephant is a prospect to conjure with), there are other portents. One elephant in a hundred at Murchison Falls has an appalling abscess on a tooth or a bony swelling on its jaw. Dr. Sylvia Sikes has analyzed various elephants up to thirty years old, the ones that have grown up since man arrived in elephant country and stayed. They show deposits of

Top: The railroad marks the park boundary for sections of Tsavo. Inside the park there is almost complete destruction of the trees, as compared with outside areas with no elephants, but only humans and domestic stock. The tribesmen are not nearly so good at clearing the bush as the elephants; setting fires does not really work without broken-down trees to provide fuel—but when railroad engines throw off sparks, there is enough material inside the park to burn for days, and for miles. Bottom left: Huge areas of Tsavo's original thick cover of thorn trees is now gone. Elephants have little to eat, there is no shade, and the ground cover —a critical factor in arid regions—is only a fraction of what it should be to protect soil from thunderstorms. Bottom right: In late 1971, the two-year drought at Tsavo left 3,000 elephants dead of starvation. This was not too calamitous for the elephants, since there are at least 30,000 in the region, even if dying with a stomach full of wood is a wretched way to go; had they been cropped in anticipation of the disaster, their carcasses would have produced almost $1,000,000 for park funds, and piles of protein for a nation with 180,000 on famine relief —and the park's environment would have been left less damaged. But even more serious from a strictly wildlife point of view was the catastrophe that overtook the park's other large animals with a large appetite and no ruminatory system of stomachs for getting every last bit of nutriment out of the woody vegetation: the rhinoceros. This is the last great congregation of rhinos on earth, and perhaps as many as 600 died. Only a few years before, a drug-darting campaign had spent $20,000 on rescuing 70 rhinos.

fatty substances on the artery walls or thickening of the blood passages. This is an ailment that leads to stiffening of the joints and early signs of old age. It can even lead to heart failure: the occasional elephant succumbs to thrombosis. Hitherto coronary disease has been attributed to animal fats, leaving the vegetarian elephant an unlikely candidate. A possible secondary factor is environmental tension: confined elephants could be reacting with the same symptoms that afflict man in stress-filled habitats. Dr. Sikes has looked at some of the remoter areas, where a few less-than-modern elephants still enjoy a wide diet, and roam over wide tracts of country, both woodlands and moorlands, free of migration barriers and molestation. These elephants do not show signs of failing health as do the elephants of the grasslands and scrublands. Yet Dr. K. G. McCullagh, an elephant physiologist, has found that nearly three-quarters of the elephants he examined reveal lesions of the aorta, with highly similar rates in all areas. While the calcification of the arteries differs from place to place, the atherosclerosis doesn't; which could mean it is a hormonal affair, a reflection of social disruption.

What is clear enough is that it is no good trying to look after elephants in what are for them handkerchief-sized plots. Otherwise you may end up with elephants subject to all manner of ills from a man-made world, a comment on those who think that elephant problems can be reduced to man-sized dimensions. Watching a herd of elephants feeding their way across the bushland, you quickly get a sense of how these creatures are capable of modifying the environment to a degree matched only by man and fire. They must have ranked as an agency second to none among the wild beings of Africa during the formation of the present scene over the latter stages of the African day. They are still modifying their environment; but this time not so much in conjunction with man as in competition with him. Unless the two can reconcile their differences there could be a sad outcome for the elephants and their environment. Man has set up the problem; he should resolve it. He might consider whether he should not intervene again, not so violently as with his thriving throngs, but by adjusting the elephants to their reduced living-space. While the overall number of elephants in East Africa has been on the downward slope for most of this century, there are still too many of them for the last few refuges. There comes a time—and it comes very swiftly—when the elephants outrun the capacity of the land to support them properly. The pressures set off a vicious spiral that continues its crash course downward unless some further force intervenes to restore equilibrium. If the elephants apparently achieve more with their birth-control mechanisms than man can within his own community anywhere, these braking arrangements are not enough without the other factors that once allowed elephants to adjust while they were developing these built-in safety valves: they do not have the space to migrate elsewhere. Appalling as it might sound, the solution could rest in giving a hefty push to the crash course, so that it can get ahead of the habitat decline. Elephants are not creatures of small dimensions in their living patterns. American deer need only a few years for a population crash, smaller creatures a single season. Elephants need fifty years. Almost every elephant population in East Africa is onto some stage of a crash. Some are halfway, some are still starting. All can be assisted. Most are scarcely being looked at.

ZEBRAS

Late in the afternoon when the heat subsides, the zebras set about grazing again. They do a lot of it: nobody ever sees a thin zebra. A zebra needs twice as much food as, say, a wildebeest, since it has no rumen to extract further fuel from the forage; a wildebeest can send it around a second time. On the other hand, a zebra can flourish on dried-out stringy stuff a wildebeest could not touch.

A Burchell's zebra—unlike the Grevy's, which lives in the arid scrubland and can go for months without water—needs water almost daily. The ranges of the two overlap only slightly, roughly along the equator.

The savannah areas of Tarangire Park in Tanzania Masailand feature a range of creatures that do not conflict with each other in their feeding habits, as is shown by Dr. Lamprey's diagram. They achieve "ecological separation" by using different food at different seasons, and by other methods of differentiating their life-styles: four are shown here. The spectrum is divided horizontally according to the parts of the savannah each species occupies, and is divided vertically between the wet and dry seasons. An arrow indicates how some species tend to spread over into an adjacent part of the scene. The problem of zebra, wildebeest, and Thomson's gazelle, which appear to occupy the same slot of the spectrum at the same season, is resolved by Dr. Bell's findings in similar savannah-land of the Serengeti.

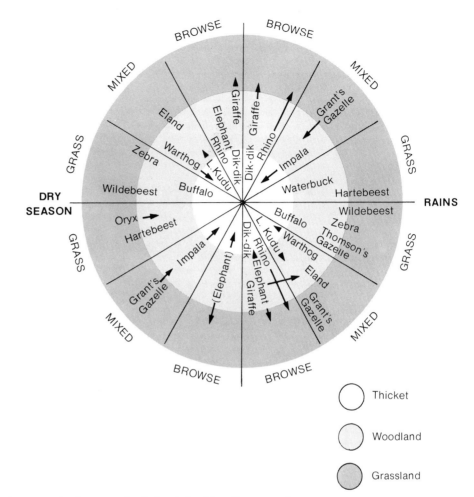

○ Thicket

◑ Woodland

● Grassland

You often see red-billed ox-peckers perched on a zebra's back looking for morsels. Zebras carry a lot of parasites inside as well as out, sometimes millions of millimeter-long worms in their intestines. Parasites notwithstanding, they invariably look sleek and handsome (perhaps because these lodgers help as much as hinder). By far the more common of the two kinds of zebras in East Africa is the broad-striped zebra, which is found right down to southern Africa. One might expect that a creature adapted to such a range of environments would be able to make its way across the whole of East Africa. Yet in most of Uganda there is not a single zebra, even though there are areas with huge herds of topi antelope, which shares a common habitat with zebra in Mara and Serengeti. The more resplendent is the Grevy's zebra, found only in the arid areas of East Africa north of the equator and stretching away into the northeastern parts of the continent. East Africa is the only area where the two range side by side.

Both these species are among the many of modern Africa's wild creatures that did not originate there at all. They stem from the original "dawn horse" of 60,000,000 years ago. From this foot-high and many-toed creature stemmed the equidae that threw off donkeys and asses of various kinds around the world, together with modern-day horses and zebras. Zebra ancestors arrived in Africa as three-toed beings 20,000,000 years or so ago, one hour back on Africa's time-scale. It was not until the Pleistocene and the last five or six minutes that the zebra emerged as you can see it today on the plains of Africa. On the same plains you can pick out many another foreigner that has become more than naturalized: the antelopes, for example, came primarily from Eurasia. Africa has long formed a kind of animal reservoir: it has drawn creatures from many regions of the earth during the course of its long day—already in far-back times there were sanctuaries of sorts in Africa—and what it received it kept. There are no zebras elsewhere, no wildebeest, no giraffes. They came and they stayed, while their ancestors in the lands of their initial evolution declined and disappeared, or passed on to other forms. The various kinds of zebras in Africa thrived as they became adapted to their new environment and its various habitats. By contrast, elephants—or elephant ancestors—continued to range across more continents than Africa, and so did rhinos. Lions still survive outside Africa, but only just; cheetah manage, too, but only just "only just." It is not that these creatures wandered out of Africa and on around the globe. The trend has always been much more toward migrating *into* Africa. But why did zebras not use the same land bridges to stray across into Asia? In Africa there are zebras for lush grasslands and zebras for grasslands that are nearer scrublands; there are lands like both these in Asia. The same with wildebeest and topi and a score of antelopes. Perhaps the Suez land-bridge became too arid for these grassland animals. If you want to see such creatures you have to come to Africa, a land that guards its riches to itself.

While he is watching the zebra grazing, the onlooker might speculate on what has made this horse-creature so much at home among the grasslands of Africa, when most of the other grazers he sees in the same stretch of plain—and there could be a half dozen others in a single savannah sweep—are so different inside as well as outside. Most of them are ruminants: they redigest their food, which helps when the food is often fibrous. But the zebra fits into its own particular slot in the spectrum. It bites off the grass, while the wildebeest and gazelle and hartebeest pluck it off: they eat with their jaws as much as with their teeth, since they haven't any incisors in the upper jaw. This distinctiveness is well illustrated in the Serengeti, where there are huge numbers of animals living together on the grassland plains: up to two-thirds of a million wildebeest, between a quarter and a third of a million zebra, and perhaps half a million Thomson's gazelles (give or take a hundred thousand). There are enormous numbers of all these animals in every square mile at certain seasons, yet there is no critical competition among all these throngs.

The phenomenon of "ecological separation" among the members of a plant-eating community has been described in detail by Dr. Hugh Lamprey in his classic account of the Tarangire, a stretch of savannah to the east of the Serengeti. He has noted how the wild animals populate the African plains in far greater numbers than elsewhere, and after following their fortunes for several years he has found how they avoid tangling with each other not only by using different types of vegetation, but—for those that overlap in their tastes—by roaming over different areas at different times of the year; or if they occupy the same area at the same period, they use different "levels" of the same vegetation. The safarist may notice how the giraffe feeds off pretty much the same tree and bush material as the rhino and the dik-dik, but each at a different height. If one objects that a rhino can get down to the same foot-high level as a dik-dik—a giraffe, too, at a pinch—then the savannah shows it generally doesn't. Rhinos prefer to feed at least a foot above the ground and giraffe at least four feet, usually ten feet or more. A dik-dik can get inside thickets where a giraffe or a rhino doesn't penetrate. Wildebeest and buffalo may share the same range for part of the year, but after a time the wildebeest move on to look for greener grazing; the buffalo can do without. The same with zebra and impala. No two species overlap in the total spectrum of their needs. None, that is, except for two that appear in many ways to occupy the same niche: the wildebeest and the zebra move more or less together around their range during the year, and they eat the same sorts of grasses —a pattern that appears to cut across some of the basic tenets of ecology and evolution.

The scientists have turned their microscopes onto these creatures, or rather onto their stomach contents and fecal remains. How things work out in the Serengeti has been tracked down by Dr. Roger Bell, who has found that zebra and wildebeest do not in fact conflict; rather the reverse. When they make use of the same food at similar times of the year, they

Left: All zebras like company: one on its own is a rare sight, whereas a lone wildebeest is less unlikely—though a wildebeest with offspring would stay close to other wildebeest with offspring for extra security.

Right: Zebras like a roll in the dust, perhaps to get rid of ticks. But not just any old dust: a whole herd often lines up to use one particular patch, ignoring other suitable-looking spots nearby. The preliminary sniffing by the leader suggests it may be a favorite patch, used day after day.

are not both feeding off the same stage of growth. Grass consists of hard fibrous stems (cellulose for structure) and soft nutritional leaves (sugar for metabolism). The animals generally need the protein when it is most concentrated in the leaves, though it can also be found stored in the stems at an early stage of growth if the grass has not grown too tough. It is in these softer parts that energy is stockpiled during the process of synthesis. Short grass contains more protein than long, tough grass. In fact—and this is a critical point—there is a greater difference in the amount of protein between the various stages of growth in any one sort of grass than there is between two separate sorts of grass at the same stage. When the plant grows tall it is more stem than leaves, so the ratio of nutritive sugar to cellulose is smaller. The antelopes can't do much about it; it is too tough for their teeth (besides being poor in protein). There is only one species that can benefit from it, the zebra, which depends less on the soft, succulent growths than on the total amount of grass it eats. Because of its specialized feeding equipment (teeth at the front of both jaws), the zebra even shows a slight preference for straggly grass over short, leafy material. This is a marginal fact in the mechanics of a grazing community, and a major factor in perpetuating the entire community. If it is the particular function of the rumen in animals like wildebeest and gazelle to break down whatever cellulose finds its way into their digestive system, how much more surprising then that the animal whose food contains more cellulose than others is not a ruminant: a zebra is never seen chewing its cud. Probably the zebra, like the horse, allows food to pass through its gut faster than a ruminant like a cow, enabling it to derive enough protein from the quantity rather than the quality of what it eats. In any case, the larger the animal, the less protein it needs in proportion to keep itself going (since it requires less energy); and a zebra is a quarter again as big as a wildebeest.

When the zebras have played their part in the system and left the tall grass shorter, the wildebeest follow to graze at the leaves nearer ground-level on the shortened stems that have been reinvigorated to a fresh protein-producing stage. By then the zebras have already wandered off to new pastures, and by late May when the rains have petered out and there is no succulent grass left in the areas where they have spent half a year, the wildebeest set off after the zebras. This is the time of their great migrations. When the zebras pass through a new area, they not only graze down the taller grass, but trample much of what they do not eat. When the wildebeest come along searching for their lower-level material, they trample the grass again. Finally come the gazelles looking for the shortest and most succulent material of all. They search out the leaves of dicotyledons in particular; this material, wholly disregarded by zebras and wildebeest, constitutes a third of the gazelles' intake. What one ignores sustains another.

But if these different species follow each other in a "grazing succession," their migrations are not all that similar in outward appearance. Migrating zebras do not move as packed together as wildebeest: they do not have to. They are not so dependent upon any limited stage of the vegetation cycle, so their herds can straggle off at stages over a couple of months instead of moving out in army-style formations over a couple of weeks. Nor are they nearly so gregarious by nature, since their living style does not require it: they are not dependent like wildebeest on enormous congregations to spot the most recent shower falling beyond the horizon. The gazelle migration is no unified trek, either. A gazelle herd eats far less than wildebeest, so their effect on the grassland is not so intense. They can stay in one area much longer, with less need for them all to move off at once. The whole system represents a high "coefficient of association," and the various animals benefit from being together rather than separate. Instead of conflict, there is cooperation. If the zebra population were to be unduly reduced for any reason, critical problems could develop for the wildebeest, and in turn the gazelle. There is more to a zebra than just a zebra.

LEOPARDS

Anyone who thinks a leopard skin looks as good on another creature's back as it does on the leopard hasn't seen a leopard. Its skin suits its owner well enough, rippling as the leopard walks, catching every surge of the animal's being.

Late afternoon is the time to watch for a leopard lodged in its favorite tree, sunning itself in the softer warmth. The body sprawls across a branch and flows over the edges. It is elegant beyond imagination. You have to see a leopard relaxed to know what it is; once you have, you won't forget. Nor will you forget seeing a leopard in a state of distinct unease. Should that snoozing leopard hear a lion walking underneath its tree, it reveals what else is inside that velvety frame. Its trigger temperament hovers on the brink. Tremors of rage flow along its back. The shoulders seethe and the haunches gather with the force of its fury. Bursts of anger sputter from the depths. There is no growl, no introductory warning, just a snarl rising from the pit of its stomach to erupt in a rush of frenzy. Down below, the lion responds just as forcefully, but not with such primordial energy. The lion is admirable and the leopard is awesome, as elemental as it is elegant. No other animal is so splendid in its savagery. The lion passes on and the leopard subsides. In a moment the fire has gone. It is a sleek cat again: it would purr if it could. But if it is svelte and supple, it is an animal cunning and daring, with an intensity like none of the other big cats.

It is precisely this adaptability that is becoming the leopard's undoing—that, together with a coat that looks so good in the wild and a fraction so good in the concrete jungle. The leopard is one creature that lives right up against the borders of man's estate. Development and cultivation don't bother it much (unless its prey entirely disappears). It can thrive without ever going out of sight of a village. Yet this ability to come to terms with the modern world delivers it into the hands of its enemies. As long as the rich and the cultivated believe they can't live without a piece of lifeless leopard, there are enemies enough. These sophisticates fondly fancy that their piece of skin shows they have some affinity for the creature that was within: "Come out of the plain, Jane, into a jugular vein," urges the furrier. Anyone who has seen a leopard knows how far such fashion

A leopard enraged is a sight to see—as long as you do not experience it too closely.

addicts achieve a skin-deep simulation; he knows what else they reveal. Such connoisseurs of the best insure that plenty of people in Africa know what to do with the leopard that lives down the valley; with their money at work there is many a man in Africa who is tempted to take a chance at a leopard. A truck was recently stopped with piles of leopard skins in the back and a European and an Asian in the front. A leopard is easier to catch than many other animals. Its tastes extend to anything meaty, no matter how old. The more the bait stenches, the more it attracts leopards from all around the vicinity. Mayfair and Monte Carlo will see that the trapper's trouble is rewarded.

This contribution to the local economy is often quoted in support of the leopard-skin trade. Leaving aside the trivial proportion the trapper gets out of the $20,000 that a six-skin coat may cost (a dozen other skins may have been scrapped, spoiled by the traps), it is a trade that cuts its throat as fast as it can go. It will last until the fashion gives out or the leopard. Nobody minds. The scarcer the coat, the more expensive and exclusive it becomes, the more potent a prop for failing egos. The more appeals there are against the fashion, the more fashionable it becomes to some minds to follow it, however many times they hear that only a single skin in a hundred is not likely to have spent its last hours gnawing off its foot in a gin trap—it shows how the wearer retains some primitive ardor against the synthetic sophistication of cosmopolitania (but then why not give these ladies the full primitive treatment?).

Meanwhile, the whole situation is illuminating for what it reveals about conservationists. Prestigious bodies have been saying for years that, yes, the leopard is quite likely to qualify for the endangered lists when there is enough known about its standing. But they do not always say it loudly enough. Other bodies have been inclined to say that they cannot really comment at all until detailed information is available—if they take the wrong side, there might be need for a rescue operation for their reputations as much as for the leopard. The furriers have been all too inclined to agree, since nobody apparently has any real idea one way or the other how the leopard is faring—so on with the slaughter. At the same time these gentlemen proclaim to their clients that leopard skins are already rare and getting rarer; they are finding it harder to get in supplies, prices are soaring; by next season ———? Most conservationists agree it might take several years to get

Left: A few moments later, the disturbance gone, the leopard is as relaxed as only a leopard can be.

Above: By the time a furrier finds a suitable "match" among the varying patterns of his pelts, a six-skin coat costs as many offspring as a leopard is likely to produce in its life-time. Considering also the skins ruined in the trap, or taken by hyenas before the trapper gets there, or lost for a host of other reasons, the coats in a single store could well account for as many leopards as there are in the 6,000-square-mile Serengeti.

reasonable indications of the status of such an elusive creature; some agree it could easily take less than that for a last-minute scramble among buyers to bring things to a crisis point. Hitherto there has been little prospect for a full-scale leopard survey: staff is short, funds are lacking, lots of other animals are in a plight that is grave and known to be grave, so they have received priority. Fortunately, an investigation is now under way in Africa into the status of the leopard (the cheetah, too); an even brighter omen is that the funds for the survey have come from the furriers themselves, who are now recognizing how much it is in their interests to have a proper appraisal of what is happening to their business potential at the source (though spotted skins are no major part of their trade: under 1 percent in many countries). Their international offices in London have urged a three-year moratorium on leopard and cheetah (not that any furrier is obliged to take any notice: many still don't), while the United States has banned spotted furs altogether. In Europe there will soon be bans in more countries than not, though one of the last will be Italy (with its film stars), asserting that it is not responsible for safeguarding the world's treasures if they are wild creatures rather than classical paintings.

But it has been futile for a long time to say the situation is all that dim and impenetrable. A single center in Ethiopia throughout much of the 1960s was exporting as many as 8,000 illicit skins a year. A recent contraband shipment seized in Djibouti consisted of more leopards than there could ever possibly have been produced by the country, supposing there were any left at all. Ethiopia's leopard trade has been running at around $1,500,000 a year, almost all of it illegal; a pity it could not be regulated by proper quotas for exporter and importer alike; then Ethiopia's peasants could look forward to an indefinite future when a man could gain as much through a single leopard skin as through several months of shepherding. Officials from Somalia in the east to Senegal in the west, and right down to South Africa, admit that the leopard is in dire trouble or on the verge of local extinction. Professionals with forty years' experience across an area twice the size of the United States believe things were growing urgent ten years ago.

There are other experts who argue that the leopard is too wily, too adaptable, to be wiped out. The occasional one will always survive. So it will. These observers do not offer views on whether conserving means much beyond sweeping up the bits left by a situation nobody can alter. Other people assert, with the gut conviction that does not burden itself with experience, that there are just as many as ever; if they are not to be seen around it is because the leopard does not advertise its presence—there could be one watching you from behind every bush. Several African countries now are taking action, but there still remain persons who say nothing is certain as yet, so nothing can be done. They are quite right: nothing is certain. Nobody knows how many leopards are taken and how many are left. The poacher does not publish any figures. There are no concise details, only evidence to support a 90 percent case. Some people believe this is no case. You must be conclusive; all the rest is emotionalism; what you want are facts.

The leopard might have to start looking after itself better than it has ever done so far. A world with fewer leopards would not be the same. It would be a world enriched for those who want something to cover their transparency, an essential addition to those who lack nothing. It would be a different world for those who like to hear a leopard snarl, or sigh with contentment as it settles against a branch. A leopard is more than its outward seeming. If it were plain gray, or as chameleon-colored as those who follow the latest fashion fads, or as naked as those who need a leopard skin more than the leopard does, it would still be a remarkable animal. It is so much at one with itself that you cannot have part of a leopard.

ANTELOPES

By late afternoon the antelope herds are spread across the plain again. You can often spot a dozen kinds, some of them in herds of hundreds, even in herds of thousands. Some think this is African wildlife at its wildest and most African.

They are all shapes and sizes. They all look different and they all look fine. Some weigh over a thousand pounds—the eland—and some scarcely ten pounds—the dik-dik. Some eat one thing, some another. None intrudes too much on another's domain for its needs, none grows superabundant to swamp the rest. None is too frail, none too strong; none is merely ornamental or dispensable. Each has its own space and place; harmony. Each has its role to play: hardly any of the usual grasses of the African plain are left to choke the others; same for the shrubs and bushes and trees. The world of African antelopes is a scene as vigorous as it is variegated, able to withstand all the forces of what is for an antelope a very competitive world.

Or possibly one should consider the whole herbivore range developing in unison as a single spectrum of animal life, the various species dependent on each other through their "functional relationships." The eland reaches for upper branches of trees and breaks them down with its horns; it eats some itself and leaves the rest for smaller browsers. Elephants smash down trees that afford cover for the duiker and the duiker's favored short-sized plants. Knock out one species and a dozen feel the blow. The tops of trees are cropped by giraffe and the middle sections are taken by gerenuk; the lower parts are eaten by a wide range of nibblers. This ecological division of labor allows for very high

concentrations of animal life. Counting the whole spread of creatures, antelopes and others together, the biomass can run to 40,000 pounds a square mile or more in the Nairobi Park, while a year-round average in the Serengeti runs to 70,000 pounds; Lake Manyara Park (primarily elephants and buffalos) totals 125,000 pounds; Queen Elizabeth Park, up to 150,000, and the great dry season gatherings of Tarangire reach over 200,000. A similar area under Masai cattle manages only about 15,000 pounds; the finest ranching country in North America hardly reaches 40,000. And these figures for African animals do not include the smaller mammal herbivores, which Dr. Hendrichs reckons at one-tenth at least, by weight, of the larger creatures in the Serengeti; when one considers that their energy needs may reach ten times as much as for the larger animals, these savannah grasslands appear productive indeed!

Moreover, these wild antelopes look after their environments. They exert a biotic pressure on the savannah through their feeding that enables the foliage to be rejuvenated. Together with the other grass-eaters, they develop "grazing mosaics" like those around Lake Rukwa in southern Tanzania, where Dr. D. F. Vesey-Fitzgerald has found a sequence of animals using the various stages of the grassland. At the end of the rains when the grass is at its maximum growth, it is first grazed by the elephants and hippo and buffalo. As the rains dry out, these larger animals trample the herbiage under, which amounts to "planting" the node shoots in the moist substratum. The result is a new grazing sward, this time short grass suitable for the lighter antelope. They graze it continuously and hold it back at an early stage, growing all the time, succulent as ever. When the pasture becomes less suitable toward the end of the dry season, the antelope move off to other grazing grounds; no overgrazing, no ranch fences to prevent seasonal movements.

It has taken the antelopes plenty of time to evolve this wild form of crop rotation. The first traces appeared during the Miocene, 20,000,000 years ago. At this stage, one hour

Ngorongoro Crater shows how several sorts of grass-eaters— the two kinds of gazelles as well as zebras and wildebeest —can occupy the same stretch of country without conflicting. (In the same stretch the eland, waterbuck, reedbuck, harte-beest, and probably a dozen other species were not visible!) They appear completely mingled in their activities, but ecologically they are separate enough through their different food needs, and other habits.

back in the long African day, there were grasslands expanding in Africa as elsewhere. In southern Europe especially there was a start to a basic antelope stock that was to spread right across the grassy plains from Spain to Turkey and eventually into China. Not that these animals developed directly into the antelopes one sees in Africa today. There were starts and stops, branchings and rebranchings, trends convergent as well as radiating. Somewhere there arose a strain that eventually produced the African array. Only 1,000,000 years ago were there finally antelopes that were comparable to the eland, kudu, impala, roan, duiker, and reedbuck. There was a larger-size klipspringer that is now extinct. There was a creature in between a springbok and a gazelle that may have been a common progenitor for both; it could also explain why there are no gazelles in South Africa and no springbok in East Africa—they occupy niches that are too similar. By the same early Pleistocene stage there were recognizable ancestors of wildebeest and harte-beest. But it was not until the late Pleistocene that wildebeest and duiker and steinbuck like today's appeared. Even by this late hour, a mere forty seconds back in Africa's day, there were no signs of the waterbuck. North America has eleven species of ungulates (hoofed animals), Europe has thirteen, Central and South America sixteen, Asia seventy. Africa has ninety. Of these, seventy may be classed as antelope (the others are creatures such as elephant, hippo, warthog). The precise number depends on where you think a species begins and where it ends—you can be a "splitter" or a "lumper."

With such a range of food in Africa's environment, and with scope for a whole range of different antelope to emerge, there was potential for a range of antelope-eaters to emerge as well. They were not nearly so diverse—to a carnivore, food is food, whether it is wilde-beest or eland or bongo. By contrast, hardly a single one of these antelopes could exist entirely off what others eat. A bongo likes the pith and rotten wood of fallen trees within its forest habitat, or it feeds off the roots of bushes uprooted by its horns. An eland lives off leaves, shoots, berries, and bits of grass. A klipspringer likes the succulent grass it finds sprouting between boulders, and it also seeks out small shrubs, unlike the oribi, which hardly ever touches them.

Sometimes one antelope counterbalances another. The topi and wildebeest spread over much of eastern and southern Africa, but in all this area they overlap in only two spots, the northwestern Kalahari and the western Serengeti. Dr. Roger Bell has looked at this part of the Serengeti and finds that even here the wildebeest tend to stick to one sector, and the topi to another. Unlike the wildebeest, the topi can cope with the taller grass, taking more stalks per mouthful—as suits its particular jaw structure and teeth— even though both prefer leaves to stems. But they fill similar places in the succession of grazers that crop the Serengeti savannah, and they seem to rank as alternatives in the antelope community in accord with what might appear trifling details to the casual on-looker, but seem rather different to the antelopes themselves. Coordination at a premium again. In fact, one should consider the array of African antelopes in terms of their overall evolution side by side just as much as the way they have "competed" with each other to produce the best adapted. What is "the fittest" is perhaps the total system, which is why there is such flexibility, such resilience (as long as it is left alone), such capacity to support enormous amounts of antelopes off vegetation that is often meager as compared with the great grasslands outside the tropics.

Grassland is only part of the scene. A bushbuck is primarily a browser, as is many another antelope. It avoids stepping on other browsers' toes not so much by what it eats as by where it eats. Both bushbuck and steinbuck feed on leaves, but they use different parts of the bushland or forest. A steinbuck likes places where there are plenty of small holes for its young, if not for itself. Even a young bushbuck would be too big for these small holes.

Almost any minor hollow can accommodate two dik-diks—they generally associate in pairs and stick to the same patch of ground. You can come around a corner of a rock outcrop in the Serengeti and see a pair of dik-dik feeding in the morning sunlight. You can come round the same corner a year later and find the same pair feeding. The dik-dik are not hard to recognize again: they generally have slight ear-notches. They are extremely sedentary, partly because they are extremely territorial—though why the whole family should go in for demarcating the local domain is not clear: perhaps so that they can find their way about a scrap of Africa that must seem huge to a dik-dik. At any rate, they all go off at once to leave a deposit on a boundary pile. Dik-diks rub their preorbital glands on grasses to warn off strangers; and woe to the stranger that takes no notice!

The smaller the antelope the more ferocious it seems to be. A duiker has a special thickening of the forehead bone to assist it in fighting. Other animals have reinforced skulls, especially giraffe bulls, but they do not wreak such damage on each other as do fighting duikers. Like the dik-dik, a duiker has facial glands, though it does not use them as much for marking vegetation; possibly the secretion serves as a sexual stimulation, since when the breeding season arrives the male starts nibbling at the neck and shoulders of the female. If he exudes the right idea, he is allowed to prance sideways before her, presenting his horns for her inspection, then rubbing his glands against her cheeks. A duiker probably has an unusually strong sense of smell with such unusually large nostrils. It already has large eyes and large ears, as might be expected considering the place where it lives, and an animal so equipped would usually have less need for a keen sense of smell. Yet if the gland message is plain to the human nostril, then to the female duiker it must be powerful indeed—even overpowering.

A bushbuck has larger ears than most. For its bush-dwelling life, sounds are more vital than sights. A young bushbuck soon produces its five-inch ears, then gets on with growing what else is necessary. Yet it has a healthy respect for other animals' eyesight. Reg Allsop has found that if you want to get a bushbuck out of its thicket for a moment to take a researcher's look at it, you get nowhere making noises, even throwing firecrackers. But if it once gets the idea it has been sighted, it is off and running. For all that a bushbuck is often seen with its muzzle to the ground, it is still browsing at tree shoots or nibbling at fallen material. It leaves the grass alone. Yet it is not really a creature of the bush world proper, even though it is never found far from bushes. It likes the ecotone transition-area

Left: This Guenther's dik-dik is only a few days old. It will scarcely reach a foot high, and its legs will always seem pencil-thin—but together with those large ears and eyes, they will be enough.

Right: The klipspringer is as much at home on almost vertical surfaces among cliffs as on the grassier patches pictured here: it can bunch its feet together on a two-inch ledge.

between grassland and forest. And it has learned how to survive in country that is dangerous for such a large antelope. When it penetrates into thickets, it makes sure there is more than one route out: if a predator appears at one entrance, that is not the end of the bushbuck. In the Murchison Falls Park there are plenty of bushbuck in various southern areas where there used to be fine woodlands but are no more, because of too many elephants. They are adapting to a niche out on the grasslands where they lead a life similar to the reedbuck's. They are an indication for the safarist who sees—and then sees what he sees.

A duiker looks serenity itself, a pitifully easy prey for a cheetah or a hyena. But if a leaf rustles out of place, it is gone: the bushes shiver and are still. Hence the duiker's name, Afrikaans for "diver." Its forequarters are much shorter than the back ones, which gives it a fair build for this particular form of escape, and its horns are swept back. Conversely, it has only a small heart and lungs, as befits an animal that needs to move fast rather than far. Some antelopes, such as the wildebeest, congregate in herds, but the smaller antelopes are not so gregarious. They have less need. They are not so dependent on limited food supplies (there are fewer of them, and each eats less food), and they are not so dependent on plenty of pairs of eyes to find food—or to spot a predator. They have legs that seem quite wrong for a creature that might have to flee for its life at any moment. The reedbuck stands only three feet high at the shoulder, and it is all gracefulness and repose. Yet it has an air of fearful curiosity. Despite its delicacy it gives a sense of wild watchfulness for the doom that may fall on it out of the next bush. In its natural state it has none of the listless vacuousness of animals in captivity. It is a wild animal and an antelope unto itself. The oribi is an antelope even smaller, a bundle of timorous hesitancy, all wet muzzle and quivering legs. Its step is sprightliness born of tension and freedom. Like other small antelopes it uses a special defense mechanism when suspicious. It pretends to graze while not actually doing so. Possibly it is trying to encourage false assurance in a nearby predator. Its jaws snuffle the ground, but the food is left untouched, then a thrust of those instant-ready legs and it is gone. The diminutive suni, all fifteen pounds of it, might give an impression of fear and restlessness, dashing from one patch of cover to another. But it is not timorous in the cowering fashion of domestic animals. It trots along in apparent acceptance of the way of things, an antelope to the height of its being—even if that is only a dozen inches. There is an assurance in its bearing that stems from its adaptation to the environment, a sense of being at one with its surroundings; it is a wild antelope in a wild habitat. It may not be a too friendly environment, but the antelope is at home here.

GAME CROPPING

In a single sweep of savannah the wildlife watcher may see gazelles and wildebeest and impala and eland and hartebeest and reedbuck and waterbuck; also giraffes and zebras and elephants and buffaloes; not far away may be hippos. He can sense the ecological cohesion and the ecological separation, how these creatures subsist together because they live "apart," how they are different because they share one community—and a community not just of panoramic plain but of grass and trees and soil and streams and climate.

Such is African wildlife. These creatures use the African earth and its prodigal productivity by feeding on the vegetation as cattle and sheep and goats do, although no cow eats grass when it is tussocky as buffaloes like it, nor when it is rank as topi like it, nor when it is withered as Grant's gazelle like it, nor when it is weedy and bitter and stringy and even half-poisonous as some creatures like it. Goats eat more than grass, but they do not eat acacia galls as giraffes do. If the safarist wants to know what makes

Top left: Gerenuk thrive in areas where there is hardly any grass, exploiting a segment of the vegetation spectrum where there is generally plenty for the few that can utilize it.

Bottom left: One of the smallest antelopes is the suni—small, that is, except for eyes and ears, which tell how it looks after itself.

Top right: The duiker has a pronounced gland between its eye and muzzle. Perhaps it evolved for marking vegetation, as in certain other antelopes, and then developed in the duiker for other secretions at mating time.

Middle right: The reedbuck is found in plenty of places, but there are rarely plenty of reedbuck. It likes areas near swamps where the thick vegetation makes it a favorite prey of leopards: it tops the list in several localities. But few as they are in themselves, and favorite food as they are for others, they still seem to flourish.

Bottom right: A lesser kudu eats leaves and shoots and seed pods and fruits, and quite a lot of grass, while a greater kudu rarely eats grass, but leaves and shoots and seed pods and fruits: a differentiation which is slight but enough.

African wildlife, he should know far more than just figures for the tallest giraffe or the smallest bird. He should know how all parts of the scene contribute something, how everything assists everything. When he considers how the ages have refined Africa's abundance until it can hardly be any other way, he has gained an insight into African wildlife that stems from more than just sterile gray facts and intellectual gray matter.

Some people look at the scene with not only this imaginative appreciation, but with facts and figures—as many and as precise as they can find. They want to exploit this animal array, not just elephants here or hippos there or eland over the hill, but the whole lot together. Every creature exploits Africa; why not exploit every creature? If Africa is productive because it has such a wide range of efficient nibblers, why not use any creature that can convert vegetable into protein, the dik-dik as well as the elephant? Africa constantly renews itself: the rains return, the soil regenerates, the grass springs up, the microorganisms get on with their micro-activities and their macro-influence, the zebras replenish their numbers season by season. The system could produce a harvest just as a maize plantation produces a harvest. As long as you don't devour the seed corn as well, there will be a crop next year; as long as you don't crop too many zebras (or the wrong ones), there will be zebras next season, and next century.

This approach is not new. It has been practiced along organized lines in a dozen parts of Africa for a dozen years, and it has been practiced along less organized lines in every part of Africa for dozens of millennia. Man has had his hunger and Africa has had its fecundity for as long as there has been man and there has been Africa. For at least 2,000,000 years man has been a carnivore and a predator; possibly far longer, certainly long before he became *Homo sapiens*. For less than two decades he has tried to benefit from this protein source in an efficient manner. But it is a long time now since the American ecologists Dr. Raymond Dasmann and Dr. Archie Mossman went to a Rhodesian ranch and demonstrated how wildlife could produce several times the profit of livestock. It took five years before there was enough wild meat on the market to stock a major Rhodesian city for months on end, or to feed a major tribal territory for a complete year. Nowadays ranches by the hundreds across southern Africa are buying in antelope. A single farm can crop 2,000 springbok from its herd of 7,000 and do the same again the next year. This resource will not run dry some day like an oil well, not unless it is refused its proper place in a world where man is concentrating on the efficient exploitation of every renewable source he can find. There are some places that are sound for livestock and some that aren't. In most regions, as Leslie Brown, a leading agriculturalist, has perceptively pointed out, Africa is little good for cattle and cattle are little good for Africa. Yet domestication is no more than a sophisticated use of wild animals. As has been observed by a leading exponent in this field, Ian Parker of Wildlife Services, Africa seems an obvious place for experimenting with such a multiplicity of specializations among the large animals as are to be found here—and found nowhere else on this scale. In Africa, do as Africa does; it is a sensitive place, highly resistant to alien mores.

Objectors say that nobody knows much about cropping—yet they are saying this years after workable schemes have produced research reports to reach the ceiling. The opposition has not always produced much evidence to resist the idea, more often scorn and skepticism if not indifference and inertia. The fundamental facts are there, certainly enough to be going on with. There has been no mystery about it for ages, except the mystery of why more has not been done about it in East Africa.

Basically it is a question of biomass. Only African savannah country can show such enormous totals. The Sahara struggles to reach 1,000 pounds a square mile: not only is the environment harsh, but it allows very little differentiation, only one or two major species instead of the twenty or more of savannah country. A rainforest is more than fecund, but it allows only six or eight large mammal species, so only two or three thousand pounds a square mile. Saiga antelope in the Ukraine, 2,000,000 of them, do not achieve

Right: An obvious candidate for game farming is the eland; there is plenty of fine protein on its frame and plenty of docility in its temperament. Game *cropping*, on the other hand, aims at taking a whole spectrum of animals in their wild state. Much savannah in East Africa features zebras and wildebeest, plus gazelles, hartebeest, giraffe, perhaps buffaloes and hippos—a score of suitable species.

Overleaf: An elephant is another obvious candidate for cropping. Some doubters protest that when surviving elephants hear a mechanized being coming along, such as a tourist truck, they will head for the horizon—or lie in wait for it. But the experience at Murchison Falls, where 2,000 have been cropped, suggests there need be no conflict between the desire of safarists for spectacle, Africans for meat, and elephants for living space. Practically every part of an elephant can be used. There is even something for those whose tastes run to elephant-foot umbrella stands. Elephant leather, selling at $4 a square foot, or over $540 for an average elephant, has been used for forty different articles. Cropping of elephants in East Africa has already earned $1,250,000, while at least another $1,000,000 worth of hide is left to the hyenas each year by "control hunters" whose job is limited to protecting plantations, not profiteering. The elephant herds of East Africa are a "standing crop" valued at $40,000,000.

more than 2,000 pounds a square mile, while caribou in their throngs reach only 5,000. Deer country in California sometimes gets up to 10,000 pounds a square mile, but more often doesn't. Virgin stock country reaches twice as much, managed ranchlands twice as much again. But that is about as far as it goes. Any major park in East Africa runs up to 50,000 pounds, several to double that, a few to still more during peak phases. Not that the temperate lands are all that impoverished. Some of them have life in other forms. A square mile of steppe country in southern Europe features only a dozen saiga antelopes to a square mile, yet the same area may support 90,000 voles and similar creatures. In the Congo's Albert Park there are well over 100,000 pounds of large animals to a square mile, but only 300 pounds of rodents (though Dr. D. F. Vesey-Fitzgerald has recently found an area in Tanzania with 70,000 pounds of molerats, and Leslie Brown reckons there are 100,000 rats to a square mile in Ethiopian highlands). It is easier to crop a 500-pound antelope or a 5,000-pound elephant than a 5-pound rodent, let alone eat one.

When compared with domestic stock in other directions, wild animals still win at a walk. They survive and prosper in country where cattle sicken and die. They exist equally well from the hot coastlands (zebra) to the upper slopes of East African mountains (eland). Local animals are far more immune to local diseases then exotic creatures. Antelopes begin to breed sooner than domestic stock and breed more rapidly. An eland is mature in three years, a cow in four. A hartebeest or a wildebeest or a topi puts on weight half as fast again as a cow; an eland puts on weight twice as fast as a cow, a gazelle twice as fast as a goat and three times as fast as a sheep. A steinbuck or a duiker or a dik-dik produces its first calf by the end of the first year, and two a year after that. Although a dik-dik need not stir beyond its one acre, whereas a wildebeest may trek over thousands of square miles during the year, what counts is the year-round average of living weight, and not just over one year but over a series of years, until there is enough to establish a fair average. It is no good quoting Nairobi Park and its 90,000 pounds in 1961 when the grasslands were overgrazed and the animals underfed.

With a sound base figure of what is on the hoof, you can then work out what will be on the carcass. Cattle carry a lot of fat, which is what they are bred for. A skin-and-skeleton affair still produces 7 percent fat; a better specimen produces 25 percent, and a sound steer over 35 percent. As Dr. H. P. Ledger has revealed at the Maguga research station outside Nairobi, a wild animal rarely goes beyond 5 percent, often a good deal less. It is the fat content that causes cattle to fluctuate between seasons, and between sexes and ages, but an African antelope stays what it is. It has no need for the fatty buildup that the cold-climate deer in North America generates and that can lead to a 40 percent range between winter and summer. Some people approve of animal fat on their plate; some people disapprove of it on their waistline; some people disapprove of cholesterol. Animals vary in the amount of muscle tissue they produce, the "lean" part. A hippo is three-quarters protein, all appearances to the contrary, and it comes at the bottom of the list. Buffalo and eland are somewhat higher, wildebeest, kudu, hartebeest, gazelle, and oryx higher still, while waterbuck, kob, warthog, gerenuk, and impala top the list with 83 percent. A poor quality cow produces only two-thirds protein, and a sound standard cow only a little over half. Of course, the edible carcass is not the same as the entire creature. Wild animals have efficient digestive systems—they can do the job off a tract only $17\frac{1}{2}$ percent of their total weight, whereas a cow needs $21\frac{1}{2}$ percent—which means that a wild animal can produce a greater proportion of edible material. Once again, there are lists showing which comes out on top of the "killing-out" ratings: domestic stock appear on the bottom half. An average cow produces well under half its carcass in edible meat, an average wild animal well over half. An occasional Zebu steer may go up to 1,500 pounds, and very well it looks—but it does not look altogether at home when it is sweating in the African sun.

It would not look like anything at all in a Masai boma, because you would not see one there unless you looked hard and long. People talk of the new era for African pastoralists. Those livestock experts who have spent a lifetime with the Masai—living with them, not just producing paper proposals for them—reckon it will take at least a generation, maybe more, before there are many good-grade cattle to be seen in Masai savannah lands. If Kenya Masailand were entirely turned over to livestock, it might—*might*—eventually earn as much as the best ranching land in Kenya, $2 an acre, which would amount to less than $20,000,000 a year. This figure could be within sight much sooner if cropping of wild animals were started at only moderate rates along the lines of trial schemes in Uganda and Tanzania. Zebras can bring in a good $50 a time to the producer, because of the valuable hide rather than the pile of meat. In the Kajiado half of Kenya Masailand there are 35,000 zebras, and these alone could earn more than the 500,000 cattle. Wildlife in Ngorongoro or Mara suggests that fewer cattle in Kajiado could result in more zebra, though it is far from certain how far zebra and cattle eat the same things the year round. One of the main grasses they share, along with wildebeest and hartebeest, is red-oat grass. (Not that it is easy to make out just who eats how much; you can look at fecal material, but some forage stays in the system for up to a week; you can get more accurate results from stomach contents, but you can't get stomach contents from a live zebra.) Preliminary surveys by the FAO ecologists Robert Casebeer and Gunter Koss suggest that Kajiado zebras make up something over a quarter of their diet from red-oat grass, wildebeest well over a third, hartebeest over two-thirds, and cattle just under a half. The three indigenous animals do not compete too much throughout the year, since they have lived side by side long enough to sort out their problems: they tend to eat red-oat grass in different amounts at different seasons. Cattle are much more recent arrivals; they came only a couple of thousand years ago. One wonders whether that period has been long enough for them to integrate with the total scene: how far can they be considered indigenous? At their present levels they can only be considered suicidal. But if they were better regulated, how far would their numbers have to be reduced before they were in equilibrium with the environment? Over much of Kajiado there is a 10,000-pound biomass of wildlife and 45,000 pounds of livestock—disproportionate, even if the livestock were to do battle with the environment on their own (and in some places the results look like nothing so much as a pitched battle). Where would an optimum lie? Abstruse questions, these; but it is on such factors that the future of large-scale game cropping depends, the future of wildlife too if the present scheme for large-scale ranching in Kajiado is to include a role for wildlife beyond the present tourist spectacle.

And even as a tourist attraction they are not doing so badly. Leslie Brown reckons that each wild animal in Kenya earns at least $20 a year, and many of them, especially the ones the visitor is likely to look at, are to be found in Masailand. Their upkeep in terms of park wardens and such expenses can be put at 25¢ each. The country's livestock also costs 25¢ per animal to maintain, but each creature only brings in a sixth as much. When it comes to foreign exchange, a powerful lubricant for an emergent economy, a wild animal brings in twenty times as much as a cow. Lions in Masailand must rank as some of the highest-earning animals in the world; the black-maned lion of Nairobi Park must match an eminent racehorse, while the elephants and rhinos of Amboseli are more than just also-rans.

Experienced organizations like Wildlife Services have developed a range of techniques. They have worked out just which is the best stage for cropping the animals; no good merely picking the dry season, since one should often aim at the height of the dry season, just before the animals have taken the last bit of nutriment from the vegetation and left it less ready to recover when the rains arrive. These pioneers have learned how to crop at night to create less disturbance; the herds do not scatter, but tend to crowd together. They have developed methods for herding animals into one particular place, just as has been done with zebras for filming—using not only vehicles but helicopters. They have learned that when you approach a herd of wildebeest, the ones that stay nearest are the ones with least experience of the world, the younger ones: no good taking a preponderant share of this age group if you want to come back and crop again another year. They have learned that cropping must often be done at strict random. There must be no choosing for whatever reason, however unconsciously—you must take thought on how not to take thought. They have learned that driving up to a hippo pool and firing at the one that first lifts its head is not the way to insure a cross section: you might take too many of the dominant bulls.

Above all, they have learned that you have to acquire a detailed knowledge of what the local population amounts to, not just how many animals there are but how many older ones, whether the female yearlings are as preponderant as they generally should be among

Many a zebra nowadays comes to a protracted end, since its hide is worth $200 to clientele overseas. One way to beat the poacher is to meet the market's demands with zebras cropped in a regulated manner (nobody poaches for beef). Another way is to ban the sale of zebra skins altogether and run the risk of having the zebra's lands cut from under it by the beef people. As long as the African rancher finds he can make as much from zebras as from cattle, he will find space for them; if not, he will react like ranchers anywhere. The present move to ban zebra sales in East Africa (even though the most intensive poaching could not make much impression on 700,000 zebras) could prove less effective as conservation than allowing the present small stream of skins to swell into a regulated flood and thus drown any poacher.

impala, how many of the older bull elephants are isolated in bachelor groups, whether the outsider buffalo bulls are outside because they are too young or too old to stay with the main herds, whether the gazelles are stepping up their breeding this year in response to a good rainy season—or last year's cropping. These are the population parameters that are paramount. It is a waste of time and worse to sally forth and blast away at the first set of animals you come across. You have to learn how to assess the age of a kob antelope by the number of rings on its horns, or the age of a wildebeest by the curve of its horns (its sex as well), the age of a female waterbuck (no horns) by the color of its coat. No good waiting until you have the creature on the ground and then finding you have taken the wrong one. You have to be able to tell all this at a far greater distance than you could with domestic stock. These croppers have learned how you can take 20 percent of the hartebeest and 30 percent of the gazelles and 40 percent of the oribi, with adjustments for all kinds of variables.

If an animal population's total doesn't matter as much as its potential—which can always be adjusted to give higher yields—then it is still not the whole story to say that wild animals achieve a higher biomass in this area but that cattle don't in some other area. What if they were swapped? A lot of evidence suggests there would still be little doubt. But that is not enough, either. You have to work with more than one method of measuring. The elephants and hippos and buffaloes of Queen Elizabeth Park sustain a biomass of well over 100,000 pounds per square mile. They could not be replaced by cattle because of the tsetse fly; but suppose they were? An elephant does not eat very much in proportion to its body weight, and it grows more slowly than most creatures. The findings of two of the earliest researchers in this field, Dr. George Petrides and Dr. Wendell Swank, show that a certain caloric intake for steers produces thirteen times as much growth as for elephants; so replacing 100 tons of elephants with 100 tons of cattle would precipitate a much higher caloric intake, far higher than the range could tolerate. Again, elephants maintain a biomass five times as high as white-tailed deer, yet the energy value of the food they eat amounts to only slightly more than the deer get through. Moreover, elephants dispose of a lot of what they eat in a fairly undigested form, thereby returning it to the system much sooner, which means that the amount of food assimilated for growth and maintenance is well under what it is for deer. What counts, however, is not the amount of living animals available at any one time, but how much more animal is produced during the year. Elephants show an annual increase above the basic "standing crop" of only one-twentieth, whereas deer show ten times as much, and meadow mice five times as much again. For all their biomass, elephants are not producing an absolute increase in protoplasm beyond two-thirds what mice achieve.

But it takes a single bullet for an elephant or a gazelle (it would be rather too much for a meadow mouse). Having got your animal on the ground, you have to deal with it rapidly in that African heat. Since there is not much prospect of getting it to a slaughterhouse on the hoof, you have to get it there on a truck. Three thousand elephants in East Africa have been processed in this way, with checks by health inspectors all along the line, from the time the elephant hits the ground to the time it hits the butcher's slab a hundred miles away or more. In the Luangwa Valley in Zambia the process is refined to an art, all the way to freezing or canning. An average elephant can fill three to four thousand one-pound tins, a giraffe or a buffalo around one thousand, a zebra something over two hundred, a warthog eighty, and a Thomson's gazelle twenty. The cost for a large species works out at fifteen cents a can, as against sixty cents for a tin of scrub-cattle beef. This game meat has been sent to Europe, where gourmets were given unmarked samples of gazelle goulash to be tested against pork, beef, and mutton. The wild meat generally came out ahead of its competitors in terms of texture and taste, and on a par in terms of hygiene.

Some advocates think that overcoming public opinion in America and Europe is a primary factor in establishing game cropping in Africa. If people can once be persuaded to buy their first can (not likely to be their last), they might be helping wildlife in a way more practical than any amount of protest about poaching. Other people say it will be a long time before zebra steak is available in supermarkets overseas, particularly when it is hard enough getting East African beef accepted. If cattle are suspected of picking up all manner of diseases from wildlife, how much worse when the cans contain wildlife itself! Infection is certainly a major factor, and not just after the meat is put into a heat-sterilized can. Wild creatures pass on a variety of diseases to man's domestic animals and man himself, notably anthrax, tuberculosis, hoof and mouth disease—a whole range of pathogens, not to mention parasites that cause muscle cysts and filaries and a series of other alarming-sounding deficiencies. It is a mistake to look at a lot of sprightly antelopes and think how healthy they are. Some of these creatures may have hundreds of less attractive creatures living inside them. A wildebeest might cavort around full of life and energy, but with a heart in desperate condition. A gazelle may streak across the plain but do it with half a lung. Yet, while three out of four gazelles in the Serengeti may show peculiarities, their neighbors a few horizons away may be free of them; and the same Serengeti population could be in much better shape another season.

The cropping potential of wild animals in East Africa has been put at half a billion dollars. What has been achieved so far, a few million pounds of meat here and a few million dollars there, is nothing as compared with what awaits. Yet there are still people who object it is not practical, hence not worth pursuing. Eat a piece of gazelle meat and you'll drop down dead. Shoot a zebra and the hide will not cover your expenses. Shoot two zebras and you cannot sell the hides, the market is saturated. Shoot three and zebras everywhere are in trouble. Certainly there are problems aplenty, including making peace with the livestock people. One way is to agree not to sell wild meat at half the price of beef or less (still feasible yet profitable), but to peg it at the same price to insure "fair and free competition." Yet what if game meat were to flood the market to the extent that not only good beef found things difficult, but scrub-stock meat as well—from the very animals that must be reduced for a range of reasons, not least to rehabilitate the environment so that more wild animals can flourish? As in so many aspects of conservation in East Africa, there are experts in livestock and experts in wildlife, not to mention economists and sociologists, and they remain experts in their own fields. The approach has too often been fragmented, thereby crippled from the start.

The safarist need not fear that the sights he is gazing at in the parks will soon be sizzling on a steak plate. It is primarily the antelopes outside the parks that are to be cropped, and in such a way as to make them produce a maximum yield year after year by adjusting the age structures or the sex ratios, even the entire community makeup. This approach, too, horrifies many a visitor. He does not want the thought, much less the spectacle, of half-modified zebras in half-domesticated ecosystems. Part of his purpose in coming to East Africa is to get back to a placid past where such manipulation has not yet arrived. He wants natural nature, not an artificial affair. But as he gazes out over the savannah, how can he tell if the zebras are modified or not? And without an appreciation of the world the zebras live in, not just a zebra world, how can he be sure they will not be modified out of existence unless they pay their way? People are appalled at the jargon of cropping, the talk of gross rates and carcass yields and kill quotas—is not "cropping" itself a euphemism for straight slaughter? The whole idea revolts their sense of esthetic propriety, if not more. There is something incongruous and grotesque in the whole thing, a pernicious abuse of nature.

Yet cropping is no fresh folly committed by the overclever sophistication of a super-modern age. It is no more to be decried than many other activities that are basic to the functioning of society, like keeping people fed with meat and shod with leather. This may be the best way as well as the final way of keeping the wild herds of Africa in existence.

The local people are not always impressed by talk of wildlife's natural attraction, and it is doubtful if they will be for some time. But there is one language they understand: when money talks they get the message loud and clear. This is a region where there is little time for the refinements of life, and if wildlife so far depends on tourism, the overseas tourist is generally a white man, a rich man, a well-fed man. For the local person, something more local might be appropriate. If he sees that an elephant can be something valuable to rival his herd of cattle, he will turn out to be Africa's finest protector of wildlife. He will know of every minor infringement, and he will tell of it with a thousand tongues. Ask him meanwhile what he thinks of wildlife, and he will say that he finds it a splendid thing, the earth is meant for wild animals and the wild animals are meant for the earth, and so forth. Ask him again, ask in a manner to make him think you really want to know, and he may say that he has never seen a lion and he would reach for his spear if he did, that his father last year got thumped by a buffalo, that his brother is doing time for poaching, and that his son is in high school in the big city where wild animals are remote from the landscape, remote from the imagination, remote from the wallet.

Despite all the problems, especially the assertions by "supporters" overseas that African wildlife is sacrosanct and must be saved by sympathy, there is still a sound prospect that all sides could have their cake and eat it, in fact a larger cake than they have had before. The leave-alone onlookers can have more to look at; the pastoralists can have a source of income that their endless herds of useless cattle have not produced in ages; the people who want to bring wildlife into the marketplace can have a task to test their best techniques, rather than a steady struggle to keep on the starting line; and the die-hard doubters can have a chance to see how far their worst fears will be fulfilled. Not that this is a new idea—just as this is not an age all that hostile to new ideas, particularly when they are being tested every day in every land. To say that cattle have always been the number-one source of animal protein and so should stay that way is like saying that man has never farmed the oceans, so why start now—or that he has survived for a long time without scientific agriculture, so why try hybrid corn. The countries of East Africa have an opportunity such as is available hardly anywhere in the world, and has been available at hardly any other time in history with this range and potential. They can still do it. Other places can't; they are already too "developed." Here is a chance for development of a different order. It could be development to make other lands wonder at.

SNAKES

Some people come to Africa and expect to see snakes everywhere. But the trees are not hanging with snakes, nor is the ground crawling with them. You could stay in East Africa for ten years and not see a single one. Even if you went out to look for them you would still find them difficult to track down. Snakes know better. They pick up vibrations through the ground—their ears have no outer appendages and are not very efficient—and make off long before those big feet get near. Snakes in trees are easier to find since not many vibrations go up the trunk. But many a visitor walks under a tree, leaving an apparent branch to stretch and relax. Still, there are plenty of snakes around. Many a house in East Africa has its gardenful, though the owner never sights so much as a tail disappearing into the grass.

You cannot really talk about wildlife in East Africa until you have seen snakes. They might not exert such an effect on the viewer or on the ecology of an area as the larger creatures or the more proliferant birds. But they are survivors from the earlier hours of Africa's long day. If you can look at a snake without letting your atavistic allergies get in the way, you can see one of the more interesting phenomena of Africa. A good time to

Left: The puff adder mother has lots more young ones still to be born. She drops them off as she moves across the terrain, never to see them again. But an infant adder is equipped to look after itself right away, poison glands and all. It can survive up to three months on the yolk it draws into itself during the last few days of "incubation."

Right: This is not a cobra about to attack, but a cobra doing all it can to avoid attacking. When it is after food, it must above all avoid being conspicuous—and hissing of any kind. When it is up against a wildebeest or a human being, it is facing an antagonist who cannot do it the least bit of good (no more than the other way round). So there is help in looking horrendous. Otherwise, the snake hopes for harmony: it has to.

look out for them is the late afternoon, when they emerge from the cover where they have been sheltering during the hotter periods. Since they are cold-blooded, their body "warmth" fluctuates with the vicissitudes of the environment. They adjust as best they can, but cannot bear too much either way. If they get caught by a sudden storm and the temperature plunges, they are more or less immobilized. At such times they are vulnerable to hawks and secretary birds, or even other snakes that have chosen a warmer spot during the storm.

Snakes stem from a stage when most creatures were covered with scales, a "skin" that did not allow for any sweating and hence permitted no heat regulation. It was a long time before mammals and birds learned how to keep their bodies at a steady level and achieve more flexibility in their living styles by the greater vitality of a warm bloodstream. But they paid for it by needing a lot more energy to stoke up the machine and keep it at a steady heat, which meant constant food for burning. Snakes, on the other hand, go for months off a single meal. A large python can swallow a 100-pound animal, then writhe away replete with its load and satisfaction to last a year or more. Needing less, it also makes far better use of its total meal than a wasteful lion would.

Snakes were branching off from other reptiles in the Cretaceous period, 135,000,000 years ago, before the long African day was a third gone. They abandoned a four-point support for the body and took to crawling along the ground. Dispensing with legs meant they could afford to be longer, which led to snakes fifty feet long in the Eocene, roughly halfway between their first appearance and the present time. Now the longest snake in Africa is a twenty-five foot python, while most do not get beyond four or six feet. There is hardly a snake that a man cannot escape from by merely walking away, unless he comes on it in difficult terrain where he cannot move as easily. Even then he need do no more than stand and look at it, unless he has tried to show it he thinks the only good snake is a dead one. Which will only leave the world a poorer place, not a better one.

When the snakes began to grow longer, they could not become thicker, too. Much better something slimmer and lighter. A black mamba is like a piece of hosepipe, and some snakes are as slender as knitting needles. This is fine for sliding up on their prey, or lying concealed. But while they have less trouble in approaching their food, they have more trouble in swallowing it. Various adaptations help. A snake can open its jaws four times as wide as the reader through a complicated system of articulations and elastic ligaments. A man can get through a meal a mere 5 percent his own weight and he has to be a glutton to do it, but a snake can manage a quarter of its own weight, while a python, a consummate consumer for any age, can go well toward doubling its size with a single mouthful. But if it feels threatened just after swallowing its meal the snake may disgorge the lot, much more quickly than it went down. The snake does not so much "eat" its prey as "walk it down." One side of the mouth is worked forward until the teeth get a hold, then the other side. There is no problem about breathing since the snake's glottis protrudes like a snorkel. A lot of saliva helps in lubrication at the difficult stages, just as it helps in turning antelope or whatever into snake. There are some snakes that anticipate this process, though they are not the ones that grease a carcass by drooling over it (snakes do that only in fables). They are the 169 venomous snakes of East Africa, and they inject a saliva of sorts to start digesting the prey while it is still alive, though of course the poison (which often contains enzymes) primarily serves to subdue the prey.

An adder strikes faster than a cobra, but it achieves only eight feet a second—fast enough if the prey is close and clumsy, but not nearly fast enough to be "lightninglike." It is much slower about getting back into position for a follow-up strike; and since no adder in East Africa is much over five feet and most are far less, and since none can strike more than a third of its length, you just have to avoid giving it cause to think a strike is the only way out; then you can stand and admire it for as long as you wish. If you recognize that it is not bent on instant destruction, you can sit and watch it all day. No snake wants to waste its poison on incidentals; it might need several days to recharge itself. Moreover, the first strike must do the job, since there is often no second chance—the prey is alerted or might even retaliate. If the prey is a mere rat the snake allows it to scuttle all over its head before the one and only strike is attempted.

When the reptiles evolved from fish they developed their own means for insuring there would be further reptiles, which represented an advance on the propagation methods of fish. Fish lay eggs in hundreds and haphazard hundreds. Reptiles lay eggs too, but they keep better control of what happens. They are still a long way from the advanced development of mammals, but they provided a big step in that direction. Some snakes "store" the eggs in their bodies until incubation is complete. A puff adder produces a batch of live-born young every six months, an average of forty. It continues to breed infants and more infants throughout a life that may last twelve years. But if only two out of the nearly 1,000 infants reach the stage where they can start producing puff adders in turn, then that is all that is necessary—and about all that are likely to survive. There is no dearth of puff adders nor is there an excess. The rest disappear, often enough in the fashion of many snakes—into other snakes.

To the man who has heard a lot about snakes but not seen many, they are all alike— long and legless and loathsome. Some live entirely on slugs and snails; others never touch them. Some die for want of a centipede. Some snakes found in East Africa are found nowhere else. One viper sticks to mountain country on the Aberdares, above 10,000 feet; another viper, a horned one, keeps to Lake Naivasha and its environs. As likely as not there are some snakes that have not been identified as yet. For diversity of shape and form, snakes stand up well in comparison with other wild creatures of East Africa. A Gaboon viper sports skin patches of gorgeous peach, blue, and brown. Python skins are so splendid they have to be converted into coverings for chic creatures that are sophisticated enough to scream if they see one alive.

Most people know less about snakes than about other creatures. Instead of watching and wondering, a more usual reaction is to reach for a stick. Yet snakes are far less of a threat to human life than many of the animals the safarist comes across during his

savannah day. The trouble is not the snake and what is inside it, but the observer and what is inside him—prejudice. There is no instinctive fear despite theories that man once had snakes in plenty for companions. Whatever the sources of this irrational urge, there is no doubt that man is one of the snake's chief enemies. Nevertheless, a few African snakes may be on the increase. Man has reduced some of their enemies, such as birds. He has reduced some of the enemies of rodents, which are a prime food of snakes. He has planted corn across the landscape, which further benefits the rodents. But poisons in the environment elsewhere kill off creatures far more widely than snake poison has accomplished in thousands of years. The whole habitat is being constricted far more silently and efficiently than a python could ever achieve. In the face of this onslaught the man who comes to Africa and looks for a snake is searching for a member of the vertebrate group that is threatened more than any other, and he is searching in one of their last main refuges. It is a lucky man who accidentally comes across a single snake in a month's safari. It is an exceptional man whose instinct is not to raise his arm. The true wildlife enthusiast may be the man who wants to keep snakes alive as much as he does leopards or giraffes.

LIONS

Toward late afternoon the lions begin to bestir themselves. They stretch. They yawn a good deal. Half a dozen muzzles scent the breeze. It is still a long time before the night's business. The male walks out into the open, moving along as if it is an effort just to put one

A lioness likes the late afternoon sun. She relaxes before evening time, even if the cubs do not feel much like lying quiet.

foot in front of the other. It seems impossible he could ever work up to a jog, let alone a sprint. He heaves himself a few paces, looking neither to right nor left; the world and its doings are beyond his caring—too much trouble, or beneath him. He flops down with a lion-sized sigh. Even in the late-day sun he is still panting at over 100 breaths a minute. Within a few hours this rate will fall to less than ten.

If the watcher marvels at the lion's demeanor, that is the only sense in which the lion is king of beasts any more than the watcher is. The lion has developed its superb strength to do a specific job: keep it alive. It has paid a heavy price for its heavily muscled body: it is a heavy animal. Because of its hunting techniques—or its hunting limitations—it is a sociable animal. It lives with others for obvious tactical purposes. In the Serengeti, Dr. George Schaller has seen lions working in concert to head off a herd of gazelles. He has also seen them trap their prey in a salient between two rivers, advancing quite openly in a fan-shape front.

Lions reinforce their sociable inclinations by indulging in much nuzzling and every kind of "affectionate" gesture they are capable of. For all that a lion in its prime can survive on its own, it rarely chooses to. Everything has to be just right: plenty of power, plenty of prey. In the Serengeti a lion on its own catches only one gazelle out of three or four, but with another lion it catches its prey more often than not. Many an aged lion comes to an end when it finds itself isolated from the group system. If the lions in an area drop below a certain number, for whatever reason, there might not be enough left to form congenial groups; they could end up in local extinction. Nobody knows how many are enough. No good saying that as long as there are a few remaining in any area they aren't all gone. Quite a lot can be too few, and nobody knows what is the critical level for lions. It might be as well to find out more of what lions know, how they really survive in a lion's world as well as a man's world, before starting to consign them to such odd patches of ground as can be spared.

The communal-living system gives rise to tensions too. A lot of lions are killed by lions. Fights between males are likely to be territorial conflicts, the resident against a challenger. These fights do not often go too far, since much depends on how far the intruder has penetrated inside the local domain. The resident lion fights hardest when he is standing in his heartland, in the stretch of country he knows best. This is where he feels safest; it is

Left to right:
Lions are given to staring into the middle distance. What the cub will see there in a few years' time could be a very different view, except in a few small areas of Africa.

While the lioness was shifting her three-week-old cub to a safer spot, and another that fell into a stream, two more were being slowly washed under. The rest of the pride ignored what was going on, despite the splashings and squeakings.

An infant lion is much more given to experimenting, to finding "how things work," than a wildebeest calf, or most other young animals. Sometimes the probing urge gets it into trouble.

Even when lions are three-quarters grown they indulge in a lot of play which is nothing if not hectic. All is great energy, all is great good humor, as only lions know how. The constant close-contact activity probably emphasizes the social cohesion that is so important for lion survival.

also his last refuge. On the borders of the territory he won't press matters unless he cannot avoid it. When he runs to meet an interloper he goes with great outward show but less inner conviction. If the intruder turns around and flees, the attacker might keep up the chase for some way, but he makes sure he does not follow too fast. He would not want a chase that was short and sharp, since it might lead to an outcome shorter if not sharper.

Just as frequent are battles within the pride itself. In Ngorongoro two lionesses of one pride—an unusually large pride—came to a violent end within a few weeks of each other. Had external threats, such as a temporary shortage of prey, set off the internal pressures? The victims were covered with wounds from more than one lion. These were no private squabbles; they were full-scale affrays with several antagonists piling onto the one unfortunate. Some foot-long paw swipes had left bruises two inches deep. In a pride of Nairobi Park two lionesses were killed in quick succession, together with a young lion. This time there were just two males to blame. One of them was suspected of unusual tendencies: he seemed to be homosexual. If any female approached his current best friend, she was promptly assaulted, often grievously. One day he was put to sleep and woke up "modified." For a while the pride got on better; then he and his partner killed two more lionesses. In the long run nothing changed except that his mane fell out. Were the females foreigners? Or were they locals that got into a fracas over food?

Males seem to maintain their own jealous view of what makes up the local hierarchy. They are all for sharing when it means taking over a carcass captured by a lioness of the pride, whereupon they are very choosy about who else shares the meal. The situation varies according to some lion code that nobody has yet worked out. A male at Ngorongoro was once seen seizing a kill from three lionesses with much sound and fury, then surrendering another carcass four nights later to four lionesses of the same pride with hardly a gesture of resistance. The lionesses were the same ones except for the additional member: perhaps she occupied some special spot in the local dominance ratings that somehow stacked the odds a little too high—or perhaps he was just not as hungry.

In fact, in Dr. Schaller's view, pride grouping seems to be a looser setup than was once thought. Males spending a few days away from the main pride readily associate with a female foreigner, but if they want to bring her home the lionesses give her a rough welcome. Conversely, a lioness off on a sojourn accepts the attentions of an alien lion, but the

resident males do not approve if they catch him at it. The least likely to wander away are the lionesses, partly because they are more tied down with domestic distractions such as cubs and partly because, unlike males, they are rarely dismissed from the pride after adolescence. Thus the same group of females may persist in one area for generations. Even so, they may not often all be found together: Schaller never once came across all eleven lionesses of a Serengeti pride in one place during the three years he was watching them.

When the male makes a move to shoo away an interloper, he is doing no more than what many people feel a lion should do. It is also possible he is keeping the area sacrosanct for the lioness to hunt in as much as himself, and George Schaller thinks the male may play the further role of protecting the cubs. Not that he does much about it directly, but he insures the females an area free from encroachment by strangers where they can

Lion cubs take a lot of training. Even when they are allowed to join in with a zebra in its last throes, they show little idea of what to do—they take hold at any but the right place. But the experience perhaps brings out instincts that are deeply buried, waiting to be activated. In this sense, they are not really "taught" anything very much.

bring up their cubs in peace. Females drive off strange females just as often as males drive off males, but if the females have to do too much of such work themselves, the cubs may suffer. At one stage a pride in the Serengeti with only a single male produced twenty-six cubs at one time (a female in season seems to stimulate others, so that several lots of cubs are born pretty much at once). Only two cubs survived. A neighboring pride with three males produced twenty cubs, and twelve survived.

Whatever their stage of infancy, lion cubs are full of high spirits if not good sense. They can be watched all the hours they are out and about. Yet a cub's life is not all sun and sport. They are strangely prone to disease. Many sicken and weaken, and in some areas less than half reach adulthood. They pick up germs that give them infected eyes, sore-stricken bodies, an altogether doleful appearance. Nursing a family taxes a lioness's strength and she needs extra food, but if she gets so hungry that her speed slackens, hunting becomes more than difficult. Hungrier soon means weaker, and she is hard put to keep herself and the household going. For all her efforts she is often luckless; the vital power in her charge is lacking, the zebras scatter, and she has to go back to feed the family, unfed herself. As she sets off to hunt, the cubs sense from her cough and grunt that they cannot go along. How she finds them again is a mystery, unless she can "remember" the lie of the land. A lioness once left two small cubs in a tangle of grass in the middle of the Serengeti Plains. They were scarcely visible at half a dozen strides. After going away briefly, it took a safarist a whole hour to find them again. How then does a lioness manage it? When she returns, the reunion is one of the sights of Africa. She licks them all over, they lick her, they gambol and play and nuzzle, and then do it all over again, just to make sure everyone knows how everyone else feels.

Social indeed. Yet to see the pride around a kill suggests that lions have not yet reached the fuller social system of, say, wild dogs. There is much snarling if not lashing out, a far more aggressive show than when the lion is making its kill (then its face is impassive). And if most of the pride is on the carcass, the cubs get a slim share—again, a long way from wild dogs, with their highly systemized sharing. Yet lions are the most sociable of the cats; a cheetah often feeds alone, a leopard almost always. The smaller the cat, the smaller the prey it can handle, size for size, until there would be less advantage for the less powerful variations—across the evolutionary perspective of the long African day—in developing a life-style in which several individuals help in the kill but everyone shares in the results. Yet wild dogs—dogs, not cats—can master a prey creature so far ahead of their own individual weight (a zebra is ten times as heavy as any dog), that they almost rival the achievements of early man in dispatching elephants. If you are going to be a small carnivore, better to be a highly social carnivore, or else a highly solitary one. The dogs have tended in one direction, the cats in the other. Not that there is anything rigid about such trends, since the lions indicate how a fairly secretive, nighttime-hunting cat—one that is adapted to close-range attack rather than the long pursuit—has responded to the specific environmental pressures it has found in Africa (and at one time elsewhere as well) by moving in the direction of the pride system. Yet this is far from a refined system, lacking the subtleties of a typical dog system where there are pronounced family bonds, and a much stronger male–female relationship than among lions. Possibly the lion system is not so much an integrated social structure as a loose variation on the matriarchal theme (or mother–family relationship), with spasmodic contributions by the males.

All of which goes some way toward saying that if we want to know how primitive man evolved we should look not only at his primate relatives but at those creatures that are akin through their food-getting techniques. In fact, since monkeys and apes are basically vegetarian, and chimpanzees and gorillas, for example, have a shorter evolutionary tale to tell than man, it might be more appropriate—as Dr. Schaller and Dr. Lowther have speculated—to work out their social systems by watching man rather than the other way round. Not that man the primitive predator developed ways of living that were necessarily similar to a lion's, but he would run up against some of the same formative forces of the environment. One might even say that if ecological kinship counts as well as genetic, then early man might have established a hunting niche where he elbowed out the saber-toothed cats, which suddenly disappeared about the same time as man became prominent —a phenomenon that has long puzzled probers of the past. After a cooperative group of human hunters had felled their prey, they would be able to guard it until they could finish it over several days, using something of the same method as a lion community employs: a few sit by the carcass to keep off hyenas (those same hyenas that would scare off a single killer from the remains—if indeed a lone hunter could prove a match for the more pachydermous prey). But such a division of labor still does not help hungry lion cubs, although a lioness on the hunt can leave her offspring with a "babysitter." Nor can the lioness regurgitate for them, as a wild dog can, any more than a human female. She must lead the cubs to the meat, provided they can walk far enough. It is not surprising that lion cubs often starve.

But for a healthy cub the African day is long, the sun is warm, and a nearby tail can be chased until dusk comes. And yet, for all their apparent intelligence, lion cubs sometimes seem born with less instinctive idea of how to survive than almost any other animal of the savannah. For a creature such as an antelope, it is not strictly necessary to undergo an extended period of parental care and tutelage. All the young one has to learn is how to eat and watch and run. But for a lion to catch that antelope takes a good year of tutelage. It has to be shown and reshown every move. The day comes when the cubs are given their first practical lesson, and the lioness is a miracle of patience. The cubs rush out all enthusiastic, long before the prey is within striking distance, then bound back to their long-suffering mother proud of what they have done. Even when the lioness catches a warthog and holds it down for them they haven't the slightest idea what to do with it. Not that lion cubs are so utterly incompetent as has been suggested. When lions that have never had any chance to "learn"—such as zoo lions—are confronted with a whole carcass, or with a creature that is potentially a source of food and actually still alive, then, according to Randall Eaton's investigations, they find themselves following the same basic patterns as do lions that have done the same thing scores of times for real. Or they play with the carcass in the singularly purposive manner of lions, showing many of the actions that speedily convert a live prey into something more amenable. It seems more than possible that various inbred patterns guide the lion when it is first "learning" from its mother: far from learning all that much, the cub has its instinctive reactions brought into play time after time, until they are reinforced enough to work with all the feline efficiency that lions deploy.

So a lion cub at play is a cub becoming a lion. It practices how-to-catch-the-moving-object, or a range of similar games that are more than games. On top of that, it indulges in an endless urge to explore the environment. Every bush is to be probed, every tree to be sniffed and scratched at. Perhaps this constant nosing about helps the cub to sense what are the bounds of the pride's territory. And there could be more to it than is dreamed of in some behaviorists' philosophies. Some people say an animal is just a bundle of reactions: it cannot do anything except in response to an external stimulus. The watcher can decide for himself how far that restless spirit is dependent on what goes on outside before anything goes on inside—whether it is by nature a chameleonlike creature, nothing but a reflection of the outward world. Other people think there is an inner urge that acts and reacts regardless of what else goes on outside: an inner world that drives the lion as much as the outside world determines it, a vital energy that must have release just because a lion is like that. According to these "vitalists," there is a motive force that allows it to "choose" what to do rather than be urged by blind forces. At the same time, this self-determined vigor is limited by what the rest of the community wants. Insofar as a lion prefers to live with others, it restrains some of its impulses—until it gets launched into a serious fight. Yet it is precisely this aggressive spirit that accounts for the restless temperament and the quizzical nature (if not the other way round: difficult to say which gives rise to which). Lions are always wanting to "find out." The late-day tourist may find one running after his safari vehicles just because it wants to have a closer look at the rear lights, however else it may seem to the occupants.

Some observers believe it is broadly correct to say that the more an animal is given to aggressive traits, the more it has a wider range of other senses for perceiving its environment—and for standing aloof when it so wants. There is a long way from perceptive apprehension to conceptual comprehension; only one creature has managed the whole trip. But whereas a zebra is not as inclined as a lion to probe around just because it is curious (and neither of them is as unenterprising as a tick in its fur), so the lion, like the other great cats, is endowed with something more than brute instincts for keeping alive. Not that it is aggressive toward any other creature—only toward another lion, or whatever gives it cause for anxiety. When it is after a zebra a lion is not fierce or bellicose or

These Kikuyu living under Mount Kenya have old-style huts alongside the new, and old-time crops such as maize together with recent cash crops such as coffee. They are among the most progressive peasants in Africa, a few managing to increase their incomes several times over in the first ten years of independence. But they are also some of the most congested in Africa, up to 1,600 a square mile, with only half the acreage of an Indian farmer.

bent on destruction: it is a creature of volition if a creature of violence, all in its own lion-like way. It cannot do differently.

It is in this sense that a self-actuating animal like a lion must suffer more than most in a zoo. A lion has to explore and roam across its country. If it cannot do otherwise, it cannot *be* otherwise. Putting it in a cage leaves it deprived in a manner one can only visualize by sensing what happens to the most restless creature of all when it is subjected to solitary confinement. Some creatures would mind such treatment less, those whose nature is virtually confined to solitary existence without much contact with the world around them or with other creatures in it. But to see the lions in their own community, to see the cubs testing every bit of their environment—rather than waiting for the environment to come to them—is to have an insight into what makes the inner lion. It says something for the resilience of lions that no matter how long they are kept in zoos, however many generations they go through, whatever morphological changes they undergo in their skull structures, they still retain the spirit of what they have always been. A caged lion never becomes a tame lion. It has its own essence. It remains superbly savage, something to awe any onlooker still able to be awed.

SAFARI INTO THE SEVENTIES

When the safarist finds himself traveling back to Nairobi after a loop of safari country, he often passes through some of East Africa's finest agricultural areas. As the afternoon declines at the end of a long day's trip—most safari lands are some distance from the city

—he looks out across landscapes with plenty of interest of their own: he is looking at something that matters as much for wildlife's future as do the larger parks. These cultivated areas with their teeming humans count, just as do areas where there are no humans at all. To gaze out over cropfields and speculate how they will help wild creatures may seem like conservation at more than one remove. But conservation means viewing the total environment in its total unity.

It is the humans who will decide the future of wildlife, by their very numbers, apart from other considerations. East Africa has a lot of people, and a lot of them are demanding extra land. Soon there will be many more. If the wild places are to be left for wild animals, then much of the outcome will be decided in places like the Kikuyu farmlands near Nairobi. The visitor who gives them a second glance is showing an indirect concern for the herds of antelopes and elephants he was looking at earlier in the day, a concern that is likely to carry more practical weight with Africans in the long run.

These African peoples are going on a safari of their own, a journey into new lands with new horizons. Their crop country is a scene of fresh endeavor and fresh achievement, in some of the best land in the world, soil more fertile and with far more rain than in three-quarters of East Africa. The "shamba" plots reveal the old staples of maize and bananas side by side with the new cash crops of tea and coffee (often better grades than from the white estates nearby). Many a coffee-grower is earning far more, up to $1,000 a year and more, from his few acres than he ever could with maize in a similar small patch. By some standards that is not much, but in a country where the average annual income rarely reaches much over $100, it is advance indeed. Furthermore, it is an advance that has taken only half a dozen years, even though Kenya's coffee often does not earn as much abroad as the extra effort should entitle it to, when coffee prices fluctuate by as much as 50 percent in a single season. One coffee country struggling to get onto its feet found its revenues slashed and its economy broken-backed overnight.

Wherever you look across Kikuyu country, every farm patch is neatly marked off. Every scrap of ground is used, particularly in areas where there is less than half an acre per person. It gives a sense of well-being, revealing how an agriculture landscape can have as much appeal as a wild one provided it represents a continuum rather than a disruption. The streams of Kikuyuland are not always running red with soil like those areas where Africa is bleeding away. Kikuyuland is largely hilly terrain, and twenty years ago this meant largely erosion; ten years ago it meant largely terracing—though in some places the situation is now slipping. These industrious people must maintain their momentum if Kikuyuland is to feed not just Kikuyu but other people far and wide. Soon it will have to feed still more around Kenya, or the more may start looking farther afield for places to expand into. And those places will include the less fertile lands, and eventually the marginal lands—which are also called the wildlands: to land-hungry people, land is land. Already there are people trying to grow maize in the Rift Valley where maize has never been grown before, but where it must be grown now, or at least planted. Savannah plains like these once featured experiments by the white man who tried to get grain to sprout, though he did no better than with many another exotic scheme such as the groundnuts in Tanzania. Still, the Rift Valley grasslands will have to be given over to maize fields and potato patches when the need is great enough.

Kenya has long been short on land, especially for a nation where four-fifths of the people make their living off agriculture alone. The situation will not improve with almost three times as many people by the end of the century. Most of the white-settler lands have disappeared under Kikuyu digging hoes; most of Kenya's arable areas are congested as compared with the spacious living of India. In Tanzania almost all the land that is fairly suitable for cultivation is now occupied by a people even more dependent on agriculture than Kenya's. Uganda has a greater proportion of good land, but most of its 10,000,000 people in a country the effective size of North Dakota (but with fourteen times as many people) subsist off less than one and a half acres each, and have already taken up the greater part of the total area appropriate for cultivation. By the time today's infant Ugandan is producing offspring, there will be twice as many people wanting their patch of land. One can understand why elephants in Uganda are now limited to less than one-quarter the living-space they had before the last war. One can guess how much will be left to them in another thirty years. Only when the Acholi farmer in northern Uganda can look on an elephant as a fine source of legitimate meat, tusks for revenue, tail hairs for tourist bracelets, hide for affluent wallets, and feet for wastepaper baskets, as well as something to lure more tourists, will he be less inclined to reach for his spear when he sees his year's maize crop disappearing over the hill inside an elephantine appetite.

So if land counts now, there will soon come a time when all the wails of the wildlife worriers will achieve nothing, nor all the research staffs nor all the funds in the world, if the savannah lands are required for other purposes; unless, of course, it can be shown in the meantime that wild areas can prove just as efficient at building a new nation as any other, and just as economic—it's no good having fine scenery and spectacle if you can't eat it (or can you?).

The Kigezi district in south-western Uganda presents a landscape as striking as any on the savannah. But so over-crowded are the people, despite terracing techniques that use every last scrap of land, that over one-third of the men are away seeking work elsewhere. As the numbers swell—and, with refugees from Congo and Rwanda, this region is reaching a 4 percent growth rate—there will be more pressure to encroach onto the Virunga volcanoes in the background, sanctuary of the last gorillas.

Near Nairobi there are farmlands with 1,700 people a square mile, as many as in the most intensively cultivated regions on earth. Like farmers in Holland and Japan, these people practice not so much agriculture as horticulture. There are similar areas around Lake Victoria and on the southeastern slopes of Kilimanjaro. If each acre supports not only its human inhabitants but domestic animals as well, then the biomass total runs well beyond 100,000 pounds a square mile, nearly 200,000 pounds in some areas. It is as much as one finds on those plains where wild animals make East Africa one of the most productive regions around the globe, far in excess of what "natural nature" achieves elsewhere. At a spot near Mount Kenya the technological capacity of man has devised an irrigation scheme for rice that supports the equivalent of nearly 500,000 pounds of biomass a square mile. But over much of Africa there are extra people appearing twice as fast as extra food. The new nations of East Africa are fortunate so far, since there is little outright starvation, though malnutrition afflicts at least half the children. One wonders how these people keep healthy at all with the sort of meat ration that outraged the British during the war, as much milk a week as an American has for his daily breakfast, and a single egg a month.

All depends on how many more places there will be at the table. These lands have population-growth rates to rival any; in fact, some observers suggest the population explosion that the world has seen so far is nothing as compared with what is to come; and these communities of East Africa will be exploding with the best of them; which is why conservationists will find more support when they give attention to too many people as well as to too few bongobongo birds.

Conservation is now finding itself embroiled with some of the most fundamental problems man has ever tackled. It is running up against perspectives that show which things count with extreme urgency and which things count first. During man's existence in the past, whether 500 years or 5,000—for the most part only 50—the problem has been solved by default: there just weren't materials or know-how available. Now there is a new stage, even if it is disguised under new default. If man is the first creature to decide his own evolution, and the rest of the earth's as well, this is the first time he has really *had* to decide, the first time since he lived by the Olduvai lakeshore. It does not amount so much to a further stage of evolution as a series of revolutions in a single outburst: a multi-revolution on a scale with the greatest of the past, even the emergence of man himself. (If there is one revolution it does not match, it is the emergence of life itself.)

It is against this kind of scenario that conservationists are reviewing their efforts and starting to speak accordingly; well might it be said that all else is emotionalist clatter. Ecologists as well as economists are questioning ends and means, and in East Africa an appraisal is being made of just what sort of agriculture is best suited to a tropical environment. This is no more than appropriate for what is still as much a pioneering region as it has been ever since the European explorers first set foot here over a hundred years ago. The latter-day explorer sweats in sun and safari shorts (no pith helmet—that was as exotic an irrelevance as the mind that went with it), and he traverses the land with a high-precision instrument in his hand and a high-precision mentality to go with it. The day is passing for the agriculturalist who preaches temperate-zone notions with intemperate enthusiasm, who visits the wilderness country and sees not the last great migrations on earth but a migration of tractors, who does not glimpse the dawn of creation in one of its final appearances but wants the last curtain call over with so that he can get on with the waving wheat.

Not that many such areas would be markedly good for wheat. Kenya averages twenty bushels an acre, scarcely the minimum to be profitable. The Masai highlands with their steady rainfall can reach thirty bushels an acre, sometimes even the world's better rate of fifty. Now there is talk of extending wheat down onto the plains. The first cultivated lowlands have run to twenty bushels an acre: what will happen in the drier country?

Above: This is a familiar scene throughout much of East Africa: as farmers run out of land, the forests fall. Despite more progressive efforts at family planning (not the same as population control) than in most parts of Africa, these East African countries have such a long way to go before their death rates drop as low as most of the developing world that they are likely to lead the largest population explosion in history.

Right: The Nilotic Luo people around Lake Victoria show much the same swift emergence into modernized agriculture with their neatly demarcated plots, and also the same hangovers from the traditional way, notably the hedgerow palisade around each extended-family homestead. Mass irrigation schemes will help, as will hybrid grains: will they help enough? The dynamic changes taking place here are of interest to any visitor; there is now a start toward encouraging safarists to go and see for themselves.

Wheat brings on plagues of quelea birds, ready to do just as thorough a job on the landscape as locusts. Tanzania has been using high explosives, even flamethrowers, to combat the quelea swarms; yet after knocking off 500,000 at a single blast, 70,000,000 in a season, and at least 500,000,000 over a period of years, there may still be more than ever.

Africa's soils are more vulnerable than most. If East Africa is a place where there is hardly any more west to be won, the remnant should not be won at the end of a battle where the spoils are a dust cloud to darken the sky for a thousand miles, as happened in another continent only two generations back. Nature in Africa usually displays a vigorous character: it can turn out frail and submissive enough when you get your hands on it, but it resists all too rapidly when it is raped, even if at other times it resists in a seemingly demure manner without complaints loud enough to be heard soon enough.

These are regions, however, where there need be little conflict between prosperity and posterity. All depends on how you go about it. The methods of your neighbor, which nowadays could mean your neighbor around the back of the world, could be as much use as doing what your forbears did. On the present time-scale, with its telescoped intensity, your father may be as little "with it" as your grandfather's grandfather. A better way would be to follow the best techniques available for your area at your time. If the immensely fertile soils of Kikuyuland can be persuaded to produce two or even three times the half-dozen bags of maize per acre it is so far producing, there will be room enough for other creatures in the East African environment. But will better methods proliferate as fast as the Kikuyu? When a Kikuyu eventually finds he can have better than only the present three chances in four of surviving to school age and that he can hope to survive beyond the ripe old age of forty, there will then be more Kikuyu, many more. In a community where over half the people are under sixteen, it is not much good moaning about developing nations and their birthrates. Even at two children to a family, the slowdown would not be sufficient for a long time: the new parents are already born. In any case, when it comes to population increase there are few nations in the "advanced" world that are truly advanced; and when it comes to overloading the planet, not just Kikuyuland, there are few to equal those affluent communities with their compulsive urge to use up every piece of raw material anyone offers around the earth.

People in other parts of the world had plenty of time to accommodate to the population explosion following the agricultural revolution 400 generations ago, and adequate time to react to the population outburst following the Industrial Revolution ten generations ago. But combine the impact of both revolutions, and you have something far greater than the sum of the two: a genie that takes some getting back into the bottle. The population explosion that is upon the world, which has been called the first real one and will certainly be the last one, is rarely as explosive as in East Africa. If these peasant farmers have not achieved more in their first ten years of going it alone—although far more than their opposite numbers in early Britain achieved in a hundred years—it may be in part because they have had to adapt in a decade to the medical advances of centuries. Nor have they had overseas possessions as an escape valve for their excess people, or any industrial resources to accommodate a concentration of their populace in cities, or any cheap sources of raw materials from colonial territories.

Thus far has man come from his days as man the hunter. The last ten generations have seen changes as great as all those before them, but they hardly compare with the one just passing, and that one hardly compares with a mere quarter-generation of the present time. What will tomorrow be? And the day after tomorrow, what will that *have* to be? It will have to be a new story. It will mark the final parting of the ways between man the hunter-gatherer and man the modern marvel, or conversely between man and his survival problems today and the man-ape with survival problems of earlier Africa. New tactics are required for fresh perspectives. Some people say that better methods for Kikuyu farmers do not need to be discovered, they are already there, if only enough people will learn about them. This requires an act of imagination on the part of the peasant as great as the effort that is not always within the scope of the tourist who looks out over croplands of East Africa and sees nothing.

In any case, if the techniques of the new agriculture are available, some Kikuyu people are no more enthusiastic about change than are farmers in other lands. Some enterprising spirits are already moving ahead; those who do not keep pace are like the farmers in Iowa who produce less than half as much as their neighbors. In the Maragoli country near Lake Victoria there is intensive use of the good earth, rivalling Kikuyuland with eight bags of maize an acre, thereby making these peasants some of the most productive in Africa. But if the full techniques of modern maize-growing were brought to bear, the crop could be increased four to six times—the soil here is even richer than in the Kikuyu hills. Yet the

Maragoli farmer is no more likely to move on to hybrid maize than is his counterpart anywhere else without a good deal of waiting and wondering first. It does no good talking to him about how the food problems of East Africa cannot wait, or about what he can do for gross national product. No more than it helps to tell his wife what she can do for gross national product by having fewer than six children. If all the smallholder maize-growers in Kenya were to turn to hybrid strains as the large-scale growers have done, the country's crop could be doubled. This would mean more food for empty stomachs, more surplus for export earnings, more land left for other crops, more land for land-seeking indigents—and less pressure on the "idle" lands of Kenya's wildlife country.

It is a pity, meanwhile, that more visitors do not go to see the extraordinary achievements of Kenya not only getting to its feet but ready to run the race against any fair rival; and not only, of course, to see what factors will allow a few spots to be spared for wildlife, but to look at a spectacle as remarkable as any one could hope to see. There has never been a time when a new community came into being so rapidly, nor when it can be witnessed so easily. Like Uganda, Kenya has been prospering more than most countries of black Africa. It has a fine array of services—health centers here, dispensaries there—surpassing most of what one would see throughout much of the continent. There are also fewer than 1,000 doctors for over 11,000,000 people; and if that is only a poor proportion of what many a nation outside Africa can show, it is vastly more than Ethiopia. It is not so surprising then that Kenya should be the first black African nation to launch an official birth-control program, especially when it found it would have twice as many children finding no place at school by the time today's child grows up. In a mere month one can glimpse the range of problems and prospects that constitute a whole history elsewhere. For all that an African trail can be bumpy and hot, there are few experiences to equal the safari into the seventies that these African countries are embarking on.

If East Africa is a land of dreams to some, and a land of practical potential to others, it is also a land where both can prosper side by side. Above all it is a land where the technologist can take on what may amount to his greatest challenge, the fitting of human beings to their environment in a manner to insure a better future for both. But he cannot do it alone, not in a developing land. Here is a project every person around the world can share in—and hardly a single person hasn't heard for years how things are going by default: not enough cash. Foreign aid has been small enough to be unnoticed by the donor and not large enough to have much effect on the spot. It was trifling in 1960 and less in 1970. From the people in Britain, who have never had it so good, the gesture has never amounted to more than the equivalent of a few drinks and cigarettes for a man who spends an average of over $200 a year on such requirements, yet still finds it hard to make ends meet. Total aid in 1970 was less than the margin by which Britain's affluence becomes more flatulent every couple of months. Kenya is fortunate among the emergent world, receiving four times as much aid as the average, but from Britain it gets half a pint of ale and deep regrets. It is a country that is doing as much toward self-help as any in Africa, and it is a country that has been described by its chief agriculturalist as periodically "wide open to famine." People in Britain spend over $30,000,000 a year on ornamental shrubs and window boxes, while some of the most magnificent environments ever to appear on earth could be safeguarded for a fraction as much—forever. It is curious that a nation with more prosperity than ever (and allegedly looking back on lost influence) should become so inturned; fifty years ago it was spending ten times as much by proportion on what was then the developing world.

The United States currently spends $40,000,000 helping people to choose among fifty sorts of puddings (and then regret its waistline), but cannot bring itself to do more for a country that has not gotten around to pudding at all (and often has an equally regrettable calorie problem). The United States national income shows an increase each year equal to the income of all black African countries put together. And if aid is questionable, then trade is something else again. During the 1960s the drop in prices for primary products from emergent countries allowed advanced countries to "save" $7,000,000,000, while the prices for manufactured goods dispatched to emergent countries went up by a profit margin of $3,000,000,000, leaving the ones holding the heavy end of the stick finding it heavier by $10,000,000,000 (as much as the total aid from international, public, and private donors). Far from increasing their support, the advanced nations might consider making a start; nobody need call himself a conservationist without considering what he is contributing. To be a United States supporter of African wildlife is to drink Tanzania coffee rather than synthetic substitutes (even if they taste better), to use Uganda fabrics rather than artificial fibers (even if they cost less), and to use Kenya pesticides, pyrethrum-based, rather than DDT-type alternatives (which are non-biodegradable anyway); it is to do all these things, and to live with the consequence of being daily too busy to support these developing nations and their developing problems. Putting out crumbs for the birds has nothing to do with it, anywhere.

East Africa is a land for the farseeing man who looks out over the plains and sees wilderness, as well as for the farseeing man who looks out and sees farm fences. It can be progressive without a progressive uniformity such as is spreading across the earth. The conservationist does not have to "put up" with the technologist; rather, he should welcome him as one who can save the wild world. East Africa could grow modern, and more than modern, while retaining its pristine panoramas—precisely by retaining its pristine panoramas, some would say. The protein potential of the savannah wilds offers a breakthrough in food production to rival hybrid maize in Maragoliland. Game cropping can hardly be "against" agriculture when both are harvesting the bounty of the earth.

The prospect of shifting ancient lands onto new pathways is a prospect to fire every side alike. The hours and eras of the long African day have something to tell anyone who listens. To some listeners the history and prehistory show only that Africa has been a wasteland waiting for them to arrive. Which is precisely why conservation needs to be presented for what it is: something that keeps Africa Africa, and makes it more Africa, and brings it to its African place in a modern world in a manner that will count for something tomorrow without leaving a rundown environment the day after tomorrow. Conservation makes a mistake if it brandishes its banner merely for wild animals alone—not only a tactical mistake, but a mistake revealing an outlook more limited and inviable than that of the diehards. There is still a notion going around that conservationists want to turn East Africa into one big animal park. The people who look at these African landscapes and look only for wild creatures might wonder how far they themselves are an endangered species (if not an endangering species), and whether their passing would be mourned. If conservation is popularly concerned with wild Africa, it is not any the less concerned, and properly concerned, with Africa as seen by the agriculturalist's eye. It is Africa as seen by the discerning visitor, whether he sees it in the primeval plains of Masailand or the crop country of Kikuyuland. It is Africa whole.

BUFFALO

Late afternoon is a good time to look out for buffalo. Like many another large animal they have to keep out of sight and sun for much of the day. During the early morning they straggle along the river banks, in and among the thickets. They are immersed in mud most of the day and only emerge toward evening. They are not such ooze addicts as hippos, and they take their slimy leisure more casually than elephants—no rolling around in the stuff, just a soak, for hours on end.

Top: A buffalo herd shows a strong sense of cohesion: when one moves they all move. But much of the day they do not move at all, lying inert in their mud patch.

Bottom left: The safarist watching a buffalo herd watching him will spot many a shiny muzzle probing in his direction. A pity he cannot be out in the environment, paying as much attention to the breeze as the buffaloes do. Then he might have more sense of what it is to be a buffalo, though the buffaloes might show that they view things differently too.

Bottom right: The buffalo is another large animal that must suffer from the heat during the day. It has no thick skin like a rhino, no flapping ears like an elephant; but it has a unique stomach system, allowing it to spend long hours in a mud bath while digesting its last stomach load.

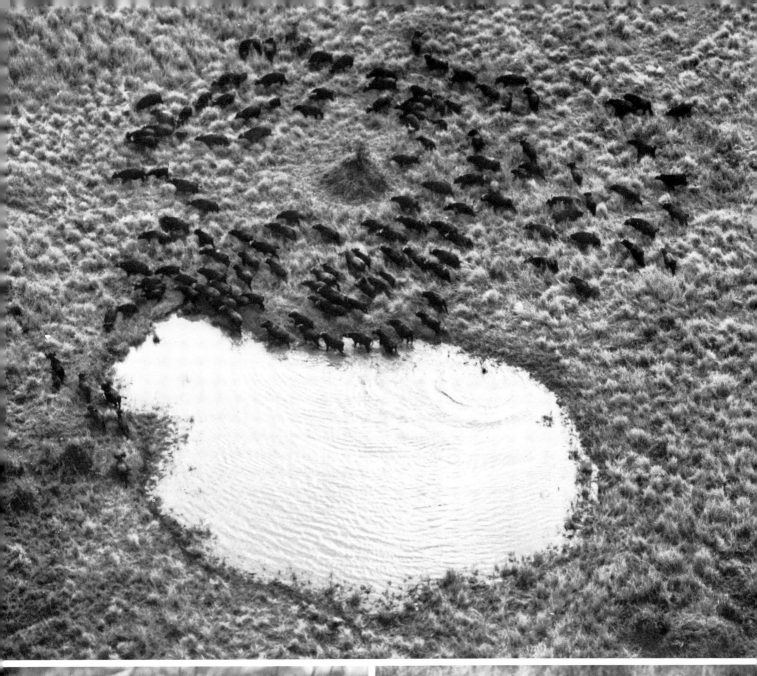

For all their size, buffalo are often timid creatures. They also like each other's company, and it can be difficult to approach a herd with all those eyes watching and all those muzzles probing the breeze; crack a stick and scores hear it. If you arrive on their scene quite openly and watch from a distance until they get used to this apparition, you can tiptoe nearer in your vehicle and end up a few dozen yards from them. They gaze at you intently—they are inquisitive as well as shy—until something upsets that communal curiosity. A sudden movement and they wheel as one to gallop off with great conviction. Fifty yards away they slow down to have another look. Not satisfied, they are the ones to come closer this time. Soon wild buffalo and safari spectator are eyeing each other at a few paces. The noses probe toward you and what you stand for: you feel there are two worlds straining in each other's direction, even if not communicating very much. Behind those lowering horns there are lumbering creatures not so indifferent to you as elephants or rhinos. But as the herd slowly unwinds from its collective tension, a fresh peace spreads over the scene. Who would ever think a buffalo is ranked among the most dangerous of animals? Then another unexpected move—or not even that—and they turn with some single-sense impulse to reveal massive backs and gallumphing gait.

Their timidity makes them not the easiest creature for researchers. Insofar as buffalo get through a lot of grass, however, and insofar as they may number many more than all the antelope put together in a place like Queen Elizabeth Park, it is essential to find out how many buffaloes there are if you are to know what is happening in the park. In the Serengeti there are 40,000 of them, not to be compared with the throngs of wildebeest and zebras, but they supply much of the lions' diet for large parts of the year. These Serengeti buffalo are especially wild. A resident researcher, Dr. A. R. E. Sinclair, has found it hard to get within a quarter of a mile of them on the ground. He can get closer by air but leaves them more disinclined to stay near any mechanical being. He has tried marking them with paint, dropping bags of the stuff on them from the air. A few he has drugged and festooned with collars. In Queen Elizabeth Park Dr. Jeremy Grimsdell has found it easier to get close, since the park and its environs are not a habitat for wild creatures alone; the buffalo have long been accustomed to humans. A skilled observer can tell a male from a female at quite a distance, and even roughly their age. The female is often browner, not as glossy-black as a bull. Her horns do not dip down in such heavy sweeps, nor do they meet in a large boss in the center.

All of which are not too easy to pick out when the buffalo are massed in a huge herd. The calves are mingled in the middle, yet this is just what the researcher must watch out for—how many young ones are surviving from how many arriving. The smaller herds are easier to investigate, easier to approach, too, since they are largely bull groupings, not so suspicious with no offspring to protect. These bachelor herds are not what make buffalo society work, not nearly as much as similar segregations among, say, wildebeest; they seem to stay segregated without the regular turnover one would find among Uganda kob or hartebeest. Lions kill twice as many male buffaloes as females, which might help to infuse fresh blood, but it is chiefly the smaller groups of bachelors that take the brunt— they are less watchful, frequently older and hence more decrepit. A large herd of buffalo in their prime can give lions a hard time. They even show some coordinated defense against a pride, far more organized than, say, eland; a single bull buffalo has been known to stand against nine lions, and stay standing.

A male is mature at four years old or less, but he does not enter the privileged ranks of the breeders until he is at least twice as old. Just possibly he could pass his whole life and never know what it is to be a full male buffalo, so strict are the breeding hierarchies. One or two males may maintain dominance within a herd of a hundred or more females, with forty or fifty other males accepting their regime. This is stratified society to beat most. If the watcher stays for half an hour, he can soon spot who's who. The leading males stride supreme through their herds, a swath of authority opening up on either side of them as younger males show a suitably subservient attitude. They rarely need to assert their rank, and you might have to watch for years before you see a fight—although it is not all that rare to come across two males who have locked their horns and find themselves unable to disengage: they may remain like that until they find themselves starving. Sometimes the social standings among the herds allow for more males, sometimes they are exclusive. Sometimes an outsider is allowed to join the system and wander off again later; sometimes he is forcibly driven out, if not actively repulsed when he first appears. Possibly the pattern varies according to the time of year, since the number of bachelor bulls can vary from one in ten to only half as many. Yet Queen Elizabeth buffalo breed right around the year with only vague peaks at particular periods. In Serengeti there are two separate calving seasons for two separate areas, one to coincide with the shorter rains and their better grazing, the other to coincide with the long rains—but the second one falls in a section of poorer rain overall, hence less rain, and more unreliable, even during the main rainy season. At other stages, when the grass gets dried up, the bachelor bulls find themselves outside the main assemblages: are they driven out, and, if so, for reasons other than breeding? Much depends on the area. As with so many creatures of the African savannah, you cannot say that what happens to the buffalo in Serengeti one year is also happening to the buffalo in nearby Manyara—or will happen to the Serengeti buffalo another year: what if better rains bring better food for all?

The bachelor herds are so small and loose they can hardly be called herds; they are more a bunch of perhaps half a dozen bulls that stick together for company or convenience. The main herds are a different matter. Anything under 100 can often be considered a splinter group. In Serengeti there are dense mobs that total up to 3,500. Each herd has its home range. The area may overlap with a neighboring herd, but they stick to their particular stamping grounds for years on end. In Queen Elizabeth Park the range usually covers only three or four square miles, since there is plenty of water on every side (a buffalo can get through half a dozen gallons of water a day), whereas in Serengeti the area may total ten times as much, even though only a portion is used, the stretches along the occasional riverbeds. A herd has its particular watering places and resting places: all is regulated if not routine. But the larger the herd the farther it has to wander to find food for all its numbers. A large aggregation not only eats more, it tramples more. This is when "density-dependent" factors set in as soon as a poor year comes along:

A cow buffalo can be picked out by its lighter horns; there is no strong downsweep, and no heavy boss in the center. It also tends to be more alert than bulls, if just as inquisitive: when it stands and stares, there is something monumental in that bulging shape and its bovine spirit.

Grass-burning, regulated and regular, is an integral part of Serengeti's conservation. It favors buffaloes as well as many other grass-eaters. The damage in the foreground is the work of elephants: the broken branches supply fuel for a hotter burn, which may mean the end of the entire tree. Scattered trees across the plain provide not only refuge for leopards, but shady spots for a range of creatures, allowing more of the savannah to be used, particularly by larger animals, such as buffaloes, that tend to overheat.

the calves cannot take the trekking to and fro, and disease takes its toll—a buffalo may have up to 3,000 ticks on it, together with other lodgers. Too little food and too much sickness means more predation. The numbers regulate themselves until stability is restored, as balanced and resilient as ever—if not more so. Buffalo have been smitten by epidemics that have taken off nine out of ten (though not all directly from disease); it takes them only a dozen years to restore their numbers.

A buffalo eats grass almost entirely. Occasionally an adult takes a few leaves from a bush if things are rough enough, and its mouth has grown tough enough. At the best of times it is a broad mouth, so not a very selective mouth. The buffalo cannot go searching among the separate plants of the grasslands for the favorite leafy parts of the more succulent grasses. It cannot bite much below two inches from the ground. It has to stick to the tops of tussocks in dry seasons, a boon to other creatures that would otherwise find these tougher grasses starting to crowd out the more palatable material. It is their readiness to accept what comes, coarse grazing or the most withered stuff, that allows buffaloes to range so widely across Africa. Every park has its grazers—zebras or gazelles or water-bucks—but many a park has only grazers of one sort and not another; or another one without a further one. Almost no park, whether swamp country or scrub, doesn't have its buffaloes. Buffaloes are not such choosy feeders as wildebeest, and so are less likely to eat a grassland to the last stalks of a preferred plant during a particularly harsh season. Wildebeest generally solve the problem by migrating elsewhere. Sometimes, however, there comes a stage when there is nowhere else to go. This is when the buffaloes show they are less careful feeders and less harmful. For all their "wasteful" ways they are more economical. During the millennia of the African experience—the African buffalo harks back to a parting of the ways from the Asiatic buffalo forty minutes ago in the long African day—their role has been worked out not just in reaction to the survival struggles among the various creatures that walked the land, but in reaction to the land itself. Land and plants comprise many different communities that compete and cooperate in a fashion not unlike those that live off the land. The feeders have supplied a "feedback" to the ground levels of their existence, thereby to the basis of the existence of the total community; which is much more than a community of everything that moves.

BABOONS

The day draws on. The various animals begin to make a move toward getting ready for darkness. Some go to where they can get food, some to where they can avoid becoming food. One creature that makes sure it is out of harm's way well before night is the baboon. The troop makes for their resting trees, or a rocky cliff area. Neither place keeps them completely safe from leopards or snakes, but it helps. It also helps if all the members of a fifty-strong troop keep close together so that they can spread the alarm more easily and give some defense to each other. They reach the overnight spot before twilight comes, and they often stay there until well after the sun has risen.

It is while they are on the way to their resting trees that they are easy to watch. They are less spread out. They are frequently moving as a definite organization, and they are indulging in the social activities that show what a baboon troop is made of. As Dr. Irven DeVore and Dr. Sherwood Washburn have revealed from their extensive research, a baboon has its primary existence within the troop. Outside the troop there is little existence of any kind: the physical side would be short, not to say nasty and brutish, in a way a baboon within the security of its troop rarely knows; and in any nonphysical sense life would be, at best, a miserable and languishing affair. Baboon experiments show quickly what makes these creatures tick. When they have been deprived of both food and companionship and are supplied with a choice of either, they make no hesitation about which they prefer: from the moment it is born a baboon hardly ever knows a time when there is not another baboon within a few feet. It spends whole portions of each day in activities that show how much it likes being with others. It rarely leaves the troop even for a few moments. If it gets hurt and lags behind, the communal life continues without it. A wild dog in the same predicament can depend on the rest of the pack to help. A sick lioness is supported by others. Elephants are renowned for their help to failing companions. But among baboons nothing must slow the smooth functioning of the social order. One might think that if the mutual-support system has grown so streamlined and efficient for those within the community it would surely succor those that fall a few feet behind it. But the baboons seem to find survival such a dodgy affair, small-sized as they are in comparison with most members of the wild, that they are often ruthless in assuring the well-being of the community. In major portions of their daily routine there is frequently little else that counts as much. Over the time of the African day since they first appeared they must have eliminated many of the tendencies that may have existed for a baboon to overexploit its capacity as an individual. If one baboon wanders away from the troop to try out its new "ideas," it might soon attract other creatures with other ideas about what a baboon is for. Some of the remoter urges to be a loner would soon be bred out.

This is where evolution and natural selection are at work not just through a single creature and its genes, but through the organization to which it belongs. The "survival fitness" of baboons has allowed them to proliferate, and to live in widely scattered environments right across Africa. There are baboon differences from one part of the continent to another, or between savannah habitats and forest zones in one particular region; as a species they have proved more "successful" than most monkeys. Their diet covers many items in a large number of habitats; more than that, their capacity for living on the ground as much as in the trees means they have come across a broader range of opportunities to exploit—which has led them to stay somewhat generalized, rather than specialized for the more adaptive niches of a tree-dwelling life. Their range across Africa covers an area that other monkeys would generally match only by producing several separate species. In fact, only one other primate has achieved a greater spread without "speciation," and he has specialized in staying general through his cultural adaptation as well as his biological evolution. At the same time, baboons have probably been constrained by the rather rigid requirements of their community-style existence: has it also inhibited the advancement that might have come to them had they been able to tolerate a whit more individualism? Baboons have had much longer than man to work out their problems, such as they are. They originated with the other monkeys in the Oligocene, 35,000,000 years ago, a good two hours back in the long African day.

As they make toward their rest trees a troop of baboons in the East African savannah broadly reveal much the same formation as they generally follow when they are on the move (though in different places, on different occasions, there are variations according to changing conditions). When Dr. DeVore and Dr. Washburn were making their observations they noticed how there are often a few adult males in front, though the less dominant ones. Behind come the females with half-grown youngsters. Then come the mothers with the smallest offspring, interspersed with the most dominant males—generally the real leaders of the group, even though they lead from the middle. In the rear come the other females with more juveniles, and finally other lesser males. From whatever direction danger comes, it always runs up against males. Whichever side is nearest is rapidly reinforced: the females scamper away a little in the opposite direction while the males carry on at a steady pace, leaving the danger confronted with a solid front of males. Even a leopard will hesitate. In fact, the senior baboon, knowing it has support if need be, might even launch a daytime attack against a leopard, or at any rate an attack display. But the senior male does not rule the roost by force of bodily strength; more likely it is force of personality. Or, more likely still, it is a collective force of several other elderly males. The younger ones might be more powerful, but they are not as attuned to living and acting as a united group. They do not generate the same cohesive action as is generated by established authority, even though this "establishment" may consist of males well past their prime or even toothless old creatures. The air of authority means more than muscle, but the junior males have their part in providing the first line of defense. A male at the height of his power can be quite a sight when he puts on a show. He ruffs up his neck mantle to make himself look bigger than he really is. He bares his teeth, and those three-inch canines are longer than those of any other creature of similar size. But the vigorous young male is no immediate threat to the central hierarchy of dominant males, the "senate," as Dr. DeVore so aptly calls them.

The whole structure is constantly reinforced by gestures toward the older ones. There is a range of appeasing moves to indicate how thoroughly the lower rankers accept the status quo, even if they don't altogether approve of it. They approach the dominant male with their backs turned. This is not a gesture of supreme indifference or rudeness; just the opposite. The older male might stress the point by slapping the "presenting" junior. If the subordinate cannot avoid looking at the superior baboon, it gives a "grin." While this fear grin may be an extension of the screaming expression, it could also be similar to the one used by rhesus monkeys when they are especially submissive. The trait may have arisen originally as an expression of displeasure: the animal tasted something it did not like, and the lips were drawn back. As a reaction it was more a form of protection. From this it extended to situations where the animal was in pain or in fear: hence its use by one baboon when it approaches one higher up on the social scale. In their attempt at "smiling flattery" the baboons have gone a way toward adapting the grin to an expression of greeting. As a pacifying maneuver it works well. The dominant baboon is mollified. All is settled, all is stable again. Everybody accepts everybody else for what he is.

In fact, there is very little fighting among baboons. There may be outbreaks of clamor, but they are mostly mere noise. If there is a particularly furious squabble, the adult males promptly dash over to restore order. The submissive gestures and the responses bring everything back to normal. Baboons, like most other well-weaponed animals, have built-in safeguards to keep them from turning on each other. Everything is given over to defusing antagonistic impulses. As primarily ground-dwellers, baboons have to be aggressive as individuals to survive; within the troop they have to damp down their aggressive tendencies if the group is to survive. They constantly find themselves confronted with sources of "competition"—food or females—but they do not go so far as to demonstrate hate for each other in any instinctive fashion. War against their own kind would be as much against their own nature as against all nature. Feeling anger is as frequent a phenomenon as killing in anger is rare. Yet toward other creatures baboons have quite a repertoire of forceful responses. Not only is there the armament of their canines and their social system to support them, but they have an aggressiveness that is not usual among monkeys, and a body build to match. At a splendid eighty pounds a male is much larger than most monkeys. But then, these savannah baboons are not like most monkeys: they have largely abandoned the tree-ranging life. They must be able to defend themselves on the spot: no good being able to swing off into another tree if there is not a tree within hundreds of yards. Hence the long canines; hence the long jaw or "dog face."

But there is little point having strong teeth and strong jaws without strong shoulders, in fact, strong structure all round. Gone is the lithe, long-limbed build of monkeys that have stayed in the trees, where they must be agile and light enough to move along slender branches. When need be, a baboon is more combative than many another creature of like size. Even a female baboon is as aggressive as the biggest tree-living monkey, while not having canines nearly as long as the male baboon's, nor half his bulk. She has less of the wherewithal for fighting—her task is not to defend the troop (and given the protection afforded by the males, there is presumable evolutionary profit in females with smaller bodies, and the more petite appetites that go with them). The patas monkey is even more of a ground-dweller than the baboon, and the male patas is twice as big as a female; the same with gorillas, which are almost entirely terrestrial. Chimpanzees spend part of their time in the trees, and the male is only somewhat larger than the female. The vervet is perhaps more of a tree-dweller than any of them, and the male is the same size as the female: no protection of the troop is required in a community that finds its first line of defense in the tallest tree.

Toward other troops the baboon is tolerant enough, if not much more. The range area of a troop of eighty members amounts to several square miles, from two to twelve. No matter if it overlaps with another troop or several troops. They all go their own way while feeding, though when they arrive at a water hole there is some rubbing of shoulders, especially if several hundred baboons arrive at once. But if troop members mingle with each other, they do not mingle their activities nearly as much. Breeding mixups are largely out of the question; some troops become so inbred that an observer can tell which baboons belongs to which troop during the melee at the water hole, so distinct can the face patterns become, even the curl to the tail. Occasionally an infant may go and play with the foreigners, but it runs back as soon as its own troop is ready to move on; occasionally, too, an adult baboon will transfer to another troop—and even back again.

As evening draws on, the baboons make for the overnight trees, probably the same trees the troop has used day after day, month after month.

The three or four miles of daily wandering brings the baboon troop up against other animals. If a rhino marches through the troop, they just step out of the way. They are equally casual toward elephants: they sense what is what. They like to stick close to impala when there are any around because antelopes have a better sense of smell and hearing. The impala in return seem aware somehow that the baboons and their alert eyes can help them; perhaps they even rely on a certain amount of protection from all those muscular males. An impala herd with baboons nearby has been seen to stand its ground when three cheetah appeared. The normal response of impala would be to make for the horizon. These just stood and stared as the baboon leaders shrieked defiance and took a threatening step or two toward the intruders. The cheetah rapidly retreated.

Throughout the day the troop attend to the business of feeding. Their diet consists of various plants and insects. Occasionally they seize a newborn gazelle fawn before it can run properly; a vervet is not beyond them, either. They go in for some scavenging. But despite suggestions that baboons show an appetite for meat, they are remarkably little inclined to go looking for it: they leave a leopard's kill untouched, easy though it is to spot in a tree fork. Dr. Washburn has seen four lots of baboons come across a kill carcass and ignore the meat scraps to be picked up from the remains. Nor have baboons had much incentive to adapt toward a scavenging life. Their troop area is so small that they won't often find a kill in it; and they have neither the nose of hyenas nor the eyes of vultures for picking out leftovers. Predators make most of their kills at night, which is when baboons do anything but wander about; and if they come across a carcass during the daytime they perhaps sense that this is a dangerous area to go interfering in (primitive man developed projectiles and similar sophisticated technology to make robbing lions a safer and more profitable prospect). But the baboon diet is so wide in other directions that they feed off 200 different types of food and more. Perhaps their varied needs led them to venture out of the trees in the first place. That bulk takes a lot of feeding, which means a lot of wide treks around the home area.

But if feeding seems an incessant affair, the baboons pause frequently for grooming. They groom each other pretty much whenever they feel like it (although so central is this social function to the community's workings that, as Dr. Tim Ransome has observed, a baboon sometimes feels itself obliged to groom a higher-echelon member of the troop whether it really wants to or not). This is a particularly pleasant activity for the females. They groom their infants, other females, or some of the larger males. In this society the male sometimes does not have to exert himself to keep a select number of females on hand, though at other times he may run up against some degree of competition. The females often make their preferences clear, particularly for the leaders. There is little sexual bond working in the community, contrary to what was once suspected. Baboons have evolved customs that serve as lubricants between the rigid divisions of the social structure, and this accounts for the importance in the daily routine of grooming. One baboon lies down and another parts its hair, nibbling out the lodgers, smoothing over the fur. The baboon undergoing the treatment reveals its pleasure at proving so eminently acceptable. As Dr. DeVore succinctly puts it, human beings gather in groups to converse, and baboons gather in groups to maintain social relations in their own baboon manner.

However much the baboon seems to have left the trees to its ancestors, it is far from being completely a ground-living animal. As compared with a patas monkey, it is still too dependent on trees to contribute much in the way of ideas on what makes a tree-dweller turn toward the ground and a new mode of life. But, more than the patas, in other aspects of its daily round it shows how it has abandoned the strictly plant-insect diet. This is a pattern once followed by an ape that abandoned the fruits of the forest and took to flesh-eating, not only leftovers from other hunters but food of its own killing. These ancestors of man gradually made their way out onto the plains. They became upright. They were the only creature to adopt that particular right-angled foot formation that allowed them to follow a path to fame and fortune. After this stage there was no going back to the trees; those feet would never again be any use for hanging onto branches. A baboon, on the other hand, cannot walk properly at all; rather, it hobbles along. Some observers think this new bodily feature ranks second only to the expanded cranium; or possibly third, after the adaptation that allows the cranium to develop more after birth than before (the other way round for baboons), and so demands a protracted period of utmost care from the parent. The brain grew larger in response to the demands upon it. It extended to wider fields of experience, which brought increased demands again: greater demands, greater brain; greater brain, greater demands. Meanwhile, the structure that allowed the human female to walk upright left her with an anatomy unable to accommodate a larger skull before the infant was born. So the changes took place in the infant rather than the mother, creating a situation where an infant could be helpless for a long time and still survive. This meant that the female of the species had to stay at home while the male went hunting; which required a home for her to stay in. From these innovations there grew a way of life that produced a creature as dominant as all the others put together, dominant not only in terms of its society but also through the expertise of each individual; and largely dominant over all the rest of the animal community combined.

Those people who think that man developed along the lines of the carnivores, and the social carnivores at that, rather than as a precocious primate, point out that a home or den where the female can look after her offspring is more the custom of lions and hyenas than monkeys and apes; a baboon mother carries her infant with her wherever she goes. But there are various aspects of baboon living that nevertheless throw light on how man evolved during his periods of learning to live with his feet on the ground. Some authorities go so far as to say that one should ask not so much how other primates are like us but how we are like them. Nevertheless, the points where man overlaps with apes and monkeys, even in the early formative stages when man was still a roaming hunter before the time of agriculture, count for little as compared with the aspects where he has quite clearly gone his own separate way. Besides language and locomotion and the pervasive intelligence that marked early man, there were traits of sharing and cooperation within a wider community that long ago set man apart as unique. He may already have revealed those qualities that some say are the finer marks of *Homo sapiens*, whether based on altruistic impulses or not. At the same time he may have been revealing those other unique features of human conduct that do not reflect so flatteringly. However one views this phenomenon, man of 2,000,000 years ago was a tool user if not a tool maker. A million years ago or a little less he had become a skilled hunter. Hunting required scores of square miles. A band of twenty Bushmen of the present day may use 400 square miles. Baboons can get by at thirty to a square mile, whereas hunting man would probably rate one individual to five square miles, sometimes a great deal more depending on how much prey was around. A short while back there were perhaps only 10,000,000 of these hunting humans in the world, but 40,000,000 baboons in savannah Africa alone. Man's distribution in Africa may have been something similar to that of lions with their hunting terrain: was primitive man likewise territorial, and for the same reasons—social breeding space as well as food supply?

Baboons eat insects; there are plenty of those in any small area. Animals the size a carnivorous hunter needs are not as plentiful. Moreover, the largest animals require many hunters to overpower them, which again means a degree of cooperative living. A mound of meat has to be stored somehow and somewhere; further planning for the future. Baboons take no thought for the morrow (nor do they have fear for the future). Primitive man probably kept his clan's hunting rights inviolate. But defending a patch of land cost a lot of time and energy, not to mention defenders. Eventually the groups of hunters must have learned to keep the peace together. The first moves may have arisen through setting

The young baboon receives constant care most of its first year, long after it has lost the black color that makes it an object of interest to the rest of the troop. This period of protection is far longer than in many creatures, such as the zebra, though it is common in monkeys and apes. Conversely, it is not a fraction as long as for a human infant, which, by standards of the wild world, is born helpless.

The infant baboon can ride jockey-style after the first few weeks, but it has to be able to cling on underneath after the first few hours. It is altogether a more advanced infant than the primate man, whose development must take place within the offspring rather than within the mother. A human infant arrives pretty premature, though its brain swiftly expands several times after birth.

up affiliation ties. In the face of the regional realm, however, foreigners were foreigners; baboons by contrast do not mind if other troops use their range (though a "core area" may be sacrosanct). Baboons leave their sick to manage as best they can; man had "homes" where the injured could be tended by other members, just as the mothers and their completely helpless offspring were protected by the same social system. Man was able to break out of the old evolutionary patterns that were largely limited to the passing on of genetic "knowledge": he could pass on stories and traditions, stores of information on how the world worked and how it could be made to work better—for him. No monkey has ever got beyond the most rudimentary vocalizations. In large measure a baboon troop is sufficient to itself for breeding, but man's communities learned to look for mates outside their own confines, with all the advantages that had for expanding genetic combinations as well as pooling ideas and accumulating knowledge. Baboons hand on what they "know" mainly within the troop. Among man, with his extensive mixing of resources, both biological and cultural, there would be a far more favorable chance of a favorable specimen evolving.

Within this social nexus man relied on custom and knowledge of "the best way of doing things," an advance permitted by his skills at language and his powers of conceptual anticipation. A creature that makes a throwing weapon for the hunt would be different from a chimpanzee that fashions a grass stalk to fit the hole in the termite mound half a mile away. The second is responding to a situation it can see, however far off; the first is reacting to the "stimulus" of what happens the day after tomorrow, perhaps several horizons beyond the next one. Man's ancestors on first descending from the trees may have learned how they could ward off dangers of the new environment by throwing sticks and stones, just as some monkeys and apes do now. Perhaps they threw them in the first place as a sort of extended threat-display, until they found how well they worked when they hit the target. Apes and monkeys can learn from experience, but they have little power to transfer the knowledge to other occasions, to shift the significance along a slot or two in their daily living. They do not reflect on the past and use it to plan the future. In all their food-gathering and fellow-living they are bound by the present. It is what suits them. They have devised an integrated life-style from which one might say they derive an integrity of their own. What they do goes beyond the demands of mere existence and aims more toward the business of living. The watcher can decide how far it is a way of life to which the animal's whole being gives consent. Baboons are conservative by nature, which leads to a life that can seem humdrum and repetitious, fixed on every side by particular habits. A man can vary his routine if he really wants to, not only by going to Africa and seeing the scene. Yet one might wonder how far humans have got beyond a vague hoping that tomorrow will be a better day, while not doing overmuch about it today. There is many a difference between man and his origins. But it is not altogether helpful to say that man is descended from the apes, at least the modern apes (and he is closer to any ape than any ape is to a monkey). Although he shares ancestry with chimpanzees, it is still very remote. Insofar as man is an ape, he is the only ape to ask what sort of ape he is.

And yet, and yet. From such stock as produced baboons sprang the forbears of man. Where and when is still a problem beyond man's exploring brain, whatever his faculties for communicating and speculating. It seems likely the whole thing took place at some recent moment in the long African day, within the last hour, possibly the last twenty minutes. A few clues are to be found in a baboon troop. Their behavior is not as raucous or random as it seems. It takes only a little while for a discerning watcher to pick out signs. His eyes may be no sharper than a baboon's—in fact, a good deal less, since he does not have to read the language of the bush every moment of the day. His senses of seeing, hearing, and the rest have not advanced much beyond what the monkeys achieved 25,000,000 years ago. They, too, have stereoscopic vision, binocular and in color. This represents a great advance over most other creatures the safarist sees during the African day. But the antelopes and lions live on the ground. Only creatures that have to run along a swaying branch or swing from limb to limb have developed the acute eyesight that is characteristic of the primates. The spectator's brain is far larger than a baboon's and many times more complicated, but the extra gray matter is almost entirely taken up with reasoning processes, together with memory, associative powers, and speech, all of which help him to go beyond a physical world into a world of abstractions. It is this capacity for conceptual consideration that permits the spectator to uncover some of the secrets of baboon society.

But he won't get far unless he looks at these animals for what they are, creatures of interest in their own right, instead of a species that regrettably failed to reach the heights of a more advanced being.

AMBOSELI

Amboseli Reserve, on the Kenya–Tanzania border, has a backdrop that is Africa at its elemental best. Sheer out of the plain soars Kilimanjaro—no foothills, no introductory ridges, just straight up to 19,340 feet. Outside Africa it is surpassed only by the Himalayas and the Andes and a few peaks in Alaska. By late afternoon the summit snows emerge from behind their cloud bank again, to dominate the savannah in every direction.

The ice caps help to feed the swamps of one of Africa's most remarkable wildlife areas. For several miles along the northern foot of the mountain a lush green marsh stretches through the arid scrublands. Around this oasis live animals in a variety and concentration hardly equaled elsewhere. Not that the oasis is wholly dependent on the glaciers—only a little, some say. The summit does not receive very much rainfall (or snow), a mere six or ten inches. No major rivers flow off Kilimanjaro's flanks as compared with the dozen that stream down Mount Kenya and the Ruwenzoris, nor is there any bamboo zone such as rings the other mountains. Probably the forest belt supplies most of the spring waters to Amboseli. Yet the massif of Kilimanjaro lies in Tanzania, so the lifeblood of Amboseli flows from a foreign land. Tanzania has plans for the forests encircling the mountain's foot, but few plans for consulting with Amboseli.

Moreover, the swamp area has been not only a necessary refuge for wild animals, but a less-than-necessary refuge for Masai cattle. Earlier in the day the visitor may have come across huge herds of livestock on their way to other watering places nearby. Trailing clouds of dust, they plod their thirsty way. Unlike many savannah animals that get by on very little water, a cow needs five gallons a day. Amboseli's volcanic soil is light and friable, highly vulnerable to the erosive action of cattle hooves. As the herds march across the plains each day, more of the precious covering blows away.

Amboseli's oasis is only a tiny fraction of Kajiado District, the size of Massachusetts. The cattle herds of the area's 60,000 Masai (eight to a square mile) range from 200,000 in hard times to three or four times as many, with huge hordes of sheep and goats; the limit the land can reasonably carry is somewhere in between these two extremes. Twenty-five years ago vaccines were brought in to eliminate the natural restrictions on unlimited growth. Extra areas had to be opened up for bore-holes. It has never been the Masai practice to excavate wells, since they scorn digging in the ground, but they do not object if white people do it for them, just as the lesser tribes sometimes did. Overgrazing soon sets in. Along the eastern approaches to Amboseli the traveler passes through an area marked on the map as "somewhat desertlike"; at certain seasons of the year this may seem an optimistic description. Within living memory there have been good grass plains here, even woodlands. But the communal way of Masai life has allowed everyone to graze his cattle pretty much where he wants, which has militated against individual responsibility for specific areas. Now there appears to be a start toward better stocking methods; it has taken fifty years to come. If it helps the livestock, it will help the wildlife too, since a regenerated habitat will mean less competition in places like Amboseli.

For years the stock and the wild animals have experienced a daily confrontation at the Amboseli watering points, with victory going to the cattle. It looked as if there would soon be no victory for anybody, only a dust bowl where no creature would want to go, Masai or wild animal or tourist. The Masai claimed they had nowhere else to go. The wild animals could claim the same, even more. Amboseli ranks as one of the wonders of East Africa, if not Africa entire. It is a place where you can see lions, elephants, rhinos, buffaloes, cheetah, hippos, and a dozen types of antelopes—all in an evening's tour. The central sanctuary is too small to support this array of wildlife and the Masai herds as well. The Masai could get by on wells and watering troughs installed a few miles from the swamp area. During the years of conflict they were offered massive sums, as much as a quarter of a million dollars, to withdraw from the wildlife refuges, but the Masai would scarcely consider the idea. They feared their land would not only be put to an alternative use, but that by subtlety and subversion it would be lost to them altogether (and the record of the past seventy years gives them fair ground for complaint). A recent offer sounded especially suspicious; it would set aside the central 200 square miles as a national park, in effect removing it from Masai tribal territory. Whatever the Masai think about the merits of Amboseli, they saw this as the thin edge of the wedge. And the cavalier way the proposal was handled did not help matters. People bearing generous gifts arrived from beyond the seas. They wanted to help (was their ready check not proof?), but they wanted to conclude the matter as quickly as possible and get off to the next threatened area. They did not even have time to go and talk with the Masai who were most directly affected, those on the ground at Amboseli; instead they spoke to the satraps in the district head-

Tourists in Amboseli have long rivaled the Masai as chief ravagers of the grasslands, since vehicle wheels on the volcanic soils can be as destructive as cattle hooves. A safari truck taking a shortcut between tracks may be accounting for forage worth a fiftieth part of a zebra. Just as bad, the close shadowing of lions, such as is shown here, leads to so many kills missed that the cubs starve.

quarters a hundred miles away. If they had had time to take tea and counsel with the twenty families concerned, things might have worked out differently. Since then the attitude of the Amboseli Masai—as they would emphasize to anyone who bothers to go and sit in their village and talk about cattle and rains and grass and at last get round to the main business of the day—has been that they will not be pushed around; and as good a defense as any against being pushed around is to step up their intransigence.

As in so many spheres of conservation anywhere, it is not nature with which one has to be resourceful and patient, but human nature. It is all well and good to say that biological problems should have biological solutions, but in the end the answer is generally going to be a political one; so you may as well go along with it from the start, especially when you are dealing with a Masai, who is as political a creature as any. A more realistic proposal

is for a "Masai park," an area where humans are excluded just as from the national parks, but which the Masai themselves would set apart from the rest of their lands as a wildlife refuge. To a Masai, land is land; it is not a convertible asset.

In any case, there are plenty of places in the world where cattle are grazed, but only one Amboseli. There is much talk about the interests of "people": which people? The area has a few hundred Masai and already 70,000 visitors a year (and a new lodge will go far to double the number). The cattle are not particularly noteworthy specimens: it is the exceptional beast that is worth more than twenty dollars. Already Amboseli is earning more than it would if it were given over to cattle, even under the finest ranching methods known. It is now producing $150,000 for the district council, as much as the rest of the region altogether, while for the national exchequer and its indirect revenues the area earns almost $1,500,000—all this from a mere thirty square miles, the present central

portion. The proposal for a minimum viable unit would extend the central sanctuary to 200 square miles. Protected for tourism, it could triple its earnings—which is money indeed in Masailand.

For a long time the Masai remained unimpressed by talk of the world's heritage and what was at stake. To suggestions that tourism was paying for schools and dispensaries, and that there could be amenities behind every bush if they withdrew their stock from the central area, they responded that they could hardly appreciate the benefits accruing from tourists when the funds disappeared into the coffers of the local council far away. To the man living on the spot and wondering where he could take his cattle tomorrow, or whether he would be met with angry words, albeit foreign, from the strange white people in cars with their strange passion for lions and giraffes and zebras, Amboseli must mean a good deal: did these foreigners have difficulty watering their cattle? The dust swirled and Amboseli blew away. The more's the pity, because the Masai are not usually unreasonable people, merely conservative and circumspect.

It was only a few years ago that funds became available for an ecologist to look into the problems of Amboseli. Dr. David Western started on the basin around the swamps, an area of volcanic soils, not only friable but alkaline—which means an area that supports only a few species of grass, in some parts a single one, with only a third the grass cover of the savannah country a horizon or two away. This is not only an impoverished eco-system, but a young one as well, a few thousand years old, a mere half tick on Africa's clock. Any major ecosystem takes a long time to expand before it can grow more complex, more productive, more durable. Still, this one was managing all right until veterinarians brought in rinderpest vaccines in 1948. Cattle have probably been in the area for ages, but it is only in very recent times that they have multiplied enough to put a brake on the infant ecosystem. In the fifteen years before 1960, they increased four times over, until a drought brought them crashing to their 1945 levels again. But after the unusual rains of the 1960s, twice the normal ten or fifteen inches, the cattle recovered to 20,000 by 1970. They made up three-quarters of the 90,000-pound biomass per square mile, an utterly inflated amount (in Ngorongoro Crater the cattle are likewise considered a problem, but they make up only a tenth of the biomass). As the years go by, Amboseli has fewer and fewer wildebeest and zebras, already less than 8,000. There are also 1,000 or so gazelles, several hundred elephants, and several hundred giraffes, plus a few dozen rhinos.

Rhinos in particular run up against competition from the goats, which are browsers; but they have far more trouble from reckless visitors. Many a visitor to Amboseli not only wants to see a rhino, he wants to see it as close as possible and then closer still. He wants the safari vehicle to charge it and see if the rhino will return the gesture, whereupon the hardy occupant drives off in a swirl of dust and bravado. Such visitors do as much damage to Amboseli as the Masai. Possibly the new lodge will hasten the end of the scene rather than give it a new lease on economic life. Either the vehicles will have to be kept down in number, or they will have to keep to the tracks (and in some parts the tracks themselves make up a network of thoroughfares to match downtown Nairobi). Certain visitors object if they are restricted in their movements: how can they get close enough to challenge the rhinos?

Outside the central sanctuary there is a plain where the animals, wild and domestic, wander out as soon as the rains start. It is a spacious area, twice the size of the 200-square-

Left: There are as many zebras as wildebeest in Amboseli—instead of the more usual two or three to one—which may reflect the stringy grass found there, better suited to the zebra's ability to digest rough stuff.

Below: Amboseli was famous for its rhinos. But the two with record-size horns have both fallen to poachers, as have many others, and the rest are finding themselves hard put to it to survive in the rapidly changing environment. Their numbers recently dropped by a third in only three years, though they might well recover if the tourists were to accept a fraction as much restriction as have the Masai.

mile eco-unit for the dry season. After observing the migrations, Dr. David Western, in conjunction with one of the finest wardens in East Africa, a Masai named Daniel Ole Sindeyo, has concluded that there will be no need to shift several hundred Masai a good way off, as was once thought, just twenty families for four or five miles. The Amboseli boundaries drawn by an ecologist's hand are less restrictive, and more effective, than the straight lines drawn by the administrators during all the long years of squabbling. The ecologist has been joined by other experts for the final planning stages: an economist to work out maximum money-flow, an anthropologist to insure that social stability reinforces the ecological equilibrium. This is what conservation must be in an area with more critical conflicts between more interests than anywhere else in East Africa. It is nonsense to see the situation as a conflict of "animals versus people." The factions are not so much diametrically opposed as ranged side by side around a spectrum; coordinated equilibrium is possible provided simplistic thinking is left behind. Nothing is "endangered" here as much as the approach of "easier" times.

In 1970 the central sanctum was enlarged by presidential decree to 150 square miles: not as much as was wanted, but far better than the disastrous situation it replaced. The Masai have agreed to pull back, leaving the inner basin to the tourists. Future tourists may nevertheless see an Amboseli of different form. This habitat, still in its formative stages, is undergoing changes that will continue even if (as has been suggested) the tourists follow the Masai into banishment to the edges of the inner zone, which would be left to recover for a season or two. Over the years it has been apparent that the splendid fever trees are in trouble. For a while the Masai—who else—were blamed. During the drought and flood periods of 1961 these trees first died of thirst, like the cattle, then of drowning—unlike the cattle. Then the blame shifted to the elephants in view of the massive modifications they are inflicting on trees throughout most of their range in Africa. Aside from pushing over trees (which do not root so firmly here in the shallow, dusty soil), elephants strip off the bark, allowing wood-boring insects to infiltrate. As the trees disappear, the undergrowth is less protected from the sun, and the rhinos find themselves on even harder times. There are spots where whole groves of trees and shrubs of fifteen years ago have disappeared; in some places it is not hard to imagine how Amboseli could soon be without trees.

Yet the culprit is not the Masai nor the elephants but the climate and what it is doing to the water table. The floods of 1961 caused lake levels throughout East Africa to rise and to remain high. In Amboseli, where the swamp lake has no outlet, the habitat has been developing a saltier surface. Plants that tolerate salt are flourishing, while the fever trees are failing. A few decades might see a shift to less salty conditions again—but it will not be a shift back; it will be an advance to a fresh scene, another step in the "successional" stages of the ecosystem's development. Amboseli is a long way from the more settled conditions of Serengeti's climax community, where the ecosystem has culminated in a state with little scope for further advance along natural lines for a while to come. Soon visitors to Amboseli will see far fewer giraffes, and perhaps hardly any rhinos, which have been Amboseli's specialty (they have declined by one-third during the last five years alone, a consequence of more factors than the poacher's spear). But the hundreds of herds attracted by the swamps will provide the tourist with spectacle enough—and there will still be the finest backdrop in Africa for his camera. All of which seems a lot more likely than it did yesterday. Then it looked as though the ecosystem of 2,000 years and the cattle of 200 years and the inflated herds of twenty years would spiral down to a final catastrophe of two years. It would have been a marvelously quick solution. Instead, there is now a solution of a different sort, of a splendidly enduring sort. What the Masai and their warden and the ecologist have achieved in Amboseli must rank as one of the great accomplishments of conservation anywhere in the world, in behalf of an environment that ranks well among the most striking in the world.

WILDEBEEST

Wildebeest are much the most numerous large animal in East Africa. When you see them in the evening, trekking in long lines across the plain, it is not difficult to imagine this. They move in these multitudes to safer grounds for the hours of darkness, looking for open country away from thickets and ambush. Or they may be on their way to different grazing, drawn by a recent rainstorm. The columns stretch right across the plain. As one line finishes, another starts. Over the rise of the hill there are still more streaming from one horizon to the other. Everybody knows there are a lot of zebras in East Africa, but there may be twice as many wildebeest. They travel in great armies, which the zebras do not, and this makes their numbers appear larger still. You rarely see 500 zebras together, but 5,000 wildebeest is an everyday sight in their own country, and 50,000 is not unusual at the right time of year.

For all their numbers, the range of the wildebeest is not all that great. Elephants are to be found right across East Africa, lions in most areas, giraffes in many, but wildebeest only in southern Kenya and parts of Tanzania. They are rather specialized in their diet, which has a lot to do with their limited spread, as well as their constant migrations (whether long or short). They are always on the move in search of the particular food they need. Most of the year there is an unending movement. In fact, a wildebeest's life is one long trek. A thousand miles a year is not unusual for the hordes living in the western parts of their range, notably the Serengeti. There are only 30,000 in the eastern habitat, and they do not wander so much. They cannot: they live in a part of Africa that they share with humans. Their range has been greatly reduced by encroaching human populations—even more by vastly expanded herds of livestock. In 1945 a part of the eastern range featured seven or eight watering points for the dry season; twenty years later there were only two. The rest had been taken over by cattle or dried up following general devastation of the surrounding country. In 1961, when drought hit East Africa, the eastern wildebeest died off by the hundreds, a third of them altogether. Moreover, the females became sterile for a year, deprived of the vitamin A they find in the new grass brought on by the rains. The western wildebeest were much better off. If there was no grazing in one spot, they had plenty of room to roam about and find another, wherever the slightest shower brought on new greenery. There was hardly any change in their numbers even though cattle in the same area died in thousands through not being able to migrate at will—they had to remain within herding distance of the Masai bomas. During more favorable years the overall breeding rate of the wildebeest in the eastern habitat is still only half that of the western wildebeest. The Athi Plains wildebeest, for instance, have less than a quarter of their former range to maneuver in, which means a sharply reduced level of nutrition. Some of them migrate into Nairobi Park at certain times of the year. They used to have several such migration routes leading north out of the plains. Now the main corridor has disappeared under tarmac, and the only regular movement is airplanes coming in to land.

Strangely enough, wildebeest seem to prosper off grasslands where grass is not only short and green, but not too thick on the ground. It has been found with sheep that too many stalks tightly packed together will slow them down in getting at the protein-rich parts they want; they do better on grassland of a "poorer" quality. It is much the same for wildebeest. A great deal more rain would not necessarily favor them, even though their habitat is often a semiarid region. When things are just right, the wildebeest grazing holds the grass back at the stage where it is succulent and nutritious. But one wildebeest on its own cannot do it, nor can twenty, and this partly accounts for their moving around in considerable numbers. If a population were to fall to such a low level that it could no longer maintain its grassland at an appropriate stage, it would be in danger of going under. Measures to safeguard dwindling wildebeest might have to go beyond protecting

Left below: Giraffe reaching up on tiptoe in Amboseli reveal how little there is left to eat at lower levels. Not that such a high "browse line" is the work of Masai cattle or goats. But goats by the thousand account for a lot of browse forage, which causes the few hundred giraffe—and elephants, too—to rely more on the higher food. In the long run, however, Masai livestock may not have been the primary factor in Amboseli's changes. The rise in the water table following the heavy rains of the 1960s has left the habitat more saline, eliminating plants that cannot withstand salty conditions, such as the fine fever trees. Changes in African wildlands often have obscure causes, which can best be tracked down, as David Western has done at Amboseli, by looking at the system overall, rather than by hurling imprecations at the nearest Masai cattleman. Even if all Masai livestock were removed from the Amboseli region (and tourists, too), much of the present vegetation would disappear—to be replaced by a different spectacle, since Amboseli, a "young" ecosystem, is still in early stages of successional development, a long way from the more developed climax communities seen in other parts of East Africa.

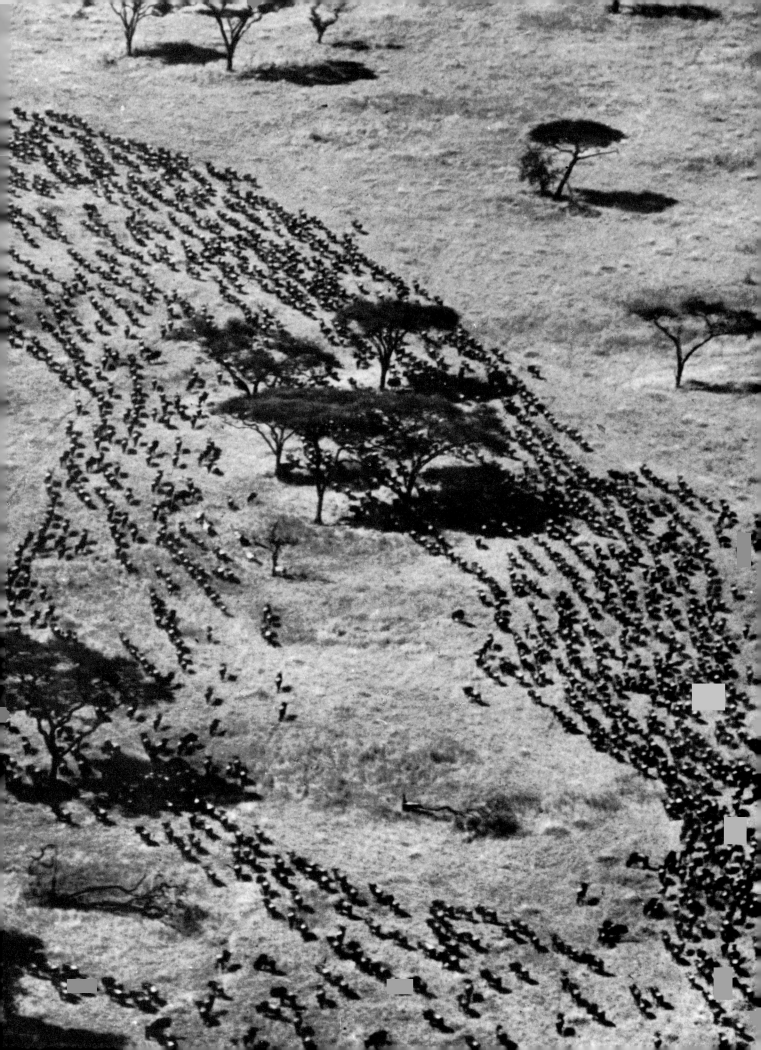

the survivors: they would have to be reinforced by extra wildebeest from elsewhere. The fresh grass they need means fresh rain. In the dry season an occasional thunderstorm sets the columns off twenty miles away. They need only to see the rain, or smell it, or merely hear it. When a storm falls right on top of them they take off in a sort of ecstatic rain dance, leaping and cavorting around the plain, sometimes bucking like broncos. They also like to drink every day if they can, once every three days at least. But some of their areas are subject to long arid spells. They have partly adapted themselves to this arduous environment by a recycling process that helps them to avoid disposing of nitrogen products from their bodies, thereby using less water for kidney outflow: they just send the whole lot round again. This means they can slow down the whole process by eight hours, which represents a considerable saving in body moisture until they can get to water again.

Since wildebeest are so dependent on the latest changes in the environment, they tend to be creatures with a highly developed social sense: an individual is not so good at spotting new grazing as a herd. And one wildebeest can't resist doing what other wildebeest are doing anyway: hence their great armies. A small group of wildebeest joins a larger congregation marching past. Large herds on the move change direction to follow still greater congregations trekking in a determined manner. While on the move they excrete a substance from their front hooves that smells like newly heated tar. The smell from thousands of wildebeest is strong enough for the safarist to make out the direction of a large herd on the move. Perhaps the deposits from these glands are a device for directing the migrations. One herd passes along the route at one time of the day (or week) and other groups pick up the trail later. But if the herd instinct induces individual wildebeest to follow the mob, it also causes them to stay put—if that means staying with the mob. A large herd may recognize a rainstorm in some inaccessible place such as over the edge of the Rift Valley. They sense it is beyond their reach (the wildebeest "remember" such things by following traditional patterns). Even though the younger wildebeest—those who do not "know"—may show a good deal of restlessness, they do not move off.

If the behavior of wildebeest shows strongly developed social patterns, there are still exceptions. Up to one wildebeest in seven at any one time may be a solitary animal; it is almost certainly a male. Moreover, the large herds of females and calves need new pastures sooner than small bunches of males, and they are keener to react to any fresh stimulus such as a distant rain shower. They are often the first to arrive at new grass. But whatever sex segregations arise throughout the year, the different herds come together in March for the rutting season. Over the next two months there are milling males and regimented females. Each male that is able to set up a territory uses a preorbital gland to mark out his space. He rubs his face or horns on the ground. Then he defends the space and tries to set up a group of females there. So long as he is successful in maintaining the female herd as a unit, it might amount to just two or three, or it might build up to fifty. Should an outsider challenge him, the intruder is met as soon as he reaches some invisible limit: a step beyond it, and the conflict is swift and certain. Not that there is any real damage. The males dash at each other with great élan, drop to their knees and wrestle with their horns. Then the two get up, stare around, snort, and return the way they came. Females are rarely stolen from a neighboring territory; rather, each male tries to set up his own group from scratch. During this time he moves about with a strange rocking gait, head held high. The posture is a red rag to another "proud" wildebeest, but as soon as one head is lowered and a normal canter is resumed the challenge is waived. Or the defending wildebeest may find that instead of half a dozen females straying into his territory, there are hundreds or thousands streaming through, wildebeest of all kinds, bent on migration. The male is torn between what he wants to do in a way no other wildebeest can do and his urge to do what all other wildebeest are doing. But either way he is engulfed by throng after throng. He may try for a while to maintain a territory on the march, but

Overleaf

Top left: When two male wildebeest joust over territorial rights the thump of their horns may sound a hundred yards away. But they do not cause any injury. It is all mostly a ritual, and it seems to serve its purpose: honor is satisfied in whatever wildebeest code is prevalent.

Middle left: Wildebeest gather at the watering points pretty much every day. While they wait to drink, there is a good deal of pushing and shoving.

Bottom left: In the Serengeti, one adult wildebeest in ten generally falls to some calamity or other during the year: some to lions, though probably only one in ten of the one in ten; hyenas possibly account for more.

Right: At the right time of the year the safarist in the Serengeti may see armies of animals trekking by in scores of thousands. This picture shows a cluster of white specks in the center; they are zebras.

sooner or later he is taken over by hordes in their hundreds, or—when the mob pauses to graze—he is usurped by another male.

This is a breeding pattern followed by the wildebeest of the Serengeti Plains. But there are wildebeest and wildebeest. Many of those at Ngorongoro follow different habits. Here there is hardly any season when the males are caught up in a migratory urge to take them from one horizon to the next (and the next) day after day. Yet within the Crater there are wildebeest that trek back and forth across the twelve-mile floor, and others that are much more inclined to stick to one spot. What counts is how many there are at one particular place, which varies from year to year. When there are a lot, they must keep on the move more, and when the numbers fall they settle down again. Hence, too, the differences in territory size. Some cover a patch thirty yards across, with others clustering around on every side, while in poor country there may not be a rival for half a mile or more. Moreover, many of these Ngorongoro territories are semipermanent. In the Serengeti you would not find the same male on the same territory day after day (or even hour after hour at the height of the migration), whereas in Ngorongoro the same patriarch could be occupying the same patch ten or twelve years later—and he stays there pretty well right around the year.

So what is a wildebeest? The Serengeti wildebeest can hardly be called "standard" wildebeest, for all that they amount to nine out of ten of all wildebeest in East Africa. They shift in their emphasis from year to year. When Dr. Lee Talbot was observing them in the early 1960s, their antics and movements might have been determined by the fact that there were far fewer of them then than the third of a million found by Dr. Murray Watson when he took a three-year look at them in the mid-1960s. By 1970 there were over twice as many again. It all goes to show that if you watch a creature at one time and one place and make comments about it, you are talking about one creature at one

At evening the safarist sees mini-migrations of wildebeest as they move away from their daytime grazing grounds to more secure areas for the hours of dark.

time and one place. Others elsewhere may be different. If you come back to the same animal a year or two later it may not be altogether recognizable as the same creature. Certainly among the Serengeti wildebeest the social mores have altered while the population has built up several times over what it was a few years earlier. They must have become more migratory, to continue being wildebeest at all. Not that this is what the archetypal wildebeest must have looked like, for all that the migratory urge is such a characteristic of the creature. Moreover, despite what the safarist sees at Ngorongoro, a wildebeest is not so utterly territorial as antelopes go. The marking glands on its face are rudimentary as compared with a gazelle's, for instance. But it is not such a primitive antelope either. It has achieved a development that few other antelopes have managed so successfully, the switch away from a forest environment—a move that some people think most antelopes must have had to attempt when Africa's forests were shrinking, before the spread of the savannahs. That was a hard shift, since grasslands are usually more arid than forests, though faster-flourishing at certain seasons. For the antelope coming out into a land of feast and famine, this difficult step could often be better accomplished at a gallop, a year-round gallop: those that could search and keep searching would live to another era. In this sense, as Dr. Richard Estes suggests, the wildebeest is nearer the more advanced bovids, those that have shaken off the ultra-territorial tendencies of primitive ruminants. The eland has apparently achieved complete independence from the sedentary strictures that lead to the territorial urge, since it can roam where it wants, even in the harshest environments. This could also explain why the eland maintains more or less equal numbers of males and females, as does the buffalo, the giraffe, and the zebra (none of them territorial): the males are not subject to the hazards of life in defending a territory; while the topi, the hartebeest, the waterbuck, both Thomson's and Grant's gazelles, the Uganda kob, the bushbuck, and the reedbuck (all of them territorial) often show only one male to every two females. If it is a sign of evolutionary advancement to leave behind territorial traits, the wildebeest does not stand somewhere in between the most emancipated and the least; rather it spans a good stretch of the spectrum, since it can adapt itself in both directions. Not that this flexibility will save the wildebeest of the eastern habitat much longer. They are hardly wildebeest. Their habits and traditions have been so constricted by the other inhabitants of their environment that they can scarcely follow the impulses that come to a wildebeest when it is doing what comes naturally. They are not yet man-made wildebeest, but they are well on the way to being man-conditioned wildebeest.

The breeding season takes place mainly toward the end of the rains in the first part of the year. Nine months later the calves appear. Practically every female can produce one calf a year, though once again there are variations from area to area. In Ngorongoro Crater three out of four females produce a calf in their first year of breeding and one every year after that. Something the same applies to the Serengeti wildebeest, but they undergo a fluctuation from year to year according to how much grass is available. A huge congregation of animals is more prone to annual variations than a much smaller number since they reduce their grazing more rapidly. In some years the rate drops to under a half what it is in a peak year. But in the eastern habitats there is hardly a wildebeest at all that is strong enough to breed in its first year. Only one in three produces a calf in its second year. After that they can do no more than reach a level that would be counted as "low" for the western wildebeest—only three out of four.

For wildebeest calves anywhere the first few weeks are difficult, but in the Serengeti there are still about 50 calves to every 100 cows after six months, compared to Amboseli with sometimes less than twenty—a reflection again of the malnutrition in the eastern areas. While the mating season coincides with the main rainy season, when vitality is highest, the birth season is synchronized with the early part of the second rainy season, from November onward. During the last month of pregnancy the female must have

enough grass to allow the fetus to increase by several pounds. With a total of sixty extra pounds to carry, she cannot flee so easily from a predator. She makes for the open plains, where she joins a large herd of other females, almost all of them in the same state. But this arrangement makes them dependent on larger supplies of forage available at short notice —a further reason for concentrating on the plains, where fresh food is not only more likely to be available but can be more easily sought out. There are some signs that the wildebeest female can delay her time of birth until things are as right as they can be. This control, however limited, is no more than is probably achieved by mice, pigs, and horses, and even to a slight degree (though equally unconsciously) by the human female. The wildebeest mother can certainly defer things for a few hours. If she is interrupted in the birth process she releases the pressure until the infant's hooves disappear again. If she can do that for a few hours, how about a few days? The rutting season is nowhere near as concentrated as the birthing season. There may be some mechanism for delaying implantation, or some hormonal control at the other end of the process making for synchronization among wildebeest females. It often appears that all wildebeest calves are born at the same time, within a space of two or three weeks. At one time the plains are covered with nothing but grown-up wildebeest, then a short while later there are small bleating creatures everywhere. This amounts to a formidable safeguard. Spread out over a longer period, the

By late day the last wildebeest herds are making for the open spaces on the plains. A calf born early the same day has little trouble keeping up.

calves might not survive the continuous onslaught of hyenas. As it is, the hyenas can become as gorged as they like and there are always plenty of calves left (though in Ngorongoro the 400-plus hyenas probably dispose of at least nine out of ten of the 3,000 calves born each year; while the 3,000 hyenas in the Serengeti, only one to every thirty calves in the mid-1960s, instead of one to every seven as at Ngorongoro, have been reckoned to take between one calf in seven and perhaps one in three, around 20,000 calves for the 3,000 hyenas!). The situation could also work out the other way. The first few wildebeest born are all taken by hyenas. Only after the main bulk arrives are the hyenas unable to keep up. This may not happen for two or three weeks after the first isolated arrivals. The process would have the effect of making all the wildebeest appear to be born at once. Moreover, it would act as a selective pressure against those wildebeest that are born "out of time." The surviving wildebeest would more likely be the ones to have accentuated the capacity for being born at whatever constitutes the right time.

When the calf first gets its feet on the ground it has four months of fine grazing conditions ahead of it. During this time the calf increases its weight four times. At ten days it can eat grass, though it doesn't really subsist off it for another three months. The mother's milk contains a number of immunizing agents, including a colostral antibody against rinderpest, which in some years can be a terrible disease among wildebeest young. After six or seven months, when the dry season is reaching its peak and the grazing is declining, the calves get worn down by constant trekking to and fro looking for fresh pastures. This is precisely when the early immunity wears off. Rinderpest or "yearling disease" sometimes swallows up nearly all the calves that have survived that far. At first the Serengeti calves amount to well over a quarter of the herds. An average of half the calves disappear in the first few weeks; half the remainder may be hit by some disease, and a further one in twelve or so falls by the wayside through drowning or getting stuck in the mud. In a single week in one recent season over 700 calves in the Serengeti drowned in a lake the herds could perfectly well have walked around. Only around one calf in five on average eventually reaches adulthood. But those that get through their first year have a good chance of living out a normal life. Full-grown wildebeest are not so susceptible to disease or other mischances, and they have a better chance of recovery.

The one mischance they won't recover from is a lion. It used to be thought that lions took a large proportion of the Serengeti wildebeest. Now it seems all the carnivores combined do not exert nearly so great an effect. In good seasons the herds swell. A survival rate of one in five among the calves is balanced by a total mortality rate among the adults of only one in ten, of which only one in three falls to the predators. Probably the herds themselves do something to regulate their own numbers. As long as there are not too many of them the wildebeest can congregate in moderate-sized groupings, big enough to afford protection but not too big for tolerable living. As the population increases the herds build up to immense throngs. During the wet season the herds are particularly concentrated. This is when the calves are born. Overlarge herds mean more movement to keep up with the grazing. More calves get lost in the milling mobs, more get broken limbs, more get crushed. The totals are stabilized again. These unfortunate consequences are likely to be more crucial limiting factors than lions and hyenas, but in the long run they amount to much the same thing, since calves disappear down the same hyena gullets before the story is finished. Whether the hyenas catch the calf on the hoof or merely find it on the ground, the outcome is the same. A calf that is lost will even run toward a hyena, looking for protection, as it will run toward any moving object—including a safari vehicle. But if there are enough hyenas to dispose of thousands and thousands of calves, what do they live off for the rest of the year? The answer seems straightforward enough: full-grown wildebeest. Nor do all those calves, especially the lost or trampled ones, necessarily disappear down hyena throats. Circling over the great herds are flocks of vultures, which might be better able to spot strays or crushed creatures. A good-sized vulture flock can dispose of an adult wildebeest in twenty minutes, so a calf would take them only a fraction of that time. Researchers who study wildebeest witness very few of these vulture orgies; they just don't arrive in time. Hence not many people have suspected until now that a prime agent in the whole wildebeest scene might be a creature as lowly as a vulture.

Yet what happens to all those wildebeest in normal times? One answer is that things never get round to being "normal." The regulatory mechanisms of a population are always fluctuating one way or another: they try to establish fresh balances in the face of a new set of circumstances. In rough terms one could say that a "stable population" of 350,000 or more wildebeest, as there was in the Serengeti in the mid-1960s, would be made up mainly of adults capable of breeding except for the 40,000 yearlings from the previous season (the males are often not allowed to breed until they are three or four years old because of the territorial system). That means there are at least 150,000 females capable of breeding. In a peak year they produce up to 140,000 calves. These newcomers could fall to 70,000 almost immediately. After disease and catastrophes there may eventually be no more than 40,000 again to survive as yearlings. Even fewer reach the stage where they enter the main ranks of wildebeest capable of producing more wildebeest. What chiefly fluctuates is the number of calves born and the number surviving the first critical weeks. If there had been a large population the previous year (a hangover from the year before that) but no exceptional rains to provide extra grass, the nutritional level would bring down the number of pregnancies to start with, and the calves born would be somewhat weaker. Unless unusual rain brings on sufficient grass to feed the "overlarge" population at its most inflated stage, the calves will be so much less able to resist environmental hazards such as too little food or too many hyenas. There can be huge fluctuations in the numbers surviving, from nearly 100,000 to as few as 20,000. From that stage on roughly one adult wildebeest in ten comes to an end somehow or other during the year.

So general are these generalizations that one can only come back to the starting point and say that what is known so far does not really allow for much generalization. A whole list of "resistance pressures" can be exerted by the environment to balance the reproductive potential of the wildebeest at any particular time. The herds in turn operate all sorts of mechanisms in their "density-dependent" manner. Rinderpest, since it is contagious, becomes worse when animals are packed close together. If the wildebeest starve in the course of a poor year, the rinderpest disease also starves; it disappears for a while, only to return at some later stage, possibly when things get "too good" for the wildebeest and the situation is ripe for another "crash." If the wildebeest do not fall to starvation, they fall to rinderpest; and the other way round. Or disaster arrives through some further agency that no researcher has tracked down yet.

If the source of this fresh disaster is far away, one wonders how it affects ideas about what constitutes a park with limited boundaries. A dynamic ecosystem must have dynamic boundaries. There is no simple process for fitting these phenomena into the tidy and static systems envisaged by human guardians of wildlife regions. If this is how millions of years and millions of trials with millions of errors have worked things out, then this is the way it has to be. In the long run the fundamental limiting factor is the environment in its entirety. Africa's limitless horizons are now limited in a way they never were when the wildebeest were adapting themselves to their particular form of life. On the borders of wildebeest country there are numerous predators, particularly two-legged ones that can take as many wildebeest in a single day as a pride of twenty lions could manage—or need—in a whole year. Poaching can still be an ecological pressure of importance. It is never a normal pressure as long as it is practiced on commercial lines. Man as a hungry predator is one thing, and the wildebeest have had to live with him for ages. Man as a hunter who takes a hundred wildebeest tails to sell as fly whisks and leaves ninety-nine carcasses on the ground is something else again.

But poaching is only one of many threats to the wide-ranging tract of wildebeest country. A greater one is the throngs of other people milling around the borders: the hoe is stronger than the spear, and fencing wire is worse than the poacher's noose. Not long ago there were approaching 400,000 wildebeest in Botswana and South West Africa. Now there are less than 30,000. The world is crowding in on the wildebeest world, even in places like the Serengeti, which has been ranked with the Grand Canyon as among the natural wonders of the world. Serengeti is not just a place, it is a world of living things as diverse and prolific as one can find anywhere. Central to the system are the wildebeest. They are creatures adapted to surviving in large numbers in a not too favorable environment. Their totals act as the fulcrum around which other creatures revolve, not just the carnivores but the other herbivores as well; the wildebeest ultimately affect all the other half-million animals of the Serengeti. This is harsh Africa and it is teeming Africa. It is Africa as few other places can be. It is—at present—the last main refuge of one of the most successful and balanced communities left on earth.

SMALL CATS

In their separate ways, the smaller cats are as interesting as the larger ones. A caracal is as specialized in its way of life as is a lion, and as different from a serval as a lion is from a leopard. The same goes for the civet and the genet, although they are smaller still and even harder to find.

The way to spot a serval is to watch for it in late afternoon as it leaps above the grass searching for its food. It listens for its invisible quarry, then tracks it down by a series of high leaps to see over the vegetation until it closes in on what it is after—a rat or some other small rodent. It is masterly at exploiting the ecotone border zone along streambeds or between woodlands and grasslands, where it finds a range of small creatures from more than one savannah world. But, like all the small cats, it has no stamina, and is limited to a shorter rush by proportion than a lion or a leopard. So it has to rely even more on surprise and instant attack. While a lion or a leopard usually hunts creatures of its own size or bigger, the smaller cats stick to prey half their size. Possibly there is not the same proportion of muscle in a smaller predator, though there is at least as much cunning and fierce spirit pound for pound, probably a lot more considering their nervous disposition and aggressive temper. They need it; they do not have the overwhelming power a lion or a leopard can bring to bear. Such small-sized cats have to kill more often and spend a much greater portion of their life in hunting; they have acquired whatever other characteristics they need to catch prey, which, in turn, is inclined to be more cautious and elusive than the larger zebra or wildebeest. A caracal has been seen to flush a group of birds from a grass clump and strike more than one from the air before they were out of range. Not even a leopard with all its speed could match that feat.

Unlike the larger cats, the small cats cannot roar. They can purr, which is something no lion or leopard can do. When their eyes meet bright sunlight, the pupils narrow to upright slits, whereas a leopard's contract to pinpoints. But they all show a common background in the faces rounded to accommodate muscled jaws. Their joint ancestry can be traced only a little over 1,000,000 years back. A few minutes ago in the long African day, or less, it is doubtful if there were any lions or cheetah or caracals or genets as they are today. The split-off occurred somewhere in Eurasia, when the forbears of modern cats ramified into thirty-odd different sorts. Eleven of them found their way into Africa and carried on with their development there. (None had much to do with the sabre-tooth tigers of recent times, which stemmed from a parting of the ways 20,000,000 years ago.) Since that evolutionary crossroads there has been no real fresh departure in the cat world,

A caracal, like other small cats, has more agility and faster reflexes to exploit that agility than a leopard; certainly more than what appears to be a lumbering lion. A caracal coming across a flock of birds on the ground can strike several of them down before they are all airborne. A leopard, fast as it is, may stalk several flocks of guinea fowl in a morning and not get a single one.

but rather a specialization of the more successful traits that have emerged finally as the feline predators of the modern world. Cats have always seemed competent creatures. The basic pattern that arose a good 40,000,000 years ago proved sufficiently suited to survival, with little change throughout all the revolutionary times of the Tertiary, when many of today's animals were undergoing constant modification from a series of starting points scarcely recognizable from those creatures that have emerged on today's savannah scene. The cats stayed much as they were: there were capable enough. Some grew huge and strong, some small and sinewy, some lithe and swift, but none became anything other than a clear cat.

Cats are like that. Watch a caracal and you sense a creature adaptable in a way a giraffe cannot suggest—or a gazelle. Other plains animals are stuck in their specific molds, suited for their way of life certainly, but not resilient or resourceful the way a cat is. A lion can turn to a giraffe or a gazelle equally, and a caracal can exploit a similar range of its own savannah spectrum. But a caracal is possibly more catlike—not just cat-sized—after the manner of a domestic cat, in that it is supple and speedy and altogether formed to fit a broader spread of its own world. You can imagine a lion coming on hard times, but scarcely a caracal.

WATERBUCK

By late afternoon the throngs around the watercourse are thinning out. A few hours later the place is deserted. Not much left for the safarist to look for. But there is one creature that chooses evening to make its way over to the river banks: the waterbuck. Most antelopes move further away from the thicker vegetation the nearer the day gets to dark. But the waterbuck makes itself a sleeping area inside a thicket. It returns to the same spot night after night. The thicket cannot protect it from a lion or a leopard, and if it always goes to the same one it seems to be asking for trouble. But waterbuck do not seem to be appreciated by predators. In much of Queen Elizabeth Park, where there are lots of waterbuck and not nearly so many other antelopes as in most parts of East Africa, only three waterbuck kills were recorded in three years. Poachers do not seem to like waterbuck either. Lucky waterbuck!

Lucky, too, in that its feeding needs do not take it far afield. In fact, it stays close by the riverine vegetation. It is a grazer and rarely browses at the trees along the riverside. A waterbuck is never found far from water, not more than a few hundred yards (it needs three times as much water as an oryx). This may partly account for there being so many in Queen Elizabeth Park, where there are great sheets of water in several areas. Dr. C. A. Spinage found almost fifty to a square mile on the Mweya Peninsula, but only half a dozen farther inland. The Queen Elizabeth waterbuck exploit a segment in the feeding spectrum somewhere between the hippo and the buffalo. Hippos eat short ground-clinging grasses, while buffaloes prefer tussocky stuff; the two together allow a whole mosaic to flourish for the waterbuck. A feeding combination of this special sort is not often found on this scale, but across the border in Albert Park there are as many as fifteen waterbuck to a square mile, together with fifteen buffaloes, a greater number of hippos, half a dozen kob and "half a topi." In Nairobi Park there are thousands of grazers but there is only a single river, so there are fewer waterbuck. Dr. M. Kiley-Worthington has found that the males occupy patches of ground that vary in area according to their ranking in the local hierarchy. The largest ones occupy a broader frontage along the river. A male with immense horns may cover the best part of a mile. (His confident bearing also makes him less ready to run from a vehicle, to the delight of the game-viewer.) A less competitive male has to settle for a mere hundred yards. Each territory stretches inland for a short way until it peters out into a no-man's-land that nobody is interested in. A male has to wait three or four years before he is sufficiently advanced to stake his claim. Guests at Treetops occasionally see a prolonged duel that shows just how lethal these conflicts can be. Males often make up only about one in three or four of the total waterbuck population. Many of the rest are probably killed off in struggles to reach the top of the pile.

Having established his boundaries, the male is as careful to observe them himself as he is to make sure trespassers do. During the day he moves about his estate in company with such females as want to spend their time with him, though they do this by their own "free will" rather than being forced. They gather in groups of a dozen, or occasionally as many as fifty. At evening they all set off for the river banks together. It is a social life. Compared with antelopes like wildebeest or kob, the waterbuck is far from gregarious, but compared with the lonesome bushbuck, it is a highly sociable being. The different patterns reflect the numbers of each creature. Kob and wildebeest are often found in hundreds if not thousands; bushbuck are hardly ever seen except as solitary individuals. Kob and wildebeest have apparently evolved their patterns of living to match their teeming populations. A wildebeest territory can amount to only a couple of hundred square yards. A kob may make do with only a few dozen. A bushbuck may occupy a fair-sized tract of land. Somewhere in between these patterns comes the waterbuck. It is less organized than the kob or

Far left: A serval has unusually large ears, as befits its way of life: it has to hunt at a closer-to-the-ground level than a lion. It often cannot see over the vegetation, so it must be better able to hear its prey. The ears rotate separately, covering almost 360 degrees at once. Not that the serval is confined to a strictly earthly existence; it frequently reaches up after low-hanging nests.

Near left: To get an idea of what the progenitors of modern cats looked like two hours ago in the long African day, one should take a look at an African genet cat.

the wildebeest, but much more so than the bushbuck; which does no more than reflect its numbers—which could, in turn, reflect its need to keep to limited stretches of ground close to water.

These are stable traditions. They allow waterbuck to stay in one place for a long time. You can go to some parts of East Africa and find the same waterbuck male as several years ago. Waterbuck are never so proliferant that they use up their food material until they have to move away for a season. Nor are they tied to a particular phase of the grass cycle by the midday heat, despite that thick coat. Oddly enough, this is an antelope that hardly varies its body temperature during the day any more than the watcher does; it loses 40 percent more moisture through sweating and panting than does an eland of similar size. Only in areas like Somalia or the Kivu lowlands, where temperatures are ten degrees hotter than in much of eastern Africa, do waterbuck seek the shade. In these areas the whole day-and-night routine is upside down. But wherever you come across a waterbuck it seems to have plenty of time for standing and staring: or just standing and being a waterbuck. Which the visitor might think it achieves becomingly.

FIRE

Toward evening the safarist may come across what seems an astonishing sight. He finds someone bent over a patch of grassland, setting it on fire. Far from trying to put it out—as should be the reaction of anyone seeing a fire in a park?—the arsonist is actually feed-

Above: Waterbuck never wander far from water. They seem well adapted to river-bank life, and approach the water's edge with little of the tension most wildlife drinkers reveal; a waterbuck in trouble makes straight for water, to plunge in up to its neck. But despite their daily need for water (three times as much as an oryx, more even than a cow), they are not especially fitted for riverbank forage: they rarely feed off trees or bushes.

Right: The horns of a male waterbuck are set at a better angle for inflicting damage than most antelope horns. And waterbuck sometimes go in for less of the ritualized pseudo-fighting than other antelopes: they prefer the real thing.

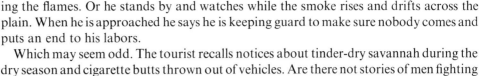

Overleaf: The man with a match in the wrong season can do more damage to wildlife than the man with a hundred poisoned arrows, and not just for a single season: this fire burned high up onto Ngorongoro Crater's walls, severely damaging the forest girdle and adding its injury to the crater's critical water table for years to come.

ing the flames. Or he stands by and watches while the smoke rises and drifts across the plain. When he is approached he says he is keeping guard to make sure nobody comes and puts an end to his labors.

Which may seem odd. The tourist recalls notices about tinder-dry savannah during the dry season and cigarette butts thrown out of vehicles. Are there not stories of men fighting grass fires miles long? He may already have come across stretches of plain blackened right across the landscape (which does not help his photographs). Fire is a good servant and a bad master. In skyline-to-skyline grassland, wouldn't fire be in complete command?

So ran the conventional wisdom in Africa. It ran for a long time. Fire was bad, it was all against the use of nature, open to the same flat condemnation as other "bad" agencies of nature, crocodiles or wild dogs or hyenas, even lions. To make its reputation worse, parks people said it was not only wrong in principle, but probably man-made in practice, and hence a mistake of the first order in pristine country. So emphatic have opinions been about wild fires in wild country that when a park warden nowadays wants to burn part of his savannahs for whatever good reason, he often thinks it best to take out his box of matches as late in the day as possible so as to avoid tourists and their appalled reactions. By morning the fire should have completed its work. In the park office will be a wall map with grid lines dividing the region into blocks, some for burning early in the season, some later on, some for burning twice a year, some once every two years. All these areas are confined by firebreaks that may be rivers or park roads (sometimes laid out with fires in mind as much as travelers) or stretches of eroded country; in other places the park staff has to go out and plow long strips across the landscape. Whatever the tactic, the strategy is a "burning question" all over Africa. Steadily and surely the idea is being accepted that fire plays a vital part in the management of wild areas. The matchbox is becoming a tool as important as the bullet, however crude both might seem. Fire has been a part of the natural scene for a long time, fire set off by fuel spouting out of volcanoes whose cones now dot East Africa. Lightning must have set off other fires. To primitive man fire represented warmth and dry living-space and food that was more manageable; it also meant easier hunting if he could trap his prey by sheets of flame. Whether man noticed it or not, those fires must slowly have had an effect on the environment. The conflagrations would have put an end to some sorts of vegetation and assisted others. They caused some seeds to germinate more quickly. They got rid of old tangles of vegetation and made room for new growth to spring up with each year's rains. In many places fires would help to spread the grasslands and the greater array of animals supported there—thus providing more plentiful food for the hunter. In other places fire would act in association with other agencies of the environment—rainfall (or lack of it) and herbivores with their biotic grazing pressures—to encourage bushes and certain kinds of trees. For thousands of years Africa changed its face in accordance with the periodic dictates of this purger of the environment. Stone Age man was using fire tens of thousands of years ago. Few actions over the whole course of man's existence in Africa have done as much to shape the modern landscape, even though fires have probably been ranging far and frequently only for a mere thirty seconds of the long African day. Eventually the more recent people of East Africa arrived on the scene, the immigrants of the last few thousand years. They had learned what fire could do to burn the environment to their more precise liking. All of which gives one pause: if the aim of the parks is to maintain stretches of Africa as they were before man-the-intruder arrived, then *which* man? The white man has turned the place upside down. Before him the black man had already altered Africa beyond the point of no return; and man before the modern-era African has marked his passing so decidedly that nobody will ever again see the vista he saw.

What fire can achieve over the ages is revealed in telescoped form in Albert Park in the Congo, where there hasn't been any for a long time. The official approach has been to keep wild lands unsullied by man's hand. Before the place was designated a park the

country to the south of Lake Edward featured rolling grasslands. Fires could come and fires could go. The landscape presented an array of antelopes and other herbivores, together with the usual carnivores. When the area was declared a park there were no more fires to keep back the bush growth, or to rejuvenate the grasslands. Open savannah gave way to scrub thickets. Brushwood shot up and animal numbers down. Earlier, the herds of kob and topi alone had totaled 25,000. Ten years later they had fallen to 4,000. Lions and hyenas largely disappeared with them. Not that every creature failed to benefit from the change. The area became a land for elephants to revel in, together with other bushland browsers such as rhinos or shrub-munching antelopes. These creatures never approached the former throngs, since browsers tend to be only a tenth as numerous as grazers. Additional elephants came in from miles around to benefit from the new paradise; by now, too, they were appreciating the protection offered by the sanctuary. They waxed many and strong as only elephants can. In less than thirty years 150 elephants became almost 4,000. The huge herds smashed down the trees and cleared out the brushwood and the thickets. The grass steadily returned. The elephants were loath to leave again because of the harassment outside the park. They did not give the remaining patches of bushland much chance. There could be no attempt to reduce them to more "natural" numbers; man could only stand and watch. As the elephants opened up the habitat the grassland revived and the great herds of antelopes flourished once more. The kob increased three times over and the topi four, while the buffalo responded even more quickly and increased their numbers twelve times. The wheel had come full circle.

Something similar is thought to have helped form the spectacle of the Serengeti Plains. The onlooker is struck by the sweeps of savannah grass surging from one horizon to the next, with not a bush or a tree to be seen. These plains may once have featured open woodlands, until the arrival of the Masai a hundred years ago or more. The herdsmen needed pasture for their cattle, so they started burning. The woodlands rapidly gave way to grass. Not long ago the traveler across the Serengeti could see sparse growths of trees along the few watercourses of the plain. Now they are all gone.

In other parts of the Serengeti the tale is similar, though not nearly so advanced. Possibly it never will go quite that far because the terrain is different, and so are the soils and rainfall. Over to the west, as well as northward in the direction of the Kenya border and beyond, there is bush country. A few hundred years ago there were probably thick forests, at stages when things must have been much moister. As a result of the feeding patterns of wild creatures and the intermittent fires that arose from natural causes—more "natural" than the Masai firemongers and their cattle herds seeking new grasslands and yet more grasslands—the thick forests gave way to cedar woodlands. In the Loita Plains the Masai clans became especially concentrated, overgrazing the area, then burning it and burning it to bring on more grass, however scant and short-lived. The woodlands were reduced to grasslands, and the grasslands to semiscrublands—hardly a balanced progression when the Masai herds exceeded the capacity of the habitat to support them. Degeneration was reaching its height when a natural pressure stabilized the stock numbers. Just before the turn of the century a series of plagues decimated the cattle herds (and the cattlemen as well). Overburning and overgrazing were brought to a halt, but the process had advanced too far for the grasslands to recover. More hardy growths moved in, woody plants such as the livestock could not use. The bush followed, leaving thin shreds of grass that produced hardly any blaze. Bush thrived in the face of less and less competition from the grasses. Another wheel had come full circle, though this time with some creaking, since the ultimate bush cover proved not nearly as flourishing and productive as the original forests. When the Masai had built up their herds again, they moved elsewhere to start off a fresh cycle.

Nowadays the Masai haven't changed their methods much, but they are running out of space to move into. They are pushing right up into the forests on the Mau highlands,

wherever they can set a fire going and bring on precious grazing for their herds. In places where the degeneration took place some time ago, one can look out over hundreds of square miles where most of the topsoil is gone, except where it is held by isolated patches of vegetation perched atop pedestals ten feet above the surrounding country. Such freak growths can be spotted on the way to the Mara Reserve, where one can visualize what this land looked like a twentieth part of a second ago in Africa's long day.

In the Serengeti there is a fresh fire problem now, this time in conjunction with elephants—that alliance so much more powerful than the effect of each working in isolation. There are only 2,000 elephants here, nothing as compared with the 35,000 of the Tsavo ecosystem. But there have not been nearly that many elephants in the Serengeti for a long time. In fact, this is hardly elephant habitat at all, and such herds as have arrived in the last fifteen years have been more likely trying to avoid harassment outside than seeking favorable forage inside. These few elephants are damaging considerable numbers of what limited trees there are: in some places over three-quarters of the trees have been barked or broken or felled, while in other places there are hardly any trees left between ten and seventy years old (these ancients are probably trees that caught hold during the late-century troubles among the Masai when grass-burning was forgotten in the face of other activities). What has happened to all the seeds that must have germinated in between but failed to grow? Many "trees" do not seem to get much beyond the infant stage; yet they are not infants—some are thirty years old. They are burned back each year by fire that spreads across the grasslands. The heavy rains and lush grass growths make

When grazing is sparse already, the zebras are confined even more by the efforts of a fire-setter who was merely smoking bees out of their nest but did not feel he was deriving enough benefit from wildlife to make certain the fire was out.

for plenty of fuel at the end of the dry season, admirable for fierce fires more capable of damaging the trees. The Serengeti wardens try to protect their trees by firing the grass-lands more frequently so that the burns are less intense. In the meantime the trees are developing stout root-systems that show many times more growth below ground than above. These trees are biding their time until a drought holds the grass back for two or three years. Then fires will not get hold, and the trees will have their chance. If they can once reach six feet they are safe from all but the hottest blaze.

Serengeti is a land of fire. It has been so for a long time. If, as is said, its vegetation amounts to some sort of a climax community, then it must be a "fire-climax": the spectrum of plants is wide but largely composed of those that are tolerant of fire or dependent on it. Some acacia seeds need heat to split their tough coats. Red-oat grass grows tall and robust under a fire regime; otherwise it becomes wiry and slender and flowers less profusely, or it gets crowded out by plants that have hitherto been held back by fire. Some people, however, think that over the long run fire must exert a degrad-ing influence. Of course, the Serengeti's conversion cycle is different from those of wetter zones in the temperate world. That does not mean it is less efficient, despite the sparse organic material in its soil. It produces more leguminous nodule-bearing plants: are they a sufficient counterbalance? There is not much microfauna below the surface to help build up the organic components of the soil—the organic material above ground goes up in smoke, and a covering of ash is not the same as a litter of dead plant material, even though it contains phosphorus and calcium and magnesium. On the other hand, fire could increase the amount of energy being brought into the system by stepping up the cycle of nutrients that assist in photosynthesis. Moreover, it is not certain that the amount of organic material in the soil is much different in burned-over territory from territory left unburned, however much experts suspect the worst. In fact, an area that is never burned might contain less than an area that is fiercely burned, and both of them less than an area that is burned lightly but often. A fire barely removes the total layer of vegetation that constitutes organic material in undecayed form, besides removing the barrier to fresh growth. Such nitrogen as disappears with the smoke into the atmosphere may be no more than is returned through rainwater, or is obtained by the unusually high number of nitrogen-fixing organisms such as legumes. Burning kills off the aerobic nitrogen-fixers but leaves anaerobic fixers undamaged. As the fire sweeps over, the soil does not heat up much below a fifth of an inch deep. On the surface the center of a burning tussock may soar to over 1,110 degrees Fahrenheit, but it cools off again five minutes later, so swift is the passing blaze—unless the fire is burning into the wind rather than before it, a factor of as much significance as whether there is any fire at all.

As the dry season spreads across Africa the fires consume the parched material. If an early burn has already traveled lightly across the country there will be plenty of vegetation left for later on. If there was a single late-season fire, then it will have been a regular bonfire, with as much as a ton of fuel an acre if the earlier rains have been good, leaving some patches of ground virtually bare. A short while later the first drops of the new rains strike this defenseless ground with an impact far greater than where there is some vegeta-tion left. Then a series of severe storms sweeping across the country can leave the bare earth beaten hard like concrete. The water scarcely penetrates, but runs off instead to feed plants elsewhere. More storms, and more impact-damage; little humus material is left in the soil to absorb moisture and get things going again. Erosion sets in. The bare patches spread ever so slightly. Next season, a faster rainfall run-off, and with greater force—more erosion. Rhodesia is now undergoing several years of "drought" even though the overall rainfall has, in fact, been slightly higher than normal. The ground has become so impacted that hardly any water remains in the soil. The rain streams off into rivers that become torrents, bringing on further disasters—floods. The balance is delicate. Once the system falls off center it shifts with accelerating momentum.

Finely adjusted factors such as these are what are in the mind of the park warden as he goes out with his matchbox. Does he want to maintain a particular kind of habitat and "freeze" it for a certain display of animals? Or does he want to achieve a greater diversity by inducing a greater mixture of grassland/bush-country/woodland? He can always elect to keep things at a "natural optimum" so that the whole mosaic keeps turning over: grasslands are switched to bushes and trees for a while, then on to grasslands again. Many of these possibilities are limited by climatic conditions, soils fertile and infertile, hilly terrain where grassland is less likely to flourish or may be less desirable. In addition, much depends on things as they already are, not just on how one wants them to be. If the rains have been better than usual there will be more grass, whereas if the rains have failed there may be hardly any new growth for the fire to catch hold of. There may be other considerations. The warden may want to protect a rare kind of antelope, a bush-browser, for a few years to build up its numbers. He may want to assist the scanty leopards in the area by fostering their stalking cover. He may want to help the cheetah by clearing open spaces where they can operate at speed. He may want to clear away the tangles of undergrowth so that he can help another of his creatures, the tourist, allowing better opportunity for viewing animals, or clearing ways into forest patches so that visitors can see what is inside. When poachers burn a patch of ground along the park boundary to entice antelopes over to the fresh green shoots springing up, he may promptly counterburn on his side.

Many of the great grassland zones of the world are thought to have been man-made—whether by intent or accident is scarcely to the point. They emerged as a result of man's actions, and there they are. Few grasslands are as extensive as those of East Africa, and none with such a variety of animals to be gazed at so easily. The grasslands of Brazil reveal far less wildlife. Across Africa there are three main stretches of grassland savannah: a belt running from west to east bounded on one edge by the Sahara and on the other by the Congo rainforest, a second running from north of the Kalahari eastward with an edge along the same Congo rainforest, and a third running up the east coast from the south to

A fire at the right time can achieve much for wildlife, provided there is enough moisture to bring the fresh shoots through at the edge of the rains. Within days there is scarcely a wild animal anywhere but on the blackened patches. When the rains start in earnest, this burned area will have a much better chance to produce proper forage for these grass-eaters. Conversely, elephants and giraffes don't benefit much at all when the brush gets little chance to sprout beyond its first few vulnerable seasons.

the Sudanese deserts. As Dr. Lee Talbot has pointed out, these three grasslands reach a rough meeting-point in eastern Africa, a focal intersection for savannah Africa, fire-formed. An African fire is a stirring sight. It sweeps across the land with an elemental surge, quick enough to clear and cleanse without destroying everything in sight. The animals step lightly through its path. It might strike the viewer as so powerful and purifying in its own place that it seems odd for man to claim that he gave rise to such a primeval force of nature. But he didn't; he merely applied what was already there, what had been a part of the long African day for ages before his own brief moment.

WILD DOGS

The late evening safarist has the chance of a sight that will fill him with fascination or with horror: a pack of African hunting dogs in action. Wild dogs are very few and far between; one can spend ten years in East Africa without ever seeing any. But if you go about your search at the right time in the right way it is not too difficult to track them down. During the day they lie huddled up in the shade of a thicket. They are sociable creatures, lying on top of one another. You might pass within a few yards of them and not know they are there. But at last light—as at first light—they are far easier to pick out than lions or leopards and other hunters of the plains. Wild dogs make no attempt to get close to their prey by stalking. They just run the creature to a standstill. No devious maneuverings such as makes a lion easy to miss at close range; no hiding in ambush such as allows you to get on top of a leopard before it leaps from cover. Wild dogs parade straight across the plain. When they sight something easy to spot from a long way, they run for miles.

An area the size of Massachusetts may contain only a dozen packs. Which is a mystery: wild dogs are ostensibly efficient creatures and need not starve. It is also a pity: wild dogs are interesting beings with an extraordinary system of communal living. If they are on the way out because of some disease or other factor, they will be a great loss. But not everybody thinks so. For ages they have suffered from a miserable reputation: they are rapacious and ruthless, they upset the game for miles around, they are a blight upon nature. This view says much about the speaker and little about the dogs. Sixty years ago there was "no official reason for attempting to preserve these animals." Since then they have been shot and poisoned wherever they were to be found. Now they have some sort of reprieve. It may be too late. If their actions were wholly destructive they would not be here at all. The wilderness is not like that. Nor do they compete unduly with other hunters. The only predator that is remotely similar in its tactics is the hyena, and nobody is certain how far the hyena is a full-blown predator wherever it goes. By their numbers and their rank in the carnivore chewing order, the hyena occupies a different ecological slot. And if there is no other member of the hunting hierarchy to squeeze the wild dogs out of the running, the wild dogs are hardly likely to exert undue pressure on any predator. They are differentiated, and they are declining.

An average-size pack varies from ten to twenty, though they have been known to top thirty, including young ones. Oddly enough, more males survive the first few weeks. One litter of nine was found with only a single female. In Kruger Park the males outnumber the females by three to two, a remarkable imbalance. One wonders how far it is an imbalance more apparent than real, as bad for wild dogs as it would be for humans. Are females unusually vulnerable, especially those with young—whether after birth or before it? The wild dog system supports incapacitated females better than do lions, much better than leopards, yet packs are occasionally found with no mother to suckle the pups. Many of the small dogs do not survive more than a few months. There are packs with a good half of the grownups under two years old, which indicates a very high mortality rate. Wild

As the dogs start to rouse themselves after the day's lie-up, they go in for a lot of rough and tumble. This seems to stimulate them to set off on a foray, and it may bolster the communal support system that will prove so central to what they do in the next hour.

dogs have been known to suffer badly from disease, but those in East Africa appear healthy enough. Or is their way of life so rigorous, entailing long miles of travel every day, that a stricken dog has far less chance of recovering than an injured hyena? Their communal system suggests that sick members are supported by the rest of the troop. Even after their persecution was stopped in parts of southern Africa their numbers continued to fluctuate wildly. They seem a strange phenomenon, and one that needs urgent investigation. No staff, no money, no time; soon there might be no time, ever.

The pack operates without a hierarchy. There is no dominant individual to set the trend for the other dogs—an unusual trait. Generally there is some adult, such as a male among lions or a female among elephants, that dominates the group. But wild dogs operate in a system where nobody is at the top of the pile, and nobody is at the bottom of the pile either. One particular dog may start the hunting process and be the first to reach the prey more often than the rest—but it does not try to exert any forceful leadership. Carnivores are equipped for violence—they have to be to stay alive—and often enough they use their weapons, or at least the threat of them, to establish a set of social standings where every creature knows its place. This goes some way to preventing fights that could eventually be harmful for all. But among wild dogs nobody seems to be top dog, and nobody leads a dog's life, though there may be some sort of hierarchy confined to each sex. A shortage of food or females could well set up friction, but it doesn't. Rather, there is an extreme inclination to appease each other, to go out of the way to be amicable and acceptable. While they are young the dogs indulge in a lot of fawning when they "beg" for food: they lick the face of a full-grown dog or nuzzle it until food is regurgitated. When they grow up they repeat this approach in almost every contact with each other with rituals that are likely hangovers from "begging."

As the long African day sinks away the dogs begin to stir. Their hunting technique means they have to rely almost entirely on sight. Smelling and listening are not for them. They set off at an easy lope across the plains. It may be a mile or more before any suitable quarry is sighted. At first they ignore groups of zebras or wildebeest in their paths, even gazelles. Nor do these animals show much alarm at the appearance of these so-called desperados of the plains. They stare from a mere hundred yards away even though there

is hardly a creature that could escape the dogs if they set off after it. Then, after a while, one of the dogs lengthens its stride. It makes for a particular group of animals; these marked-out creatures turn and flee. The pack follows some way behind. Soon they are strung out across the savannah, only a few of them maintaining the flat-out chase. The pursuit goes on across one stretch of country after another until the prey weakens. Sometimes a couple of miles is enough, but the chase may be two or three times as far. The dogs do not take turns to wear down the prey, as has been alleged. One dog keeps in front, and the others make a strike only if the prey turns or weaves. An escape tactic of this kind is often tried, since prey animals have eyes at the sides of their heads and tend to run in zigzags; or when they tire they change from outright flight to a series of dodges.

Which unfortunate creature is to be singled out at the start of the chase is not clear until after it has all begun. Perhaps the dogs do not pick out any individual until it is clear which is a weaker one. The hunter launching an attack from ambush might select its prey before it moves. When wild dogs get their eye on some individual, they follow it right past other animals even within closer range, right through the middle of herds that just stand and watch. Flee as it might, the prey is now often down to its last few minutes. It is not long before the leading dogs are snapping at its heels. Occasionally the wretched animal does something about defending itself. But if it is a gazelle or a warthog or a young wildebeest it is generally too exhausted and shocked to do much. Not that fighting back would make much difference: the end is just as rapid as with a lion, if not more so.

Left: After singling out an ailing wildebeest, the pack pursues it across the plain. If need be they can reach forty miles an hour, and keep it up plain after plain.

Middle: But this yearling wildebeest soon turned at bay. Not that it can do much about fourteen wild dogs. As soon as two or three get hold, it is gripped at every point . . .

Right: . . . with dogs tearing at its neck and sides and haunches. In under a minute it drops to its knees.

One dog rips at the skin of the stomach, another thrusts its head deep into the gap, the prey lurches forward and the contents fall out on the ground. The animal staggers, and in a moment it is in pieces.

By the time a lame dog arrives, or an elderly one, the carcass may be gone. No matter; it still gets its share. It lets out an especially effusive greeting and pushes its muzzle into the corner of a mouth already fed. It promptly receives a regurgitated piece of meat. Or if there is still some carcass it may try to get a place by showing extreme subjection to another dog. It flattens its ears, lays its head along the ground and makes docile twittering noises. Eventually the feeder feels obliged to forsake its place—unless it can prove itself more submissive than the interloper. The same goes for half-grown dogs: as soon as they arrive the adults are forced to surrender the legs, the head, whatever remains of the

Above left: Suddenly it finds itself released by the dogs. It staggers to its feet, to find itself confronting another hunter that has been attracted by the dogs' excited twittering.

Above middle: The lion bowls it over, and a single bite through the neck puts an end to the prey.

Above right: But whose prey? The lion does not have time to feed at the carcass before the dogs are back to dispute the quarry. They circle around growling, while the lion backs off from the carcass without surrendering it completely.

Below right: Finally the lion makes off, harassed as it goes. The dogs rip the carcass apart, and another vulture flies in overhead to join the dozen that have already arrived.

carcass. No member of the pack goes hungry. One for all and all for one: this is a community where it really works. After their instant meal the dogs start back to the den if there are young ones to go back to. Near the warren they are met by a guard dog or two. More regurgitation from the late arrivals as well. Still nearer the den the hunters are met by the pups. Regurgitation once more, even from the guard dogs that have just received their share. A piece of meat reaching a pup's stomach may have seen the insides of several dogs on the way.

Efficient hunters, these. They cover huge distances. If there is no den to go back to they may cover thirty miles a day during their foraging expeditions. Obviously they do not clear areas this size of other wildlife; nor do they seriously reduce the numbers of whatever they prey on. One pack was reputed to range over 1,500 square miles, and their effect could have been no more than that of other predators of similar size and numbers—or even of far greater size and far greater numbers. Sometimes a pack covers only a small area. One group of twenty-three stayed in a mere twenty square miles as long as prey was plentiful and only extended to three or four times that area when quarry got scarce. It was not that they drove the animals out, but that the migration season had come round again. Another pack subsisted in Ngorongoro Crater for several years while using only part of the 100 square miles open to them. Nor do wild dogs set up much disruption while they are on the hunt. An occasional antelope herd may be dispersed, but this could be no bad thing if it prevents the group's becoming isolated as a unit. In Ngorongoro Crater Dr. Estes and Dr. Goddard watched a pack for almost a year. They found the dogs caught gazelles on two out of three hunts, most of them full grown Thomson's gazelle males. If these were territorial males they would be reluctant to abandon their territories until the last moment and possibly hesitant about encroaching onto another's territory; which makes them more vulnerable than most. To make matters worse, they tend to circle round toward home again. Only a few of the male gazelles have territories at any one time since there is not enough space for them all. So the action of the wild dogs could eliminate a steady number of these males and allow others to take their place, which helps to achieve a regular turnover of fresh blood for breeding. Wild dogs kill twice a day, so they could dispose of almost 500 gazelles a year. But this does not seem to have had an undue effect on the 3,500 gazelles in the Crater. Something over 300 wild dogs in Kruger Park are accounting for over 10,000 impala a year out of a total of well over 100,000, which may be

less than a quarter as many as are taken by the lions and leopards and cheetah. Without the wild dogs and the others the impala would not get on so well as they do now. In the old days of "predator control" the antelopes grew old, they got sick, most of all they got too numerous—none of which is any good for a healthy community in the wilds. Despite the onslaught they are subjected to at present, the impala are maintaining their numbers and more, even if they are not increasing at the suicidal rates of olden times.

There is more concise evidence still of just how much havoc is caused by wild dogs, or how little. The Ngorongoro pack was calculated by Estes and Goddard to make an average of six pounds of flesh available to each dog each day. If one follows the calculations of another researcher, Dr. B. S. Wright, wild dogs, like lions and certain other predators, need to kill at the rate of one to one and a half pounds a day for every ten pounds of their body weight—and wild dogs in East Africa weigh around forty pounds (though they abandon well over a third of what they kill—the guts, the hide, the bones). The number of animals accounted for by each dog every year could vary according to the size of the pack, though any pack, large or small, seems to kill twice a day; in Dr. Pienaar's view it would range from thirty-five to fifty. It would also depend on the prey creature: a full-grown zebra is worth ten times a Thomson's gazelle. But a zebra does not often supply their food. They prefer to go for medium-size antelopes such as gazelles and impala, or even smaller creatures. If they succeed in capturing one of the larger animals it is likely they have spotted a sick one or a lame one or a very pregnant female. They often seem to cover a narrower range of prey creatures than any other major predator. A short survey in the Serengeti by Dr. Hans Kruuk and M. I. M. Turner showed that almost two-thirds of their diet can consist of Thomson's gazelle, with the rest shared among wildebeest, topi, impala, and Grant's gazelle. They also include the occasional zebra, reedbuck, bushbuck, duiker, or warthog. There has been the odd instance of wild dogs killing an old lioness. They occasionally take an ostrich or a sable antelope or a roan, even an eland. Nevertheless it is a restricted regimen. Leopards with their more variable hunting techniques account for twice as many different creatures.

A pack setting off across the savannah is one of the sights of Africa. The outcome may cause you to shudder. It should also cause you to wonder: how can this particular predator be on such hard times? If wild dogs are disappearing, the wilderness traveler will hear fewer hunting calls across the plains. Some people still think that would make the world no worse place, just as some people would like to put an end to that dog-type hunter of more northerly latitudes, the wolf. Other people think that no more wild dogs would make the world merely different—or perhaps *less* different than it is already with all its diversity. Meanwhile, the safarist at a last-light kill may see more yet if he stays to watch the array of guests that arrive for leftover scraps. Some are straight scavengers and some are rather more than hangers-on and sweepers-up. The wilderness is supposed to contain predators and carrion-eaters, and never the twain should be confused. Now it seems there are all sorts and conditions of creatures, some predators, some scavengers, some predator-scavengers and some scavenger-predators.

One group of safarists had a chance to follow up a scene that revealed the interplay among these carnivores. In the late evening they came across a wild dog pack loping past groups of gazelles, neither taking much notice of the other. Then the dogs topped a rise, and there was a large herd of wildebeest. Hobbling around in the middle was an injured yearling. The dogs were after it in a flash. The yearling stopped hobbling and ran as best it could. Too late: it was singled out. In terror it made for the one large object that promised safety—the safari truck. It cowered right up against the door. The dogs gathered around in a half-circle, a dozen yards away. Perhaps they did not recognize the wildebeest with its outline concealed by the vehicle. The safarists looked out between the wildebeest's horns and saw what the cornered creature saw, wild predators with their intentions all too plain. The pack circled about, twittering as they do when they are excited. Suddenly their twittering changed to growls. A hundred yards away a lion was approaching at a businesslike pace. He was hardly interested in the dogs, but he had seen the wildebeest during one of the moments when it had not been obscured. Now he too stared at the vehicle baffled. Dogs and lion looked at each other and at the spot where the wildebeest had "disappeared." The lion lost interest and moved off. The wildebeest stepped away for a moment. The dogs were onto it. They seized it from all sides and dragged it down. Their twittering filled the air again—and the lion came rushing back. The dogs scattered. The wildebeest was freed of its attackers and staggered to its feet. It was felled by the lion, and this time there was no getting up.

The lion had its carcass and the dogs had their frustration. They ringed the lion, snarling. The lion did not take long to decide it was better to abandon the kill than risk becoming a kill himself. The dogs fell upon the carcass. The sight of that rending flesh was too much for the lion. He came bounding back, tail lashing. The dogs did not dispute him. They backed off—but not very far. The lion was caught in the same quandary as before. A single group of wild dogs in front of him might be something he could cope with. Dogs circling on all sides was something else. He retreated, and the dogs dashed in for another mouthful. Back came the lion. The shift and turnaround repeated several times before the lion finally sensed that while he could take possession of the carcass he could not eat it as well. He turned away.

The dogs now ripped the carcass to pieces. Five minutes, and it was half gone. By this time the first hyena had arrived. It came too close. A single dog dissuaded it, repulsing an animal four times its weight. Another six hyenas turned up, but they all sat around at a distance. If they had combined forces they would have been far more than a match for the fourteen wild dogs. But hyenas do not have the impulse for concerted action that is one of the sources of the dogs' success. They merely lay and watched while the wildebeest carcass grew smaller and smaller. Another ten minutes, and the dogs were almost sated. Some of them began to leave. The hyenas still did not get their chance. The lion had returned, at a discreet distance, watching for this moment. He charged in, full of hunger and hope. This time the few remaining dogs did not challenge him. He set about the remains. But he had hardly swallowed a mouthful before he was harassed off the carcass again, this time by less likely looking competitors. Even while the wildebeest was still on its feet a vulture had swooped to the ground. Vultures, like hyenas and jackals, sometimes follow wild dogs or other predators while they are on the hunt. By now the one had become fifty. The lion resisted for a moment while vultures flocked in from all sides. As soon as he cleared those in front, more pressed in behind. He moved off again, and this time he did not come back.

The carcass disappeared under a hissing mob. The other scavengers, the hyenas, made a short attempt to dispute the picking, but as more vultures fell out of the sky they drew off to sit and wait some more. Only when there were mere bones left a few minutes later did the hyenas feel it worth staking a more forthright claim. This time it was the jackals that were obliged to watch and wait. They were to be too late. One hyena made off with the head, another with the rib cage, the others tore the limbs apart. All that was left were patches of blood on the ground. By next day these too would be disappearing as the ants got to work. The following evening there would be nothing left except flattened grass to mark the spot where animals had been and gone.

JACKALS

If the safarist has not yet seen jackals around a kill, this is the time of day to look out for them. For much of the heat they have been lying up in their dens. By evening you can hardly miss them.

Jackals are another example of how far the popular image can be from the real one. Their niche is not so close to the main predators as a hyena's is, and they are not such complete consumers of carrion as they are often made out to be. And not all jackals are alike; there are different species with different food habits. Not all areas are alike, either; some are fine for jackals, some less so. Some jackals have an easy time of it, while others have to work to stay alive. Ngorongoro Crater shows a more rapid turnover among the plains animals than the Serengeti: there are more predators preying on a more stationary supply of food. This could mean a greater supply of jackals as well. The Crater contains 500 jackals, many more in proportion than the Nairobi Park with its semi-migratory plains prey animals. The main hunters in the Crater are hyenas—at least 400 of them; and hyenas leave far less carrion than lions. But if the lions are recovering their former numbers, how will they change the situation—not only for the wildebeest, the zebras, and the hyenas, but for the jackals?

What *is* a jackal? When a wildlife-watcher comes across one he has found something worth looking at. It is not the rough, moth-eaten creature often imagined, of mongrel-like appearance if not mongrel-like habits. In the evening sun it looks sleek, especially if it is a golden-backed jackal, a resplendent creature. It looks an alert creature, all probing sharpness. Its long ears and nose tell what it amounts to as much as its reputation. If it were a mere hanger-on of the hyenas, a scavenger of the scavengers, it would scarcely need the slight frame, better adapted for hunting on its own account. A jackal looks as if it could look after itself without others to help. Perhaps it would do more hunting if it found itself with no alternative. But so long as it can scavenge off others it does not need to very much. It can get by on little food: scraps are enough. All the same, it probably makes more effort to catch its own prey than people often realize.

There are jackals and jackals. There is the golden-backed and the black-backed, sometimes known as the silver-backed. The two do not overlap much, whether their range is viewed as geographical or ecological—and the second counts as much as the first. The black-backed jackal extends throughout Africa but nowhere else. The golden-backed appears in eastern Africa but its main home is Asia. Both live side by side in East Africa, another example of how this place is a meeting ground of wildlife worlds. There are major differences in what each eats and how it gets it. In the Serengeti practically all the jackals in the bush country are black-backed, while out in the plains they are mostly golden-backed, especially where the grass is shortest. John Wyman has found that for the first part of the year they both live off young gazelles and insects, roughly half and half. The golden-backed jackal on the plains finds insects easy to come across with all the huge herds of plains animals providing droppings for dung beetles and others. Later on, after the great herds have migrated into the woodland country and the gazelles are mainly in the borderlands where the bush and plains meet, there is a change; for once you see both jackals together. The black-backed jackal has much more carrion to feed off once the hordes of wildebeest and zebra have moved off into the woodland country. It hardly bothers with insects now, whereas the golden-backed still relies on them for about a third of its food. In both ranges they flourish best where the grass has been grazed very short, leaving less protection for ground-nesting birds and small creatures like rats. Nor does the occasional fruit or wild berry go amiss. Bits of grass, even cultivated crops, all help. Anything is good for a jackal, anything that comes to hand—or claw and jaw. In Ngorongoro Crater the golden-backed jackal eats twice as much carrion as in the Serengeti, but still only a twentieth of its needs. The black-backed jackal finds no more than a third of its food in somebody else's leavings.

So are jackals to be classed as scavengers or hunters? When the right prey is available they do a good deal of hunting. They kill gazelle fawns with astute ease when they go at it in pairs; two together are successful much more often than not. One jackal bothers the gazelle mother, which may already have run off to distract the intruders, while the other takes its chance. In Ngorongoro Crater more gazelles fall to jackals than to all other

Left: Jackal cubs show how various species differ. The golden-backed (shown here) are born in the early months of the year, while the black-backed arrive a good six months later. The golden-backed average two cubs a litter, black-backed twice as many—which could be a reflection of feeding habits, along with other factors.

Below: Jackals scavenge less than is often supposed; and when they get a chance at a carcass they may get less of it than is often supposed. The vultures need only a few moments to take over by sheer weight of numbers if not by sheer weight of individual vulture (a Ruppell's griffon or a lappet-faced is as big as any jackal).

predators put together. Jackals also hang around the wildebeest herds when they are calving, but they go for the afterbirth rather than the calves themselves. In Kruger Park, where there are no gazelles but impala by the hundred thousands, a very large part of the jackal diet is made up of impala fawns. In other parts of southern Africa, outside the parks, black-backed jackals have been found living mainly off insects such as termites, locusts, beetles, or crickets, with quite a few spiders, and an odd rodent or small reptile thrown in. Carrion is no more than a random extra. But in some parts of the Transvaal, where jackals can get at sheep or poultry, they do much more "hunting," though this could be because the major predators from which they would scavenge have been eliminated.

Wherever it lives, the jackal does not find it easy to get its food. Nor does any carnivore, but jackals have to be more careful with their stocks. Bits left over from a kill or a scavenge are buried, usually near a rock or a bush that may act as a pointer for finding the spot again. Having eaten its fill the jackal trots off to its den. If it has left young ones behind it announces its arrival before it reaches the hole. The cubs race out to greet the parent with much fawning and licking. Where greeting stops being greeting and moves into something else is difficult to say, but the effect is the same: the adult puts down its head and regurgitates food for the little ones. They snatch up bits of meat and run off to gobble the half-digested lumps. The same for a jackal parent that has stayed behind to act as a guard: there is food forthcoming for everyone. Around the den the adults maintain an area as their territory, often a mile or two across, though the range can vary according to how many jackals there are in the locality. They defend it against other jackals of their own kind. A stranger is warned off by a complicated series of threats, but with hardly ever any fighting. Yet a golden-backed jackal does not mind if a black-backed wanders across its territory.

Both male and female have a hand in bringing up the cubs. They show a strong bond-relationship to each other. This is no more than common for the dog family, but quite different from the cats, which further indicates the niche the jackal occupies among the carnivores, whether canids or felids. If you want to learn what an animal is, one way is to find out what it isn't. You sort out how it fits into the passing scene with an array of other creatures without treading on their toes—and the jackal is not a creature to dispute its rights with another animal since the opponent is almost certain to be larger. It is no more built for true scavenging than is a domestic dog. As Dr. Richard Estes has pointed out, the jackal does not have the jaws and teeth that mark the hyena for its role. Nor does it have the specialized digestive system that enables the hyena to get nutriment from bones and offal and other tidbits that hyenas alone seem to appreciate. A hyena's diet can include camp ropes and pegs, boots and socks, not to mention an odd tire. No jackal is a scavenger supreme of this order. Moreover, hyenas are gregarious enough to live in communities of several families. A jackal scarcely shares such traits, though it is still more sociable than hunters like the leopard or the cheetah. A group of eight jackals was once seen chasing a leopard off its kill, but this kind of tactic is much more the exception than the rule. A jackal has something of the deep chest and long legs that characterize the dog family; they hunt by running their prey to a standstill. Yet a jackal catches its prey by getting close enough through its acute doglike sense of smell, then making a catlike pounce. It grabs the prey with its jaws, like the other dogs or the hyena, also like the cheetah (which is a cat). It uses its claws much less than a lion or a leopard, because it has neither their more developed armament nor the powerful forelimbs that are needed to deploy such weapons. Nobody has seen enough jackals on the hunt to know whether they attack from the back like most dogs or from the front like cats. But since the jackal has little to offer against the defensive weapons of a prey animal, such as the horns of a gazelle, it probably follows the dog pattern.

Whatever the jackal has learned from its experience in the long African day it has

Near right: Warthog piglets recognize their own mother, but they are not particular where they suckle; any nearby source will do. Similarly, a female does not seem to mind which male is parent of her litter, despite stories that warthogs are one of the few creatures in Africa to practice monogamy.

Far right: The bushpig offers much the same front to the world as the warthog: a long broad snout, fine for digging up plant roots, especially with its bone disc at the tip, and eyes set high up on the face, fine for seeing out over the countryside when so much of the action is at ground level. But the bushpig and the giant forest hog, the other members of the pig family in Africa, have developed a life style in complete contrast to the warthog's: they do not emerge until the warthog is generally underground for the night.

evolved as a highly efficient scavenger-predator (or predator-scavenger—for some jackals at some seasons in some places). Its double-barreled approach allows it to follow the common carnivore path of least effort, and much more easily than most. This is why the jackal is sometimes found where there are no lions and no cheetah and no wild dogs; and wherever it is found it is worth a second look.

WARTHOGS

A land that features so many creatures of elegance also produces the warthog. A warthog can look becoming only to another warthog. As it pauses in its feeding and swings round to the intrusion that is you, the whole animal twitches with curiosity. It sizes you up with a stare of incredulous surprise—how can any creature look like that? Then back to its feeding. To stuff the grass in more quickly it kneels to the job and moves about the same way. Feeding goes on as if the warthog feared the grass might run out any minute: not a moment to spare.

Not until dusk, at any rate. Then the late-day traveler might come across a warthog family on its way back to the burrow. They will not have far to go, since their range is only a few hundred square yards. By dark they like to be down their holes. They trot along with tails aloft like so many periscopes. In fact, their tails are probably a means for the warthogs to keep in touch with each other. The faster they trot, the stiffer the tails. When they disappear into long grass, all that sticks out are the tail tips, like tassels. Then they emerge again, to snort and sniff and gaze around, blissfully ignorant of their superb ugliness.

But while their appearance might appeal to one's sense of the comic, that face helps a warthog to avoid experience of the tragic. The warts protect the eyes, which are of greater importance than a sense of smell in the wide-open spaces where the warthog lives. The upper tusks, long and curved if not curvaceous, are not so fearsome as they look. They are more developed in the male, so perhaps their main purpose is no more than show. It is the short lower tusks that are used for combat. They can do a good job on an antagonist, as more than one lioness has found out. When they are used against another warthog, the upper tusks are handy for holding the opponent's head out of the way while a strike is aimed with the lower tusks at the throat. But whether both sets are for looks or lunging, they are not for anything so lowly as digging; wrong shape for that.

And anyway, why dig a burrow when there is often an aardvark den to be taken over? A hole has to be big enough to accommodate several of those squat bodies. As Dr. R. M. Bradley has described in his lengthy account of the Nairobi Park warthogs, the entrance may slope down for half a dozen feet, then branch out into two separate chambers a yard long and a foot and a half high. Or there could be an extended passageway that opens into living spaces. The hole is generally on top of a slope, where there is less danger of flooding, or in well-drained ground where the soil gets packed hard, discouraging to a passing lion that wants to dig a warthog family out. If the lion succeeded, it would most likely find more than one warthog family. Warthogs are gregarious creatures, perhaps because they need the greater watchfulness of several pairs of eyes when they are out and about above ground. Or perhaps they are sociable because they like to huddle together in a heap underground, a way of keeping warm without using too much oxygen. The tunnel down into the den has passing places so that the occupants do not have to come out in the order they went in. Piglets go down head first. Eventually they get too big to turn around inside. Then they learn the adult style of going into the hole backward, not only to give the tusks a quick strike at an intruder, but to avoid a warthog posterior being presented in a vulnerable position when coming out. At the first sign of danger a warthog makes for its hole. After a few moments of silence down beneath, a cautious nose appears above the ground. It is followed by suspicious eyes and bristling forehead. If the warthog is satisfied that danger is past, the whole animal emerges grunting resentment at the world. Another strange move and the body disappears in a flash. This time it will be longer before the nose appears. On the Mweya Peninsula in Queen Elizabeth Park there are a hundred holes to a square mile, so that one is always close at hand. It represents their only real means of escape, since there is little cover in the short grass areas they frequent. Mweya features warthogs by the dozen, two tons of them to a square mile. They are proliferating to such an extent that their numbers should act as a warning of what the hippos are doing again to the habitat. The hippos are multiplying after the cropping schemes of recent years have been brought to a halt. Hippos eat the grass very short, which is how warthogs prefer it. Like the Egyptian geese around the water holes, that can also serve as signals of overgrazing, they may act as a barometer of stormy times ahead if the hippo herds are not checked.

The warthog has little time for anything but eating and wallowing and an occasional rest. It spends frequent moments in passing on warthog greetings. It touches noses or lays its forehead flat against the broad brow of another warthog. All is accompanied by a good deal of sniffing and squeaking. Several times a day they go rubbing. They have their favorite spots on banks or on hillocks, and if there is nothing handy then another warthog will do. The piglets spend a lot of time playing. They have short stumpy bodies like blocks of wood on spindly legs. Their urge to see what is behind every bush takes them out of the mother's grunting range, until their terror-propelled legs bring them scampering back behind the lowered tusks. As often as not they are fleeing from their own shadows, so back to their games. A popular one is racing in circles, with a sudden about-face in midflight—a useful practice for dodging predators some day, or turning to get down a hole at speed.

In East Africa there are usually two rainy seasons. The warthog birth season is generally at the start of the short rains, except in Queen Elizabeth Park, where it can be at any phase of the year. This part of Western Uganda is almost on the continental divide, where there are changes in the pattern of climate. In Nairobi Park, by contrast, the warthog young are born in October, when the lesser rains are getting under way. One might wonder, why not the long rains? If the births are to be timed for when there is plenty of grass growing, this seems less than the best way of going about it. But the long rains come at the end of a longer dry season, which would mean less grass for the mother-to-be. Moreover, heavier rains bring a greater prospect of flooded-out burrows.

The piglets are born full of life, and into a world full of dangers. By six months, half have disappeared. Eagles take some, jackals others, and then there are lions and leopards and hyenas. Among those surviving this onslaught females may outnumber the males by three to two, after starting off level. What accounts for the difference? No one knows; what is sure is that a preponderance of females would make a monogamous society difficult for a species that does not practice hierarchy among the males. Even after they are grown up, life in a warthog world is still a chancy affair. Warthogs in zoos can live to be twenty, but in Nairobi Park they do not get far beyond six or seven years. Not that warthogs are not courageous fighters; two of them have been seen to hold off a pack of sixteen wild dogs—a feat that would daunt a wildebeest or a zebra. But a warthog sees life from a low level, though hardly lowly when you see the jaunty way it faces its environment. Not being able to see very far, the warthog has to rely on warning snorts from antelopes and baboons, or ox-peckers and ground plovers. Which is not the same as being able to spot dangers oneself.

Warthogs are not what might be called the most handsome of creatures. Should they be called anything? Their appearance must be considered an example of functional beauty. It does its job well enough. When a warthog fixes you with its sprightly gaze, it is something worth looking at, glorious warts and all. Nobody ever saw a sleepy warthog.

Toward evening the hippos rouse themselves. One member of the herd may pick out a partner especially notable for refinement of feature or delicacy of deportment. The two begin overtures, trying to out-stretch each other's jaws. The interlude may last half an hour before there is a relapse into an ecstasy of ooze.

HIPPOS

Throughout the day the hippos lie immobile under the heat. They are almost submerged in the best mud patch they can find. From time to time they take a walk along the bottom.

They can stay under for four minutes, or longer if they have to, in part because they have a larger number of red corpuscles and absorb more oxygen into the bloodstream than the watcher can. When a hippo submerges, two small flaps inside its nostrils close off automatically. Away it goes for a subsurface stroll.

These flaps are what makes things difficult for the researcher who wants to drug-dart a hippo so that he can look more closely at what makes it a hippo. Tranquilizing drugs act as a depressant on the nervous system, causing the hippo's flaps to go out of operation. Drug-darting in water generally proves of little use: the hippo promptly drowns. So the scientist waits until the hippos come out on dry land. By evening they are emerging for their night-long feed. If the evening safarist sees somebody taking aim at a plodding hippo, he should not be surprised. The scientist must let his target get far enough away from the water so that it cannot get back again before the drug takes effect—usually seven to ten minutes. A hippo in trouble makes straight for where it feels safest and that is the nearest stretch of water. But hippos are not all that cooperative; sometimes they prefer to stay in that glorious slime until after sundown. Nowadays Africa is becoming more modern. Only a dozen years ago there was no drug-darting of wild animals at all. Following the pioneer work of Dr. Toni Harthoorn and Dr. John King, drug-darting has become a refined technique. Dr. Pienaar in Kruger Park has developed a drug that acts less completely than knockout drugs, more suitable for use on hippos in water holes. Armed with a crossbow, he perches on top of a bulldozer and drives straight into the wallow. He fires at a hippo's neck, where the skin is not too thick. Nothing happens for ten minutes; then the hippo begins to go popeyed. It staggers about with an agreeable expression of alcoholic lethargy. It has just enough strength to keep above water. A rope is thrown around it to haul it ashore. This technique is generally used for capturing calves, since there has been a need in Kruger Park for shifting hippos to areas where they have been poached out. A calf is easier to transport than a full-grown hippo, especially if it has to be taken 100 miles or more. The sight of a calf disappearing behind a bulldozer is something no hippo mother can watch with equanimity; but what to do against a bulldozer, when not even a rhino can do better than a draw?

The late-day watcher is not likely to see much more than hippos just lying there. Only eyes and nose are visible above the water. A short time back in the long African day the eyes were taller periscope protuberances, probably to allow as few inches of hide as possible to escape that mud-clinging bliss. Around 3,000,000 years ago there were no proper hippos, but their anthracothere ancestors were already showing signs of a mud-basking life. Eventually hippos arrived in Africa from the Orient, during a time when Africa was experiencing much greater rainfall and northern regions of the earth were under ice. The dried-out visage of Africa was changing to lakes and rivers, just the place for hippos. They rapidly spread across every part of this primeval landscape. They were soon acquiring much of the form they have today. Grotesque as this appearance is, it is not as remarkable as an albino hippo, blancmange in color with two-inch freckles along the back. Some people say it looks "boiled" or "naked." It does not strike other hippos as all that odd. Albinos are allowed to join a school just like the rest. A school of hippos generally totals around ten individuals, though the areas around the park borders, which are particularly vulnerable to poachers, regularly run to 100 hippos in a single school, or on occasion huge mobs of 500 packed together for greater security. But wherever they are, hippos usually crowd in as if this were the best mud hole on earth, and the last.

With the fading light of evening the hippos look around. They give forth prodigious yawns. The straining mouth rears out of the water to gape at the skies. If the hippo topples over, no matter: a roll might be the ultimate treat. All four feet flapping around on the surface look a bit strange, but the hippo doesn't care—its head is in the mud. All in all, it is a creature that makes no bones about its appearance. It certainly doesn't try to pass itself off as a natural beauty or a *jolie laide*; not what you would call a hippo-crite.

Giraffe males sometimes fight several times a day. Why they are so inclined to combat is not clear: they have no territories to defend, nor do they necessarily fight over females since there are often no females around. Possibly they are trying to make a place in the local hierarchy, even though the herd structure usually appears vague.

GIRAFFES

A giraffe swaying across the horizon at sunset is as serene and graceful as it was at noontime when it moved across the heat-haze mirage as if it were walking on water. Now the heat has subsided; Africa is benign and genial. The cool light is a different world, but the giraffe is still the giraffe. Behind it the sun sinks fast and red. Soon it will be night and a different time again, a time of the hunter and the hunted. But for a brief while the savannah and the giraffe and the luminous languor of sundown are a scene to remember when the lion's roar sends word of a new stage in the long African day.

It is always worth pausing to watch a giraffe, whatever the time and whatever it is doing. There it is, this phenomenon, right before your eyes, a marvel of adaptive forces, just *there*. That neck is displayed to unusual advantage when the giraffe is indulging in love-play or fighting: one often merges into the other with a fluency you would expect of giraffes. They demonstrate affection by rubbing their necks together, and aggressiveness by stepping up the rubbing into a vigorous buffeting. Fighting bulls stand shoulder to shoulder, sometimes facing each other but more usually side by side. They swing at each other until one gets out of position, and then a well-aimed lunge from the other is a sledgehammer blow. Their heads are especially adapted for fighting. The sinuses bulge out in lumps to form the bases for the horns. These are not horns with bony coverings like cattle horns, nor do they fall out periodically like a deer's antlers. Only the giraffe has "giraffe horns." The male's horns grow rapidly for two years, then more slowly. The whole surface becomes covered with extra bone, making them massive and hard as ivory. They are supported by layers of more bone on top of the skull. The entire structure increases by as much as twenty pounds over the years. A female's skull is much smaller. Her horns are lighter, and they taper toward the tips. The male's do not develop points, since they would be weapons far too dangerous for the good of giraffes. But fighting aims more at playing out a ritual than inflicting real injury. The females do not fight at all.

Nor does a male use its horns for defense against a predator: the forelegs are more useful. But that clublike head can make a dent in a piece of timber. The idea is to dominate and deter, not maim or kill, though a vanquished male may occasionally be left unconscious on the ground. Constant fighting makes the horns lose their fur covering. This is convenient for people who want to distinguish a male from a female but see only a head sticking out of a bush. Possibly the fighting stems from some sexual significance. Males often intertwine their necks in gestures amicable enough, followed by a demonstration of homosexual tendencies. Presumably the neck-rubbing goes some way to stimulation. But then the affectionate gestures are suddenly escalated to very different intentions. All another phenomenon of the African scene whose subtle beauty is rivaled by its mystery.

The giraffe has taken a long time to reach its present form. It came into recognizable being during the Miocene, 20,000,000 years ago. This was a stage when the mammals were enjoying a golden age of adaptation to nature's environment and Africa had not finished settling down. The "giraffe" of those days was related to an ancestral deer that was developing in a new direction, away from the cervids and toward the bovids. To this extent, the giraffe is related to deer and cattle. A long while back there were giraffes from Europe to eastern Asia, sixteen species in all. Some of them were short-necked creatures, no bigger than a calf giraffe. Eventually they must have been unable to stand the competition from better adapted forms. Another interlude, and today's giraffe emerged. As Dr. Spinage has pointed out in his lengthy review of the giraffe, it has been a prime example for various theories of evolution. Everyone knows how it is supposed to have developed its long limbs and neck in order to get at vegetation that was out of reach of other creatures. But how about female giraffes, since females are generally shorter than males— how did they compete when there were better adapted specimens of their own kind? And how did young giraffes ever survive to grow up and reach the stage of producing more giraffes? The theory is not so supersimple. The main answers were provided by natural selection, as Darwin theorized, rather than by the dynamic "yearning upward" that Lamarck proposed. Any giraffids that did not stay the course were eliminated. There can be no deliberate or inspired passing-on of desirable traits. The evidence of modern genetics would put Lamarck in a tougher spot still, since there is a further principle to evolutionary theory that is just as central as the older parts: when two individuals combine to reproduce their own, they regenerate through an individual which varies slightly from the parents with no carbon copy of either. Some giraffes would be born taller than others; they would survive and pass on their genes. So runs the idea in grossly simplified form. But why then did no other creatures develop long necks or long legs? Possibly a need for long legs became paramount at some far-back period of the long African day. When all this stretching and straining was taking place, there were bigger predators than today's lions, some of them possibly faster. Moreover, the teeth of the modern giraffe suggest the creature was once a forest-dweller, as is the okapi today. The giraffe had long legs even in those days; yet there is no need in a forest to be constantly reaching high in competition for a limited food supply. Such conflict would rather arise in the open bushlands or on the plains. In a forest there is plenty of food for all creatures, whatever their height, and a forest would give little opportunity for flight. So possibly those legs helped

For all that a giraffe's neck is long, it is not really long enough when the giraffe is reaching down at a salt lick or at a water hole.

their owner to spot danger a long way off. Yet a forest environment is the place for a hunter wanting to creep close.

One can try another approach, and ask not so much why or how the giraffe grew *up*. In older times there was a tendency toward the outsize among many creatures, a feature which has declined. Possibly the giraffe evolved as just a big creature anyway for whatever primordial reason, and not only big but bulky. The elephant handled a problem of that sort by growing tusks for defense; it was too heavy to run away, so it would stay and fight. The giraffe might have evolved in a different direction, aiming at speed: a lighter body was needed, so the limbs grew more slender. Instead of the head growing upward away from the body, the body tended to contract and the head found itself in lofty isolation.

Whatever the explanation, these changes occurred some hours back in African time. The okapi shows that the short rump, the setting of the elongated neck on the shoulders, and the characteristic gait had all arrived at some far-back stage of ancestral develop-ment: no major changes since. There is still room for speculation and many basic clues are left open for combinations and permutations. The giraffe remains a marvel and a mystery. It is still evolving. Whether it will evolve much further is another question. More creatures than just a lion want to see that elegant length lying broken on the ground. The watcher gazing at a giraffe in Nairobi Park with the city skyscrapers in the background might ponder which represents the greater achievement in vertical engineering. Giraffes gaze at the jets flying into Nairobi's airport bringing the latest load of tourists for a look at East Africa's world much as it was before man became upright. These travelers might consider whether there will be many giraffes in many more years' time. If not, the fault will lie with local hunters with an eye on the bucket market and those tourists that fly off again with the best bracelets.

The giraffe has a regulating device for its blood pressure that may yet teach those onlookers with their city induced blood pressure how to manage a control if not a cure. But it should not be necessary to consider a giraffe's uses. It is worthy enough as the world's tallest living creature and as a graceful if grotesque part of the African scene. Yet these are like vital statistics: what they reveal is significant and what they conceal is vital. Just look at a giraffe in the wild and see what it is all about. It is a wonderment of nature—just by being.

PARKS

Late in the day the safarist starts back to his lodge. He may wonder how far the park meets his expectations. He may wonder what his expectations were. Has he seen a special world that is separate from the ordinary world, or is it an extension of the ordinary world, a world he does not leave behind because it is all one world? If certain features remind him of his more usual world, should they be increased, or reduced, or both, depending on how far they reflect the better features of any world?

Parks are a new idea in East Africa. The concept of wilderness as a place to be ap-preciated is newer still. It took centuries for the locals in Europe and North America to get over their feelings about the fells and fens; once again, East Africans are having to catch up twenty generations in ten years. If, in the meantime, they look on their parks as economic entities, they are hardly to be blamed. These parks cater to the idea of wilder-ness in the minds of affluent foreigners who come to visit them—even experience them. Many of these would-be samplers of nature are people from urbanized communities, from habitats like cages: gilded cages, perhaps, but cages. They live lives of synthetic sameness, as bland as planned. There comes a time when they are less than satisfied with their silky-

smooth surroundings, when they want things roughened up a bit. A little disorder helps to get things straight. What price then the shambling disruptiveness of an elephant or the mindless meanderings of a rhinoceros? If wilderness is sometimes made out to be fearsome and forbidding, that could occasionally be what is needed: such sensations are part of the total human experience and just as valid as feelings of elation or sadness, grief or ecstasy. Just as a life of incessant sweet pleasure might become a cotton-candy illusion, so the good life is more than the life of goodies. But is wilderness a state of nature or a state of mind, or a state of nature and human nature together?

Not that people come to East Africa on a rehabilitation course. They come on a vacation. They might also come for recreation in its literal sense, re-creation. They might even go away with something new, especially if they can avoid seeking a situation where experience gives way to enjoyment, and enjoyment to mere entertainment. East Africa features wilderness of all kinds, some of it still wild enough. Nowadays park country is often understood as woodland landscapes with nice shady spots, a place that looks like "parkland." But can't desert country also be park-land? And if desert can be fine scenery, can't it also be fine experience? Or perhaps people are looking for a place they did not go to last year. Some people come with packaged program and packaged minds, bent on becoming a bit more like the élitist herd by visiting the latest jet-set place—provided it is not too strange. Some people come to play bridge. Others come for the world of the travel brochure, which is as genuine as come-on propaganda ever is: these sophisticated safarists from the ends of the earth, are they so susceptible? Not everybody comes to Africa to see the wild animals; they come to see more of the same people, with the wild animals thrown in as an extra. But many a traveler to Africa nowadays is going to a place he knows something about, more than a patch on the map with JUNGLE and DESERT written across it. To his parents it was a place of prickly plants and pythons; to his children it is a photograph from a spacecraft, part of the over-the-fence world they know from television. He is also going somewhere before it disappears. He has heard it said (and he will hear it said again) that what wilderness is saved in the next few years is all that will

In a park elephants' rights should be paramount, together with those of other wild creatures. But in most parks, the dominant influence is already man's, and will become more and more so as the people who never go into a park make their presence felt: the cultivators and pastoralists thronging around the borders and causing unprecedented congestion inside the borders. As soon as the wild animals start turning the park into a sanctuary on this scale, it is headed toward a wildlife slum, unless the pressures inside can be halted in time.

ever be saved; or that the problem is not *where* wilderness will be tomorrow, but *whether* it will be. So he'd better go and get the thing looked at while it is still around.

But although the tourist trickle is swelling to a stream and will hopefully surge to a flood, these African parks have not yet reached the stage where you enjoy your solitude amidst multitudes, except perhaps Nairobi Park, which nears saturation at weekends and where you sometimes see more autos than antelopes. In the middle of the Serengeti you still get the feeling of wilderness as a place big enough to have a place beyond it, a place where you do not know how many places there are beyond it. Serengeti and its 6,000 square miles has already been pegged at 600 visitors at a time; after that, there is "crowding." Of course, more of the Serengeti could be set to work if people could be persuaded to venture beyond the central zones into the other nine-tenths of the park. But then, the wild animals are not so cooperative elsewhere; wild animals that are really wild won't stand and be photographed.

Parks mean different things to different people. Ask the visitor to East Africa what the parks are about and he is less likely to say wild places as wild animals. And yet African parks are places where you can sense a single wild community, rather than a place for the swiftest and the strongest and the tallest, or even the bravest. If a park is a whole, the experience should be a whole, too. In this sense parks are anything but museums, living or any other kind, nor are they places for collecting curious experiences as if they were natural oddities. The visitor should not be encouraged to look around with lists of creatures: scattered scraps of information suggest a world with no basic wholeness (or wholesomeness, either), a place for looking at but not a place for living in.

So what is wilderness Africa-style? Obviously it is more than a place where you don't pick the flowers. Is it a place where the hand of man has, so to speak, not set foot? If that is what people are after, they will be disillusioned. There is hardly a locality where you can achieve the idea—let alone the ideal—of a national park as a place untouched. At the same time, parks in Africa are not like those where the main attraction is scenery. In an American park you can get out and look around, which, say some people, gives you a closer contact with nature (some say it gives you a closer contact with people). In such places the view does not alter much if you look at it with droves of others at your shoulder (or does it?). While you are looking at giraffes or leopards or zebras, things are not the same, especially when those other people are taking up far more space in their safari truck than vista-viewers on foot.

An African park without animals would scarcely be an African park. In some senses the animals emphasize the we/they standing; in other ways they could reduce it. They could make man less obtrusive, or they could make him unmistakably everywhere. When a piece of land becomes a park, it becomes a place titled and treated; like it or not, you cannot leave it virgin and innocent. The day is gone when the best way to protect a stretch of wild country was to look at it and leave it, tiptoe away, and say nothing. Once a park becomes somewhere for man to disport himself as well as watch animals disporting themselves, it is not what it was. The landscape becomes laced with roads, even though tracks should allow insights into the natural scene rather than insights into the road-maker's art. How about when such tracks are paved, as has been done with one main thoroughfare in Nairobi Park to allow visitors to see something even at the height of the rainy season? Roads are built for the express benefit of one creature, even if they then become express roads: perhaps the answer to the heavy-footed driver is to build only the most rudimentary tracks and then not bother to maintain them.

At a time when more wildlife areas could be set aside in East Africa but aren't (the official phrase "set aside" says something of the approach to wild lands as something separated from the usual stream of affairs), there are sites being designated from Florida to California where people can see African animals "in natural surroundings"; even in Great Britain, tight little island that it is, there are people making a hundred times as

Above: In contrast to Tsavo's 35,000 elephants, a mere 2,000 in Serengeti are causing extensive damage to landscape that has few enough trees to start with. Certain elephants seem to be going on a rampage, especially middle-aged bulls at certain stages of the year (a "delinquent" elephant is a force to conjure with). But Serengeti often has shallow-rooted trees, light soil, and strong winds. Moreover, the regular fires in some areas would mean hardly any trees left in a few years anyway, elephants or no elephants: there are no young trees coming along to replace those soon to disappear from old age, no matter how many overturned trunks the Serengeti staff prop back in place.

Right: Tsavo Park, home of the largest assembly of elephants left on earth, is rapidly becoming less capable of supporting them (or the largest collection of rhinos left, or some of the best baobabs, etc). Fifteen years ago this habitat was bush too thick to walk through; now you can not

much an acre out of "lion lands" than out of normal agriculture. After the next few years in East Africa the doubtful situation of the present will not be doubtful anymore. It will be plain to anybody what the new crowded era amounts to, with up to 1,000,000 people streaming out of the jumbo jets looking for places serene and secluded. Some of them may not mind sharing their seclusion with thousands of others. Some may want Africa, a region still safe from the prospect facing parks in other lands where you can listen to the latest pop singer on half a dozen transistor radios, where you can socialize with as many people as in the middle of the big city you are escaping from, where you can be glad you are in a place big enough to throw beer cans, where you can do what you want—even be robbed or raped or murdered.

All of which might seem a long way from root-factors of conserving Africa's wild spectacle. But when everybody wants to come to see the spectacle, how do you keep it worth seeing? You have to fit the needs of the visitors to the needs of the animals as best you can; or vice versa. You can get wild creatures to be cooperative in a hurry by laying out inducements for them, special water holes and salt licks. It might mean dislocating the normal movements of the animals, but aren't parks for people, too? If migrations allow portions of the country to recover from their seasonal concentrations, the migrations of visitors to East Africa will not (hopefully) prove so seasonal. If you have to sell

only walk for miles, but you can see for whole horizons—which is considered an improvement by some. Moreover, several of the main watercourses are silting up through erosion in farming areas as far away as a hundred miles or more. The Voi River disappears altogether in the dry season, now that the Teita people, in whose lands the river rises, have doubled in numbers during the past twenty years and are undertaking more intensive cultivation on ever-steeper hillsides. There is little use thinking one can safeguard elephants only within a park, and not within their total environment.

Africa and sell it again, your customer is your customer, and if that means presenting a packaged product that is sold and soiled and sullied, he might not know; he might not care.

Such a customer is not all that common. The situation can still be saved by the stubborn soul who refuses to conform to the computerized image of the average tourist (the "mean" tourist, as he is sometimes called). Coming from a homogenized world, he wants Africa because Africa is different and he is different. Different in what standardized way? Or perhaps the visitor is so sated with everything he wants he is not sure what he wants. He should watch his fellow-visitors as they disport themselves around the lodge at times when the urge for creature comforts is greater than the urge for creatures. At several

localities you can do things you don't need to go to a park for, such as take a swim in the pool. In time the visitor might find every opportunity to do what he really wants, and all not too far from the lodge (which allows for more lodges, more visitors, less crowding). He goes for a morning trip to an artificial dam where the animals are bound to congregate, since the pools roundabout have been diverted to this superspecial watering point. There will be ample scope for fine viewing since the reeds are cut back, however helpful the old-style streamside vegetation might have been for grass-eating antelopes and antelope-eating carnivores. The visitor sees hippos where there weren't any before because they have been brought in from elsewhere, while other creatures have been thinned out to make way for these added attractions. On the way back from the water hole he passes spots where stretches of grassland have been burned to attract a suitable array of antelopes. If the grass grows too high, mow it; if it refuses to grow because the rains have failed, set out water-sprinklers. The visitor views the spectacle while reclining in air-conditioned comfort, rattling his martini rocks at the rhinos. Back to the lodge, and a quick glimpse into the compound where the tourist who was unlucky in the savannah can check further animals off his list and take a few photographs to prove it. After lunch there are local dancers with all the color of modern-uniforms. For the afternoon there is fishing in trout-stocked rivers at sections sealed off from wild animals. A game of tennis when the late-day cool returns; it means the guest misses the evening run, but what does that matter—he can always see a film after dinner presenting African wildlife at its best, all the finest spectacles packed into a single experience.

Such conveniences are already available in one park or another in Africa. For the less modern locality, there is still the problem of protecting the landscape, however much the park manager might want to avoid leaving his fingerprints on it. You have not only to manage wild places to change them, you have to manage them to keep them as they are. Tsavo is becoming a place where man has been kept out as much as possible for as long as possible, and what results is a natural scene sadly reduced in its diversity. Too much notice has been taken of KEEP OUT notices on the borders, in men's minds as well. And if a wild area is to be managed, you have to decide what it is to be managed for. No environment is a static affair that need only be put behind a fence for it to be safeguarded for weekends and vacations. You could aim at an ecological slice of time and try to "freeze" it. You could aim at the broadest array of animals and plants in your area, while changing the status quo as little as possible. Or you could aim at a direct, positive, continuous manipulation of the whole thing from top to bottom. Not everyone would agree with those who suggest that since any ecosystem exists only at a given point in space and time, you cannot look at the same one twice because it will have changed (as with the Greek philosopher who noticed how quickly a river became another river, so you might not be in time to jump into it once, let alone twice). But there could be more agreement with those who say that what wilderness is to one person it isn't to another; and what it is to one generation it won't be to the next, so why not handle it as a sociological concept as much as ecological? If it is futile to try to recapture the past or hang on to the present, how far can you plan for the future? Well, you pay your money and you take your choice: you review the possible range of plant associations and animal communities and then say "that one, for the present."

To which some people will object that the result is not wilderness—at least those who believe that to touch is to defile. A more usual approach is that you manage it as little as you have to—but you manage it. And yet, and yet: what do you manage it for? If you define your aim, you might find it disappears by the time another season comes around with too little rain (or too much). You try to keep out stray fires: how about stray birds? Or stray diseases? All of them on occasion can exert an impact on the system. And what if the intruders from outside are stray elephants, 2,000 of them as have "invaded" the Serengeti? One approach proposed by Dr. E. M. Russell for the Serengeti is to "conserve the present variety of the different habitats within the park and of the different species of fauna using those habitats, and to maintain them as nearly as possible in their present distribution and proportion." The elephants are hardly residents of the Serengeti since they only started to appear ten years back, and there were none for a hundred years before that. Where do you draw the line?

And if the Serengeti is the "land of the lion," should one try to increase the lions—or the leopards, since this is the best area in East Africa for seeing leopards by day? Or should one try to find out what visitors want and then aim at giving them a maximum of what they "prefer"? The park might then turn into a zoo, where the animals are there at man's behest for man's convenience. If the animals are so wild and wanton that hardly any of them appear on some occasions, do you listen to the visitor's complaints? If man and all his works are to be eliminated from this primeval area, what about the blue gum

As well as studying the wildebeest, the researchers study what the wildebeest live on. An "exclosure" at Ngorongoro indicates how much the grass grows when the grass-eaters cannot get at it. The grass is not only growing taller, it is growing much less vigorously, especially after its first month or so; grass kept down to two inches produces twice as much more grass (through replacement growth) as grass eight inches high.

trees and sisal plants at Ngorongoro, brought into the Crater by German settlers fifty years ago? And the ruins of their houses? Or the burial mounds of people of 2,000 years ago that dot the Crater floor?

However man-made a park may become, it should scarcely permit interference like feeding starving animals. Perhaps, perhaps, one could make an exception for lion cubs, especially those from the local tourist-show prides, more especially still if the lionesses have been disturbed in their hunting by some of the same tourists. Assisting thirsty animals is another affair. When there is a drought there are cries for artificial water supplies, whereupon the creatures are induced to stay in one area close to a constant water supply and become reluctant to go off to remote parts of the park for fresh forage. Piped water supports only pipedreams.

And if an African park for African animals usually means the larger animals, there are many smaller ones and nocturnal creatures that should not thereby become expendable if a conflict arises. Tsavo Park features a wider range of birds in its bushlands than in its grasslands, but the bushlands are disappearing. Some of the more gorgeous rollers frequent baobabs, as do hornbills and a whole assemblage of others, which could be a further reason to protect the baobabs from the elephants, unless, of course, most people go to Tsavo to look at elephants and more elephants (and if not elephants, then zebras), with the birds way down on the list of "true tourist needs." In American parks you can fish, on the grounds that not only is this a nature-inclined pastime but that nobody sees fish under water anyway, which is akin to the Tsavo tactic of running a commercial fishing venture from one of the Park's artificial dams—in this area that is a citadel of the preservationist's "don't touch" approach. Some people might want the lesser kudu brought back to Lake Manyara, where they were shot out some years ago. Perhaps impala should be introduced to the Arusha Park where they "would surely go" if they were not prevented by a belt of newly arrived cultivators. Perhaps one should bring back plants in like manner, replanting the elephant-felled trees in Serengeti on the grounds that they are attractive (to tourists).

Some people suggest that the parks should aim at a "vignette of primitive Africa." Even if this could be achieved easily or completely, it is not easy to set a historical starting point. If the arrival of the white man is some sort of watershed, what about the Bantu peoples? Or the earliest agriculturalists? Having decided what you want, it is not so simple to reconstruct those times even if you have people to tell you what they were like. If Africa had remained uninhabited by all sorts and conditions of men for all that time, the place would still not have remained the same. Nature moves. The natural areas that have undergone the greatest transformation in the past few years (those that have not been turned into crop country) are all too often the areas that are set aside for the protection of the wild world. It is primarily the elephants that have caused the change, but it will not be long before East Africa is like those regions farther south where a park is not immune from all manner of conflicts with the outer world hundreds of miles away. Kruger Park has had to be fenced in to stop the wild animals from getting out to mingle with the purer stock outside (apart from eating their fodder), which means a radical disruption of the animals' movements. There is no outlet during hard seasons, and there is overgrazing during all seasons. Not only elephants and hippos are having to be cropped, but zebras, wildebeest, impala, buffaloes, even giraffes: giraffes have multiplied prodigiously following a ban on fires as a man-made contrivance, and the consequent spread of bush vegetation on all sides. More than that, some permanent water holes are no longer so permanent, some of them even nonexistent; rivers that were once year-round are now seasonal at best, following an overtaxing of the system by water-demanding farmers well out of sight of the park boundaries. This is a measure of how far a park can be carved out of the environment as an independent scheme of things. But if it is still a part of the continuous ebb and flow of the environs, where do these environs end? In an area twice as

During the 1970 drought, the Serengeti wildebeest migrated thirty miles beyond the park boundary, farther than they could move inside the park in any one direction. The total Serengeti eco-unit varies between two and three times the area of the park, depending on how many animals are feeding off how much forage, a range of factors that changes from season to season. An overall approach would ring the park with a buffer zone to absorb its periodic "population explosions" such as seemed to occur during the 1960s. A park in Africa should be considered as providing scarcely more than a heartland within broader stretches of wildlife country. Parks as "island sanctuaries" are far too vulnerable to disease disasters, do not allow enough genetic exchange, and in other ways are hardly ever adequate for long-term conservation: they form only a fine framework on which to build.

large as a park? Or ten times as large? Or the whole region? The whole country? A whole section of the continent? How about those parts of eastern Africa that are threatened periodically by locust plagues from Asia?

The Serengeti is a scene that is severely threatened by the future. A world "young and fragile," as the entrance gate proclaims, it is also aged and enduring, and has been so for long before man-the-tourist made his way here. While it could be valued beyond compare before the century is out, it will be subject to pressures beyond compare in the interim. The park is less than half the size it needs to be to constitute a self-sustaining unit. To make things even more difficult, the Serengeti region—which includes the stretch of land surrounding the park—is not considered a single entity by officials or politicians. If the hinterland itself were to be the responsibility of a single authority, then much more could be done to safeguard the scene. But it isn't: there are half a dozen different authorities, each functioning in its watertight domain. These wilderness environs are being developed out of existence overnight, especially when modern Africa's ability to alter its environment makes the techniques of thirty years ago look positively steam-age and those of the turn of the century Stone Age. Moreover, there is all too little consultation between those running things inside the park and those running affairs outside, which means that real conservation of the entire Serengeti region cannot even get onto the starting line as yet. The park is little more than a few lines on a map, whatever the wildebeest might make of it.

The long run probably requires a more refined approach to conservation than the concept of a park sanctuary with borders inviolate. Even if poachers are kept at bay, it is hard to say what is a "border," when what is fine for one year might not be so good the next. An ideal would be a fluid system allowing for minor adjustments along the boundaries from one period to another—and requiring major adjustments in the minds of administrators both inside the park and out. It would be possible only with the widest cooperation throughout the entire Serengeti territory, and in a world more practical than the present "practical" arrangement. A gesture in that direction was made a few years back when the "excess" wildebeest were to be made available to local people for hunting as the migrating herds passed through the border areas, regulated hunting by hunters who stick to bows and arrows—no firearms to shoot a score where an archer would get only one. Then it was found the wildebeest had made less mistake about their numbers after all, even if the plan had got beyond the Africa-paced arguments about hunting rights in different territories. The approach was abandoned.

Which was a pity, because there could be fine prospects for people roundabout who tend to look askance at this alien entity in their own land. For all that the Serengeti habitat verges on a "biological famine" classification by standards of temperate-zone vegetation, it is prolific with a reckless extravagance. Dr. Murray Watson suggests the wildebeest alone could supply up to 24,000,000 pounds of canned meat a year, without removing more than the natural increase and without depriving the predators of their food. Toward the end of 1970 enough wildebeest and zebras died of starvation to give 50,000 Africans as much meat as they normally eat in a year. Some people think the visitor might find it inhibiting his aesthetic appreciation to know that some of the herds were migrating into a canning factory. As long as such ideas are deemed wholly incompatible with what a park stands for, cropping could be considered for areas outside the main sanctum. The first such scheme has been tried in the Loliondo area to the northeast of Serengeti. It could have been a major breakthrough for Tanzania, but it ran up against several snags, not all of them of nature's making. Local beef barons put up resistance to a product that could undersell their own, though they were no more obstructionist than their counterparts in North America who oppose the sale of elk meat from cropping programs. If the preliminary scheme works out at Loliondo, however, there are many wilderness areas of Tanzania that could supply meat to a protein-hungry land and money to a peasant-based populace.

Not a single one of East Africa's better-known wildlife areas is an independent eco-unit by any sort of viable measure. These are mostly paper parks, much as they were when set up by their white originators. How about the future, and the workings of a society like Kenya, as dynamic and changing as its great wild ecosystems? Parks are no longer surrounded by miles and miles of more Africa; they are becoming surrounded by ranches and maize fields. One way to safeguard these areas is to view them as economic enterprises contributing to new nations: this is what will make them—might even make them more. Twenty years ago land meant land; today it means development, too. In modern Africa as elsewhere land tends to drift toward its most economic use. Those people who protest that not everything should submit to the test of the marketplace should go to East Africa and listen to some of the other protests. Several parks are already being run as multiple-resource areas, however much their wardens would be appalled to hear them described so. Sometimes the prime aim is wildlife, sometimes it is tourism; sometimes fishing, sometimes other activities. Sometimes the area is exploited legally, sometimes illegally, sometimes in accord with ecological law, sometimes in accord with no law.

Backed up by his researchers, the warden does what he can to meet day-to-day difficulties. But what is wanted is not a day-to-day approach, but a long-term approach that has to be achieved with hour-to-hour urgency. Not that there is much scope for working out integrated plans for conservation when many a park has no policy: nobody is sure whether it is trying to earn money, or international status, or local acclaim for producing protein. A properly planned conservation unit is a combination of various factors that are greater than the sum of its parts. On its own a forest or a habitat might fade away, the wildlife too, but together they can subsist indefinitely. The parks are sometimes described as where East Africa is striking oil. Supposing oil *were* discovered? In a park that recognized the multiplicity of its resources, and therefore the multiplicity of its activities, it might be possible to have oil derricks nodding to the ground in one corner and giraffes nodding to the ground in another.

But not in most of East Africa's parks: they are not yet set up to meet more than one purpose, even though when an African looks at his park he must be persuaded to see it as a prime part of his country's makeup, a source of fortune and fame and future. Other parts of the world can afford the argument of whether parks are for parks or parks are for people, but in Africa it is plain what they must be for, even if for people who will never go near a park. Ruaha Park in Tanzania is a huge stretch of country across the southern tsetse zone—no good for human occupation. Nevertheless, it does not run off nothing; nor does it run off visitors, since it is too remote and too wild to attract most seekers after far fastnesses. It also has too many elephants. A preliminary appraisal is under way to see if it could be run as an elephant range for protein and profit, for the time being at any rate. A revolutionary departure; a center for secluded contemplation given over to Mammon. But better that than giving it over to whatever passing phase comes along, fragmented away without regret and without return. Ruaha Park may have a different future if the future has a Ruaha Park. Similar plans are proposed for the Selous Reserve, also in southern Tanzania's tsetse belt, a 15,000-square-mile area almost the size of West Virginia, that is to be devoted to sight-seeing safaris, roughing-it expeditions, hunting trips, cropping schemes, and whatever else can be welded in with the master plan of allowing every kind of use that does not conflict too much with the other uses. This is multiple-use such as East Africa has rarely seen before, and could see much more of. Parks are not yet for profits, but they are for some purpose beyond "being there."

Parks are also for prestige. It is a poor country that does not have its parks. The parks of Africa that have survived, some of them backwaters away from the mainstream of the country's life in the early days, are now setting out into a new era. Even if the visitor looking out over the park is looking back on a time as remote as it is tranquil, the park itself is undergoing a change as tumultuous as it is recent.

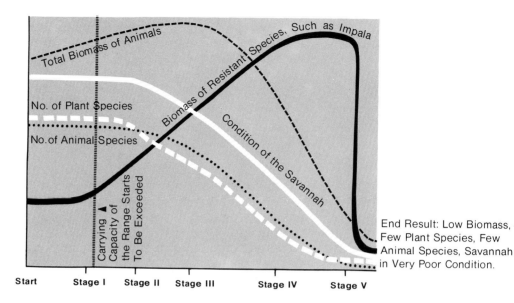

Total Biomass of Animals

No. of Plant Species

No. of Animal Species

Biomass of Resistant Species, Such as Impala

Condition of the Savannah

Carrying
Capacity of
the Range Starts
To Be Exceeded

End Result: Low Biomass, Few Plant Species, Few Animal Species, Savannah in Very Poor Condition.

Start   Stage I   Stage II   Stage III   Stage IV   Stage V

This diagrammatic representation, based on Alan Savory's findings in the Zambezi Valley, indicates what can happen to a wildlife area when the animals are increasingly subjected to pressures of man's populations in the surrounding environment but are suddenly protected from his predation pressures inside the sanctuary. Instead of migrating to new pastures when they are needed, the herds are joined by other animals coming in to escape the harassment outside: all are trapped, then overprotected. From an initial stage, when a wide array of mammals, birds, reptiles, insects, and others live among a wide array of plants on sound soil with proper water supplies, the process starts on its plunge as all forms of hunting are halted in an overloaded community, and the larger creatures which generally have no predator but man (such as elephant and hippo) are free to multiply as they may. Under the impact of their appetites, the better plants are overeaten, perennial grasses give way to annuals, and the more nutritive forms of vegetation are usurped by shrubs and herbs and "weeds." The process is accelerated if the one agency that could help to keep things in some sort of balance—fire—is kept out as "man-made." By stage II, the grasslands are thinning out to bare patches, or are being invaded by scrub growths. This decline favors a few browsers such as eland and impala, but many grazers decline, notably sable and roan antelope and reedbuck; nevertheless, there may be a temporary increase in total animal numbers while the impala undergo a population explosion, a surge that serves to conceal the deteriorating conditions that cannot be halted at a later stage for a fraction of the cost in time and money as now. By the end of stage II, the rainwater soaks in less easily on the bare, hardened soil, and the greater runoff leads to silting-up of pools, even of some streams. As the water table sinks still more in stage III, and the more palatable shrubs give out, there are marked browse lines appearing on trees, an effect of overfeeding by giraffes; there is a start to tree-felling by elephants, while young saplings, especially succulent, don't get a chance to survive infancy to replace the trees disappearing. Coarse grazers such as buffalo may hold out in fair numbers, and the impala continue to boom, perhaps outnumbering all other herbivores put together; there is as yet no fall-off of lions, leopards, and other carnivores that are considered a chief attraction of a wildlife area. By stage IV, the damage to the trees is rapidly increasing. The annual plants that have widely replaced the perennials are less able to resist the dry season with their poorer root structures and quickly wither away to make the dry season seem longer and harsher; when the rains arrive, there is less ground cover, or "litter," to hold the moisture while it soaks in. Those creatures that are most sensitive to disruption of their habitat are now fading away, especially rhinos, bushbuck, bushpig, and others, together with many birds, reptiles, and insects which cannot survive a grossly degraded habitat. Meanwhile, there is hardly any low-down vegetation to obstruct the tourist's view of exceptionally large concentrations of animals around the few remaining water holes. By now, the few surviving grasses and shrubs have less chance to make any recovery with the rains, because the water almost all washes off in flash floods, leaving a drought regime. Three quarters of the trees are dead or dying. The devastation spreads to sheet erosion as the unprotected soil becomes vulnerable to wind damage. Only a few plants and animals survive into stage V, in a landscape that is now well on the way to becoming a desert.

INTO THE NIGHT

The light fades in a display to surpass anything the immense sky has shown during the long African day with its many changes. The sun gets bigger as it falls faster. There is no slow decline to the day on the equator. A fireball stands on the horizon, dropping behind as you stand and stare. The last arc slips out of view and the sky is shot with the brief splendor of twilight. There is a flare and a glow, as is in the nature of this land of the brilliant and the transient.

Night falls. An hour ago there was full sunlight. Now there is darkness. The day ends suddenly with a glory that matches the sun's rising; how long ago the dawn seems now, much more than a day. Yet it is a day complete as a day ought to be, if one has not gotten too much out of touch with the rhythms of the natural world. Nothing essential has been left out. It takes time and a readiness to watch and see and listen, to learn what is new and not just what confirms "old-hand" beliefs. And then it takes more time, and still more. Time passes; it is not chased. That is the attraction of Africa: it follows real time, not a clock-kept ticking.

The traveler moving across the sundown savannah has witnessed a world going about its day's activities in accordance with its hourly needs, in accordance with the patterns of a thousand such mornings, a million such middays, a billion such evenings. They are all similar yet not the same. By infinitesimal shades of difference things are moving in fresh directions. The balance of evolutionary pressures has been shaping the animal life and its environment toward new forms of living. The visitor can hardly discern the slightest trend, but it is there and it is going on all the time: it is part of the experience of Africa, and you sense it is possible. One African day is the merest flicker in another long African day, and you are in both together.

The watcher puts away his binoculars and his camera and puts himself away for the night. Among the boundary trees there is a lion coughing. The sound sets off zebras a little way farther off. The safarist cannot see either; his watching is over for the day. But the day has not ended for most of the denizens of the area. For almost every creature but one the day merely enters another phase, for many the most active phase of all. As the tourist makes toward the light of the lodge he notices how the shadows streaming across the plain are matched by herds of antelope moving out into more open country. The aardvark emerges from its burrow to go on its evening exploration. The galano, better known as the bushbaby, swings around the branches of a tree looking for insects just as it has been doing for the last two hours of Africa's long day. The cheetah and wild dog are now at rest; they cannot exploit their skills at night unless there is a full moon. The hyenas and jackals are on the move, however, and on the move as they rarely are during daylight.

The dark uncovers another side to the creatures, and a fresh side to a fresh set of creatures. Across the wild areas of East Africa there are doings at night that you can only visualize, even if you can hear them well enough. The visitors around the campfire listen to the excited barkings of zebras, or pick up the distant trumpetings of elephants (and wonder how distant). They hear the snort of a wildebeest, and wonder what can be upsetting it. There is a grunt from a leopard, and everyone draws nearer the fire. They hear the roar of a lion and they fall silent, straining to pick out the answering calls from the rest of the pride. They turn toward the nearby river and an outburst of frenzied splashing. They listen to a hyena laughing, and someone remarks it sounds like the noise of a person being raped who decides halfway there is no point in resisting further. But the

The onset of dusk finds the zebras and wildebeest doing what they have done at the end of African days without number: making for the open spaces.

laughter dies as a rumble of hooves erupts and everybody wonders which hooves; another cough from the lion, and everybody speculates how much nearer it is than last time.

Few things are better than watching a pride of lions in the evening sun, then returning to your safari camp and sitting with the night orchestra listening to those same lions going about their night's business. To lie at night and hear the sound rolling across the savannah is to know where you are. If the lion sounds a bit close to your tent, that does not matter, since a mosquito net or even a string six inches off the ground is enough to keep it away.

From the fringes of the safari camp you can sense what a changed world the same world has become. That tall-grown thicket, is it an elephant? And that black shadow, is there something moving in it? Those creatures moving across the plain, are they a group of gazelles or a pack of hyenas? When the moon comes up you can make things out better, oddly enough by using binoculars—there is enough light to pick out things a quarter of a mile away. And you can see a good deal by moonlight with the naked eye, not by looking directly at the animal but slightly to one side: then you can tell an eland from a buffalo. If you are still out and about in your safari truck, you get a finer sense of what a lion's world is like, too. A snoozing lion suddenly sits up and stares into the darkness. Far away a herd of zebras is appearing over a hill. He is on his feet and away with a steady stride. When he is still a hundred yards off he can make them out clearly enough to tell if one is turning in his direction: he becomes a stiff shadow, one paw raised. Suspicion passed, he moves along, belly to the ground, legs moving in long, raking strides. From behind a clump of grass he stares some more; he stalks some more. The zebras start grazing. They think they are the only ones on that patch of plain. They move nearer a dip in the ground. Fifty yards away the lion moves toward the opposite side of the same dip. He glides into position. He watches every one. Not one watches him. They stray closer still. A cloud crosses the moon and a shadow of tension runs through the zebra herd. They start, then trot away. The lion watches them move out of range. Back to his snoozing.

Finally the tourist turns to bed and hope for another day. What will it bring? What group of creatures will loom out of the morning mist? Will that group of cheetah be on the hunt again? Will there be vultures circling aloft to show where the lion pride has got to? Will that pair of crested cranes still be dancing about on the river bank? Will the rhinoceros and calf have found their way back to their particular patch of swamp after moving far out into the plain at twilight? Will tomorrow be clear, with Kilimanjaro sparkling above the cloud banks?

A few visitors wonder not only whether the lions will be lying out on the plains in a few hours' time, but whether they will be lying there in a few years' time. Or whether there will be a further set of lions there in a few more years' time. Will there be any lions at all in a few decades' time? Lions are little affected by poachers unless their prey is. It is the antelopes and zebras that come onto hard times when poachers move into their area. There may be scores of thousands of animals a year falling into traps and snares, devices of grotesque cleverness and cruelty. Yet poaching in itself is not the worst ill to beset African wildlife, not the direct slaughter. The killer may light a small fire to trap his prey, or he may need a fire to smoke the meat before he makes off with it. If he does not put the fire out, he isn't bothered about whether it destroys a dozen animals or a habitat for hundreds of dozens. A score of other reasons can set off scores of unwanted fires.

Fortunately, due to the wardens' efforts, the antelopes are often freer than they were to escape this predator they can't outrun, the carnivore in a truck with a shotgun (and there are hundreds of thousands of old-time muzzle-loaders in East Africa, left over from the colonialists' wars). But the small-timers wreak havoc enough. If a poacher catches enough meat in one area, he leaves long lines of animals elsewhere to die in the snares; or

he hamstrings a number, to dispose of them at leisure another time, provided they haven't hobbled off too far in the meantime—so better cripple more than enough to insure some to spare. Snared antelopes attract predators, and before long there is a terrible toll of lions and leopards in the traps, animals that total hundreds instead of thousands or hundreds of thousands. One leopard is worth more than a hundred wildebeest, to the park and poacher alike. The Serengeti Park is losing 40,000 animals a year to poachers (probably twice as many as to the lions), which is little more than pinprick poaching *only* as long as wardens spend a great amount of time and money in intensive patrolling. A recent patrol picked up 1,000 snares in a single week, while a similar swoop came across a gang with 60,000 pounds of meat on the drying racks. One wonders how many snares are not picked up, how many mass-slaughter gangs are not caught red-handed, how many animals would be taken if it were not for organizations like the Louwana Fund, the Munitalp Foundation, and a range of others supplying cash. On the other hand, if you see a single animal with a month-old snare around its neck, there is nothing to wonder about: the position is quite clear.

Poaching outside the parks is another thing again. Experts in Uganda estimate that at present rates there will be little wildlife left outside the main sanctuaries in five years' time—and that would mean a good half of Uganda's wildlife. Not all these poachers

The lions respond to this final phase of the day by testing the scene with nose and eyes and ears, sensing the vibrations of their lionesque environment.

A leopard sets about its twilight stalk: by tomorrow morning, when it returns to its favorite tree, it may be bringing another creature with it.

operate as commercial organizations: there are a lot more people nowadays, and they are a lot hungrier for meat—in some places, local people make up at least half their meat diet from wild meat. A factor greater than the racketeers is the poacher's fellow tribesmen, who bring forth an average of six children, because "many are good" or "some might die" or "they can help you in your work and your old age" or "there is nothing you can do to stop them."

Poaching used to be a low-level affair. Although the Wanderobo existed off nothing else for generations, they limited themselves through stringent regulations: one could only kill a certain species at a certain time and a certain place. They never rushed in like those who shoot off every bison in sight or every whale. Now poaching is often big business. The white man has all sorts of lucrative inducements to offer the local with a leopard pelt or a crocodile skin, just as the brown man has plenty to offer the local with a rhino horn or a set of elephant tusks. All goes to boost deflated egos overseas: all are hangovers from the days of primitive passions and primitive ways of meeting pseudo-passions. Poachers nowadays not only use their shoulders to carry away the proceeds, they use fleets of trucks. They not only use bows and arrows, they use guns and automatic guns. They not only kill wild animals without a thought, they kill rangers with less thought. Poaching is wasteful and cruel and highly profitable. Not a dime that is given to resist poaching is not well spent. Ask the warden who used to trek across the bush on foot and now leaves aside his jeep to take to the air: he will tell you what it is worth.

Not that poachers are likely to be the prime factor in making any creature extinct. They have pushed the rhino near the edge, but only after what the white settlers and hunters have done to it. And not that many animals in East Africa are near disappearing altogether, though how many are near the point of no return (a different matter) is anybody's guess—and that is just what it amounts to, a guess, until more is known about how many dibatags make enough.

East Africa is lucky. North Africa and South Africa have been under the influence of the outside world for longer. The Barbary lion has gone; so has the Cape lion. So have several more creatures, while several others stand on the edge. In eastern Africa the Somalia wild ass is threatened, as is the Walia ibex of Ethiopia. When one considers the creatures of which one sees a single individual—if one is lucky—where once one could see a hundred, the list is a lot longer. Judging by the noise people make about the animals that are gone, one wonders what future people will say about those who felt they could afford to be the last to see a gorilla in its own place, let alone a crocodile or a cheetah. No good responding that they just never thought there would be an outcry—or that they were hungry, or that they wanted to save the creatures but that the situation wasn't ripe: it wasn't ripe for the dodo.

It is a part of nature for a creature to go extinct, even if it should not be a part of human nature to drive it extinct. Extinction is the usual way of things, not survival. The creatures alive today are the merest part of those that have ever lived, and in time they will be a smaller part still as their roles are taken over by more new creatures (always supposing the full evolutionary process keeps going). Nobody really knows how many species have emerged, existed, gone extinct. Some people put it at ten times as many as are alive now, some at ten times more again. The total number which may have existed since the first flickering of life could reach as many as 500,000,000 species. Even so, this is an age that is not far from being the most interesting ever, even if we are a long way from knowing just how interesting: 10,000 new species are discovered every year. The mammals only number something over 4,000 species, fewer than there were a short while back, but

An aged tusker heads for whatever an elephant needs to do at night—usually eating.

the present time is still part of the great age of the most advanced beings to arrive on earth. If the mammal group has been slowly declining for a few million years, it is nothing as compared with the last 2,000 years when over 100 have disappeared, and that is nothing as compared with the last 100 years, when three-quarters of those 100-plus have been kicked off the planet. The story is much the same for the birds. And that again will be nothing if the present age keeps up its energy: over 1,000 species are on the brink. So much is known: what is not known is how many lesser animals have been eliminated, and how many plants—probably far more than the mammals and the birds (and probably far more are threatened). Man is master of creation: why not get on with it and prove the point? It would be a task to challenge his ingenuity, though not for long. There is no doubt he could manage it. Then he would be lord of all things and alone. No more argument.

Some people ask why bother about these creatures—nobody worries about the dinosaurs (though they might if there were a chance to see a brontosaurus coming down the street). But dinosaurs and other forms of prehistoric life not only disappeared many millions of years ago, they took millions of years about it—though the disappearance of the dinosaurs has been called fast beyond belief. In comparison, the modern rate of extinction is instantaneous, as if the whole of a species were shot off at a single stroke. In the natural way of things it takes a mammal species—even a mammal genus—as much as 5,000,000 years to go under, or be superseded by a fresh form of the old stock. The great eraser is not extinction but evolution, even if it amounts to the same thing. Sometimes a mammal species lasts only a little over 500,000 years. The mean life of a bird species has been placed at around 2,000,000 years, though some of them last far longer. Occasionally a new species appears with astonishing speed, like the snake of Somaliland that is reckoned to have taken a superswift 175,000 years, possibly a third as fast again. Some people say the rhinoceros is suffering from racial old age: it is on its way out, and can no longer adapt to what has been a new world for a long time. But that is different from saying that it should be given the final shove in a few years flat. Why not let it take its own time about these things? It might even shift onto something else. If it were to go under as fast as the dinosaurs, it would be a longer time agoing. None of these natural events has been so momentous as what started in a few years around 1620, when the *Mayflower* arrived in New England and another group of white people touched shore in West Africa. Within a day or two there was the sound of a shot over two continents, a sound that has never stopped.

A rifle is not the only weapon man can aim at his environment. Of the ninety-four bird species that have gone extinct since 1600, less than one in four has disappeared for natural reasons. Much the same for the mammals. Man takes with him not only his gun but alien predators and alien diseases to ravage local communities that are virtually defenseless against foreign incursions. He also takes bulldozing equipment and bulldozing ideas of how to use it. He takes chain saws that slice through ages-old forests and through ages-old ways of doing things. Sometimes there is cause to wonder whether man is leading his technology, or the other way round; getting the cart and horse mixed up is all right, as long as you are in the horse-and-cart age.

There are still plenty of people who do not attach much importance to the disappearance of unfamiliar creatures with unfamiliar names. Will the next be *Diceros bicornis*, that rhinocerine relic of ancient days? It seems an object of amusement as much as interest to some of the people who are fortunate enough to see it. How far do the rest see it as an integral example of African wildlife? Or do they see it as a creature of the same value as a unicorn or a two-headed donkey? Or something massive and monstrous and marvelous, something that would leave a big gap if it disappeared? Not all of them would view it as a single item removed from the page, an isolated being to be thought of in isolation. Others would think of it as a reduction of that marvel called "African wildlife,"

Right: And a lioness heads for whatever she needs to do at night. She prowls across the savannah with less of the relaxed diffidence that marked her stride an hour earlier.

which consists of lions and gorillas and ants and butterflies and chameleons and zebras and zorillas, but which is far greater than all these put together and all the other wild things as well. A leopard in the savannah is not the leopard you see in a zoo. It is an African creature in an African setting with a lot of other creatures that can be African only in this particular way. The person who has seen a leopard—who has *really* seen a leopard—will scarcely see it except as part of the larger whole. It is not a creature on its own, and you don't need to know all the intricacies of its ecology to sense that this is something integral as well as interesting, fundamental as well as fascinating, a single part of a single scene as well as a singularly splendid part of it. If the rhinoceros disappears from Africa, more is lost than the rhinoceros. African wildlife in its last few remnants amounts to more than lists of creatures that are endangered. It is not that twenty are endangered, or two hundred; it is that an individual species under threat makes the whole prospect different.

The tourists, it is said, are to save the wild animals. How far they achieve it depends on the tourists, not the wild animals. It may seem strange that more is not done to expand a source of earnings that is already greater than any other in Kenya and growing twice as fast as any other. Yet it may seem equally surprising that tourists view wild animals in a way that does not always help in the long perspective—and Africa is a place for seeing

Overleaf: At night the wildebeest on the open plain listen for silences. In the herd there is a constant shuffling; so there is little point in making a warning sound if something goes wrong, since it might not be heard. As long as the wildebeest feel secure, there is a steady, soft "grunt-grunt." But if a sudden silence spreads across the herd, something is amiss. Moreover, the hunter has a harder job locating a silent group, and the wildebeest can pick up grass stalks being crushed at a dozen yards away—which a human ear would miss at a few feet.

far. When he is in a park the tourist is in an area which has been set up at least in part for the benefit of creatures other than himself; in fact, man should come a steady and solitary last. Somehow it does not work out that way. There is much talk of how you soon learn to sense the least quiver of a bush; but you have to be able to clamber out of your man-made conveyance to do that. Perhaps the visitor is influenced by what he has read in the past dozen years. If he has read about animals, it has frequently been about animals and people. The setting has been the human setting, into which the animals inject their presence. There have been human ways of doing things, human ways of looking at things, human ways of being. How then can the visitor adjust himself to what happens to the animals—or happens *among* the animals—in a corner of the world where man is supposed to be a non-starter? The watcher may scarcely have heard about how to look at wild animals and see wild animals. Instead he has heard about how the leopard shared my breakfast, how the elephant shared my siesta, how the rhino shared my life. This has done wonders for getting people to look in the right direction; now they might look beyond the creature with a pointing arm and see a few other creatures for what they are.

Wilderness is supposed to be where man can feel at home with the earth. Why then the demand for a home away from home? There is no doubt that people feel an urge toward the open spaces—possibly a hangover from their origins in the savannah lands of Africa? In America the city dwellers now number three out of four; soon they will be four out of five, then five out of six. Many of these people have never seen an animal except for the occasional dog or cat. If there are plenty of African children who have never seen an elephant, there are plenty of American children who have seen an elephant but have not seen a sheep. The new traveler is less inclined to go off searching for ancient buildings unless he can take them in en route. He wants to get away from artifice and artefact to find something simple and straightforward, and he will find it in a land where the animals are not faceless ciphers, not subdued or ordered or altogether man-dominated like cattle in a field at home (if not in a big factory). Antaeus needed contact with the earth, and so does modern man, even though by Herculean efforts he has lifted himself away from the earth. There are places where the world is no longer his earth; it has become too worldly, and he has lost the myth and mystery of his contact with his source and support. In the broadest sense he needs to keep his feet on the ground. Yet the visitor to East Africa finds it hard, stepping as he does from airport tarmac to city street to hotel carpet, thence to safari vehicle and game lodge doorstep. He steps less than he might on the African earth. And yet he wants the invigorating impulse of contact with nature: the winds of the savannah will blow the cobwebs away, the African sun will thaw out the frozen attitudes of the drilled and docile urban life—in Africa he cannot miss: this is nature with more impact than elsewhere. So runs the theory.

If he has come looking for a place untouched by man, however, he will be far from finding it, even if he really wants to. He does not have to be a Robinson Crusoe and gaze in horror at wheel tracks on the plains to sense that a park is now a habitat not only of wild creatures (whatever official policy says about the absolute dominance of nature). These untrammeled places are now available to a creature that will hardly leave them untrammeled. One way out is perhaps at the way in: limit the number of entrants. Which will bring a storm of protest. Some people argue that wildlife is an asset to be exploited to the limit; madness to turn away good money. They think that the golden goose can be persuaded to lay its eggs flat out, whatever it is accustomed to. But there are also those who say that if the open wilderness is not open to all, then what is the use of it? Nobody is sure how far virgin nature may be seduced by how many visitors. But—say it again—in a region where there may be jam tomorrow but hardly bread today, there is little room for talk of wildlife "for its own sake." The visitor is to be allowed in on more than sufferance; he should be welcome once he has been through the ticket office. Furthermore, one may wonder how far parks should ever have to earn as much as they cost—part way, certainly;

A lioness at night reveals how this is a scene separate from what has gone before; day seems a long way off, a world away—and so it is, a world apart. But it is the same lioness that strides back to her cubs at dawn, at the start of a new African day.

but they are hardly to be run as commercial enterprises, or as public amenities which no more have to show a profit than the fire department. And if some of the park expenses have to be paid for by the taxpayer, then which taxpayer? Where are the people who talk of the Serengeti as part of the world's heritage?

If it is sometimes hard to know what to do with the foreigner (except to hope that he will keep on coming), *Homo touristicus* is a species which occupies a prime niche in the total spectrum, a pivot on which other species largely depend. He promotes an increased turnover in that fundamental nutrient of any contemporary community, cash. His antics benefit scores of species; without him, they would find their habitat rapidly shrinking, and would be subject to a new onslaught of predation as intensive as it was insatiable, powered by a technical efficiency and a commercial incentive which the wild world has never run up against before. A future bleak and short.

These tourists are coming to see the old-time Africa, the Africa of sun and sand and safari, Africa as everyone knows it, Africa the wild, Africa the unchanging. In this one part of Africa there is wilderness and wonder, snowcaps sparkling across heat-shimmering savannah, desert and rainforest side by side, an ancient world and an abiding world. But should wilderness be seen as an antithesis or an antidote to civilization—or as an extension? Is it to be protected because it is rare and remote, or can it be as economic as esoteric? The Bible sometimes looks on wilderness as a place accursed; more often it looks on it as a sanctuary where you can be alone with your thoughts as well as secure from the evils of society. But nature protected for tourist repose, and nature protected for conservation, are not always the same thing. Tourism is an exploitative business, and the aim is to get your wild nature to produce the shekels. It will not run out like a coal field, but it might become less wild in the process. Much depends on whether the visitors treat the wilderness as a glorified zoo: if they want a zoo now, they'll get it soon enough. Or do people get that mysterious uplift when confronted with unmitigated nature? Perhaps the only uplift they are sensitive to is the elevator to the twentieth floor. If nature can pull it off, perhaps modern man with his inquisitive instincts and his acquisitive passions (especially for new social experience) is the only variant of the human species that senses an urge for a world of pristine origin; or is he merely indulging in his old game of social reaction (one tourist brochure calls it social intercourse), with a fresh backdrop against which to disport his jaded sensitivities? Like South Sea islands of the tropics and traditions, Africa is perhaps a land of sunshine and serenity without end, hence a place generous enough to absorb whatever oddments of litter an outsider inflicts upon it.

If it had not been for the tourists and their foreign exchange, not to mention their foreign ways, these East African countries would not have achieved their remarkable record in conservation. Hopefully there are more tourists to come, bringing more conservation. Africa is still a land for the man who gazes across empty space and sees it full of many things, a new land and an old land and a strange land. It is part of a flimsy biosphere-film that has produced a zebra, a leopard, an oryx, a fish eagle, a lungfish and a naked molerat. Nobody knows if the naked molerat is the only one in the universe. It could be. So could the rhinoceros. Yet man wants to take the rhinoceros off the planet because he feels so decrepit. He wants to do the same to the leopard because he feels so naked. He might leave the naked molerat alone unless it proves so wretched as to have some quality that can prop up man's impotent, not to say imbecilic, ego. East Africa represents a race in conservation as dramatic as anywhere, and the tourist upsurge represents one of the best bets so far.

Another man central to conservation in East Africa is the pastoralist. He lives in areas which the wild creatures share with him by his good grace, the savannahlands that *are* East Africa (the parks and the cultivable portions are by far the exception). Range lands around the world are coming under pressure to develop—or else. It is these parts of East Africa which will see much of the change in the next few years, especially when they have hardly changed in centuries.

There were cattle people in East Africa well before the time of Christ, perhaps as far back as the apocryphal equivalents of Abraham or Isaac. The Masai patriarch watching his herds file into the manyatta at evening time is a scene out of the prophets. He is ancient and autocratic. He has now come up against a vision he had not expected. There is promise of change, and not at some stage in the remote future. Change can be change, or it can be disruption. Wildlife protagonists in the past have tended to ignore the rights of local people: they might not be "right" rights, but they are there and the locals will hang on to them. Ecological ideas are one thing; idealistic concepts are another, when they see people on the ground as something to be ignored, or at best as statistical variants. The wildlife will survive in these areas not just because people overseas want them to survive, but because people living with them day by day want them to survive. No good the wildlife supporter firing off streams of biomass data and upholding the wild creatures as paragons of ecological virtue, when he does not have to go home in the evening and wonder whether he will wake up to find his cattle carried off by a lion or his watering points modified by a rhino. The time could be coming when the Masai will view wildlife as worth having only when it is dead, just as they see domestic stock as worth having only when it is alive.

Any scheme that aims at better stock husbandry strikes at the deepest roots of these people and their whole value system. The problem is—as in much of East Africa—that

A leopard is distinguished at any hour, but at night it is a leopard as much and more again. Secretive and stealthy, it matches the darkness more than any other carnivore.

there are plenty of programs leading to progress, but they do not always run in conjunction. Because they operate in tight little worlds of their own, the overall upshot is often something nobody would call "progress." Nor is it any good for munificent conservationists in their citadels overseas to fire off assistance ultimatums that amount to offers to "buy" a stretch of Masailand for wildlife. They are about as helpful as those who think that Masai development depends on Masai dress. A Masai in ready-mades gains no more in stature than an Elijah put into trousers and given a social security number. The dignity of Job does not bother about keeping up with the Joneses. Nor are the Masai yet accustomed to the ways of avarice. But it will come, together with whatever else lubricates the modern world.

Fortunately, East Africa and its range lands are not saddled with the deep-seated religious attitudes that hinder advance in Asia. In times when many a now-ism amounts

to a was-ism, Kenya is lucky to have a dynamic social basis in what is known as African Socialism, just as Tanzania has its "Ujamaa" community-living concept. This is not so much an ideology as a way of life. It has been founded on what is already there, not on what should be there or what might be there some day. It focuses on the communal nature of many African societies, the self-help attitudes, the live-and-let-live approach which too often in the past dwindled to desultory existence but which in the future might lead to more constructive frameworks, where people exist for something else besides making money out of their neighbors.

All this is work that can only be done by East Africans. The outside world can watch, and learn as much about the Masai and their problems as about the wild creatures and theirs. Beyond that, there are all kinds of ways people can help—if they want to. Most people say they do, but they don't. Not that East Africa is going it alone in conservation. Plenty of people around the world remind East Africans that wildlife is not just the heritage of Africa; fortunately a few of them are prepared to do something about it. It can be an expensive business. Running Tanzania's parks costs two-thirds of a million dollars for Tanzania, which would not go very far without even more from abroad. Tanzania itself is spending five times as much on its wildlife as it was in the colonial days, and this is a land with as little affluence as almost any in the world—and other things to spend money on, when its medical expenses per head per year are less than many an American spends on tranquilizers every day.

Foremost among the outside helpers is the World Wildlife Fund. It is one of the more enterprising organizations, even if not enough people across the United States have heard about it to put their hands in their pockets. It does not hesitate to raise its voice in the marketplace, and that is a lot more than some do: a single ad can bring in thousands of dollars. During the last ten years the fund has raised $7,500,000 to meet crises around the world, which is a lot—and a long way off the $5,000,000 required to meet minimum needs *every year*. It is also half the cost of a jet bomber, or 1 percent of what the United States spends on such essentials as skiing each year. The man who tells you there is nothing he would rather do than help, but he has taxes and troubles, and tells you as much over his second martini before lunch, is retelling the story of the bison. One martini less a month might put off his coronary for a while, and might put off sudden death for the animals of Africa and everywhere else, forever. He has his choice, a choice to be observed by people in the future who may no longer observe a rhino. East African citizens are each contributing more from their impoverished pockets, much more, than many people who are ready to talk about how the world's treasures belong to the world.

Around a water hole there are many comings and goings at night, especially by the larger animals, which have less to fear from lions. At Treetops, there is a steady throng of elephants, buffaloes, and rhinos, some of them getting in each other's way at the poolside.

The World Wildlife Fund is generous toward Africa. Although the continent ranks third after Europe and North/Central America in the total it receives, it features more projects than the rest of the world combined except Asia. Half of them are in East Africa. Several other organizations are in full fray. The African Wildlife Leadership Foundation is a major funding source as are a number of Zoological Societies across the United States. Dr. Grzimek in Germany sends cash to support anti-poaching patrols, and to support schools for the anti-poaching patrols' children. The Ford Foundation keeps up a steady flow; so do the Nuffield Foundation in Britain and the Thyssen Foundation in Germany. Many of these organizations channel their contributions through the intelligence center on the ground, the East African Wildlife Society. There are organizations that send in money for the most crucial crises, just as there are those that send in cash for deciding whether a hartebeest should have this Latin name or that. There are organizations that have to think twice before picking up the telephone. One such is the International Union for the Conservation of Nature, allied to the World Wildlife Fund, the only global organization that keeps tabs on which is going extinct where. Its staff sometimes hitchhike to conferences. It is the only organization supported largely by government funds around the world, which might explain its parlous state. It has plenty of other affairs in the red: it maintains books listing endangered creatures, with lucky ones between the red covers—every month or two a sheet is taken out and moved into the black, In Memoriam.

All sorts of people support conservation organizations, and all sorts of people lead them. The full-time conservationist is a man whose activity is now likely to be of as much consequence as most, and *not* just in saving wild animals. He might even be among those who help to shape the future patterns of civilization. Conservation now means the most rational use of the environment for the greatest benefit of man: how much talk of animals there? And what creature sits at the climax of the definition if not their "enemy"? Put another way, conservation aims at the use of natural resources for the greatest good of the greatest number for the longest time; which after all is a change from the assumption that everything belongs to the first-comer—the fast-buck approach. Modern man has come a long way from medieval times when it was thought not uncommon to enhance the landscape with a cathedral, a project to last several generations.

The conservationist should be the specialist leader of what is everybody's business, even if all too often it becomes nobody's business. Conservation should not be run in the spirit of a small club of nature fanciers, but as a broad social movement of life fanciers. The conservationist is trying to put over the message that although nature can get by (and probably a lot better) without man, man cannot get by without nature. He is trying to suggest that man should think about escaping from his own ingenuity. Fortunately, man has the power to do it, in his imagination. It is not that there has been enough intellect; the consequences would be disastrous if intellect were brought down a peg or two; but what is needed is for imagination to be brought up a notch or three. Man will have to start getting to grips with the concept of the totality of earth. It is a big expression and rather too big for the intellect to grasp in its conceptual consequences, but man may as well get used to the idea, since it is going to be with him for a long time.

This is what the new conservation is about. Conservation was once equated with plugging the wounds of a zebra foal when it has been saved from a hyena. But saving a leopard is not like saving the leopard. Some efforts by animal protectors, however inspired, might achieve little more than Lady Bountiful dispensing charity around old-time England: much done to alleviate individual suffering, but hardly affecting the cause. Syringes for antibiotics are scarcely more than a pinprick approach. Moreover, there is not much good in trying to save animals unless it is apparent that by saving them we are saving ourselves. There are plenty of people who agree that wildlife should have a very high priority, should be the subject of crash programs and last-minute strategies, in fact should have every sort of priority except for one, and that is people. With that sort of approach, the wild animals are doomed. Not that they should come before people; they should come side by side, just like any other part of nature. The conservationist who says that people are all very nice, but what about the animals, is doing as much to bring about their end as is the poacher and the dashing developer and the most irresponsible hunter. Those who weep over the animals are likely to drown their charges in a flood of tears, because too much of the world takes too little notice of that sort of thing. Those with such a perspective might wonder what their own survival value is, whether they are not in as much trouble as the rhinoceros, thick of skin and short of sight. What is needed is the latter-day economist, who can show how wild animals can allow local people to enjoy a life with wider horizons to match the land they live in. And if the aim is a higher standard of living for people in East Africa, it is an aim for those outside as well—a real standard of living, not just a sense of existing.

Conservation has been viewed as not so much about what people can do as what they can't. But people are not like that: they can be persuaded, while they won't be prevented. Conservation shouldn't be a case of don't do this but of how better to do that—and a score of other things besides. It is not a restriction of activity so much as an immense widening of experience. The modern-day conservationist should develop a sense of the jugular. He must be able to encounter the unbeliever and tell him in one minute how he will be impoverished if he does not listen for another five, and after five how his life will be impoverished if he does not impoverish his pocket.

And beyond that the conservationist has to learn yet other languages, those of the economist and the engineer and the agriculturalist and the planner. Until then he will be a voice crying in the wilderness, and a wilderness of a different sort. If it is time to leave behind the purely aesthetic approach, it is past time for the purely zoological approach. The wildlife researcher can no longer be the strict biologist: if sociologists are now having to learn something of ecology, and lawyers too, why not the other way round? The wilderness scientist in Africa might realize what forces are being generated beyond the horizon that may turn the wild places into an ersatz wilderness. It is as pointless for the wildlife researcher to work "as if man does not exist" as it is for the old-time economist to work "as if nature does not exist." The leading ecologists of recent years are noted not only for their contributions to their scientific discipline but for their contributions to community living of a different kind. There are few researchers now who are not consummate at computerized communications among themselves, yet when it comes to speaking with the people who will call the odds in the long run, they can hardly get

Rhinos at night are more nervous and irritable than during the day, perhaps because their poor eyes put them at more of a disadvantage. They react to any creature that crosses their line of sight, or scent, and they do not spend long at the water hole before lumbering off into the night, like some mammoth retreating into the dark of prehistory.

beyond preliminary programming. Not that the man-oriented approach should penetrate too far into the field. Trouble has begun when man thinks he is big enough to take the protection of nature into his own hands, rather than merely give a bit of assistance. When much more is known, nature will still need nobody to hold its hand.

East Africa is not yet blessed with those marvels of modern living which make life in the multi-million metropolis not so much a case of acting as reacting, where persons become "other people" to be avoided as much as individuals to be encountered. East Africa has few of those fanatics who wish to look out over the world through smog-colored spectacles. It has not yet reached the sophisticated stage where beauty amounts to the latest fashion, and where perfume smells better than flowers. The Africans could always chicken out of the rat race, as some persons have put it, though there is nothing of that spirit in President Julius Nyerere of Tanzania when he tells his people they should beware of confusing material advance with what is intrinsic to Africa, a sense of community. At a time when these emergent countries want to take their full place in the world, it is to their credit that they do not want to take it altogether on the world's terms—which takes a lot of doing. Yet this is one way these African people can preserve their African integrity. If it is a choice that is not always easy, it is a choice—in East Africa—that is not

always necessary. They can have a fair measure of both; indeed, some people say it is difficult to see how they can have much of one without the other, if they decide to exploit their ancient African landscapes in the most efficient manner.

The African leaders do what they can for their wild spectacles, in the knowledge that if they kill off all the creatures at one stroke, all the papers around the world will be full of it, and nobody will be in any doubt where Tanzania is on the map. But if they do the sort of thing that could set them foremost among the nations that have appeared on earth, the world will still know of Tanzania as a place near Algeria (or is it Angola?). Already they can look back on a record to compare with the best during the formative stages of any new nation. In fact, they have done enough for them to recognize that it would be less than fair to say everything is perfect. What is being asked of them is a breadth of mind and an enterprise of spirit to set them apart from the dreary conformity spreading over the earth; and what is being asked of people outside is a tolerance and patience toward these departures to match the scale of the new endeavor. It is a great deal to ask, something that has never been asked before and is unlikely to be asked again. It is a massive responsibility and a massive opportunity. Those elsewhere can either watch and wait, or they can take sides and take part.

No other community has ever had this chance. Africans and non-Africans alike have an opportunity such as the Greeks never had, nor the Aztecs nor the Manchus nor the Founding Fathers nor the Victorians—they did not know, and if they had known they would not have had the means to do much about it. Everybody lives once and everybody has the chance to stand up and be counted once. He stands up for what he thinks is worth something, or he stands up for "don't know, haven't time." Either way he is counted. He does not have a chance to lie down and keep quiet till his life is over. How far the wild horizons are retained in their present form depends on the horizons in the minds of people all around the earth, people who are often called the faceless creatures of anonymous societies. Yet there has never been a time when the individual counts so much. He can show what sort of a face he has, and how to preserve a face of the earth worth looking at.

For the people of East Africa there are no neat solutions to easy problems. Only rarely is there a right side and a wrong side. Nor is it a case of both sides having a lot of right, since there are not two sides but two dozen. Some of these African leaders recognize

Below left: All at once the night is split by the sounds of hyenas at a carcass. Three lionesses hear them and race over. By the time they arrive the wildebeest kill is ten minutes old and half gone. The lionesses scatter the hyenas and set about the remains.

Below right: While the hyenas sound their objections, the lionesses chew and snarl, occasionally breaking off to issue a warning.

that whatever they do, many an onlooker is going to be taking aim at them. They have to make a move, while those behind cry, "Forward!" and those before cry, "Back!" They have to take the most significant decisions, significant for their people, significant for whatever is fine in Africa, significant for all those watching, significant for now and for all time. They have very few precedents to guide them. This is an exploration as difficult as any a hundred years ago, an exploration into the interior of Africa to find out what makes Africa. They are up against an African environment that is thick and tangled and thorny, with an atmosphere that is invariably overheated, and with thunderstorms all around. If they use the maps offered from outside, they might find they are not maps for Africa. These African leaders have the opportunity to become some of the finest land managers on earth—and that is what makes a citizen of the late twentieth century. They do not need to follow the old-timers like a group of wildebeest. They can go straight to the head of the line, migrating into a new land. They will have to reveal the wisdom of Solomon and the tenacity of an army of Solomons, just as they will have to show strong sales resistance to the peddlers of a synthetic society. After all, many an outsider has strong reason for wanting to convert East Africa to his contrived cause: as long as there is an environment fit to meet the real needs of the community, not just the money-grabbing antics of a few, it will be an offense to be different from the old-stage world.

The true technologist refines the world rather than refashioning it, following the dictates of balanced nature rather than of unbalanced man. The days are gone for those technicians who had something in common with the tunnel engineer, who used their restricted vision to dig around in the environment insisting all the time that they alone saw the light at the end of the shaft. What is needed is a revolution in thinking if not a revolution in doing. It is of little use to say one is against revolutions, when there are several revolutions *going on* at once. The only way to stabilize the scene is to get several bigger and better revolutions going in a single direction.

The conservationist is not against the bland technological present. Far from trying to stop progress, he wants to make it. There is nobody who is not on a chariot of progress that is bent on a headlong dash down the road, at a faster and faster rate. It only got out of low gear comparatively recently, a couple of hundred years ago; a couple of score years ago it began to pick up speed at a remarkable rate—yet even today it is a long way from

Left to right:
As the lionesses gnaw and growl, the hyenas howl back, which attracts other members of the clan. As more hyenas arrive, hungry hyenas, the pack edges closer.

The lionesses gorge faster, the hyenas grow bolder, harassing the lionesses from all sides.

The lionesses half devour the kill, half defend it—while a jackal nips in to snatch a bit.

The lionesses get fuller while the hyenas get hungrier and more numerous. The screeches and snarls reach a crescendo until finally the hyenas rush the remains, and the lionesses scatter.

reaching high gear. The conservationist should be as capable as any of the other passengers at steering the vehicle along the road, though the main problem is guiding it round some of the larger rocks and the more precipitous holes. Slamming on the brakes might not have much effect beyond throwing the whole machine off course.

Man will need all his faculties for this feat. Some people view him as a hubris-harried being, a self-blinded creature as ambitious and limited as any tragic hero of ancient times. Yet he is only half-blind, and there isn't anything much heroic about the security-ridden worship of his modern-style golden calves. And if there is a tragic quality to the situation, this could still be a human comedy to make the gods laugh—except that there will probably be no opportunity for man to pick himself up and try again. If he is still to be a tragic figure, he won't show all that much surpassing stature, nor will he have failed in any time-transcending endeavor. He will arouse a bit of pathos and not much else.

Development in a score of fields is progressing at a rate unprecedented even yesterday, even this morning. History is accelerating beyond imagination. It is a time when prophets and seers are of less help than usual, even though they are needed more than ever. Twenty-five years from now is as remote a period as pre-Renaissance times five hundred years back. But there is one trend accepted by all the crystal-gazers: there is to be a steady progression to conformity as efficient as it is featureless. All the more appropriate then to try to preserve those parts of the world that represent interest unmatched.

As progress progresses, and an age emerges which has been called the post-historical era—when people and places are so conformed to patterns that all is controlled and all can be predicted, with nothing new happening, when history has been brought to a halt —then man may look for a place where there is still change, even if it is change that has been going on for millions of years, a change of infinite variety at an infinite pace—so that he may get intimations of infinity in a strictly limited world. He might then delight at a serval cat on the stalk at evening time. There is something about a wild animal that sets it apart from the onlooker. It is mobile where he is bound; it is simple where he is complex. No man, no matter how complex—or cultured or civilized—but will react to the essentially naive, the elementally simple. East Africa is a land of the past, of the immense past, and it could be a land of the future.

This book is not a polite plea for wildlife. There have been dozens of those in the last ten years and if there were scores every year—given the progress that has been achieved so far—they still wouldn't meet a fraction of what is needed. Because there is no other measure: what matters is not whether a lot has been done, or a lot more than a lot, but

whether it is *enough*. There is little point in saying we have come a long way; we might consider getting on the starting-line. There are few people who can say they have donated as much as would be noticeable to their pocket a month later, or a minute later. But even that much is not required from everyone; what counts is a mere trifle of what is given over to the gargantuan extravagances of affluent existence: that much would be more than enough, forever. One can keep one's waistline from going excessive, and keep the wilderness from going extinct.

So this book is not a plea. It says that we do not want wild animals—we, living far away from Africa, far away in imagination (even if not really farther than the end of the television tube) we do not want wild animals. This is a time to see wild worlds right around the globe as easily as never before. It is also a time to see to it that they are there to be seen again. Everybody knows more about an elephant than Socrates did. Everybody also knows how to keep elephants in being for millions of people who will not be a Socrates but will want to know. It is no good saying that Africans should do more (or even do it all). Communities elsewhere can look to their record in their first hundred years of nationhood, let alone the first ten. Tanzania started off independence with one park; now it has ten, and it gives three times as large a share of its national kitty to its parks as the United States gives to its own, out of a total budget amounting to what New York spends on ice cream. Yet there are still bystanders who object that poachers in East Africa enjoy a field day, so why don't the Africans do something about their problems. Not that the richest nation on earth has resources to do as much as it might about poachers by the hundred in a trifling tip of Florida, one four-hundredth part the size of East Africa. Other people protest about the population explosion in Africa, but families there have not been producing more children than many a household in pioneer America or Victorian England; rather, today more are surviving, many more. People complain the world is losing the world's heritage in Africa, but when Africans ask for help they hear how hard the world is finding it to make ends meet.

The story is known well enough: we all know it, the entire tale. What we don't do is *visualize* it, using our refined senses to recognize what is happening, then using some common sense to do something about it. People will look back and wonder why the latest toothbrush counted more than the last cheetah, why the multi-martini mattered more than the modern Masai, why the spread of the most capable civilization ever could not find space for what was there before civilization got out of its cave. Which may be why it takes the supreme sophisticate to value what was there when he wasn't or what is there where he isn't. People one day will wonder why there was no time for what was called

In a few moments the hyenas have disposed of everything, with bones disappearing in all directions—while two lionesses watch from the background.

the timeless; they will wonder why—when there was more to spend on making life less of a bore than there had ever been on making life possible—why we, on being asked for a few dimes, sent our deep regrets. People will wonder how we could watch and wonder—and wait. But we are no longer waiting. We have decided. We do not want wild animals: we only want to want them.

We can change our minds. If we want some sights round the back of the world different from our own backyard, we had better say so. Some people think Africa is only a little way beyond the end of the airport runway, but it is far closer than that. Voices nowadays cross continents as fast as they cross the local suburb. What is needed is not only a change of thought but an exchange of thought. Fortunate it is that we are to be matched against this moment with the means to confront it. The wherewithal is overready; the time is overripe; the crisis is over—where? One can either be a statistical stereotype, or one can be an individual, an individual as never before. There are people to talk to, people to write to. If it costs something to write a check, there is that other piece of paper that costs

less and costs more, and that is a personal letter expressing a personal opinion. Kenya covers the entire expense of safeguarding its wildlife except for a mere 5 percent from outside. The parks of Tanzania need the cost of one destroyer to keep them going until today's child grows up, but at the present time these funds are not fractionally forth-coming. If more could be done in East Africa, it is because more needs to be done outside East Africa. Talking about letter-writing and fund-finding may be a prosaic way of ending this book, but it could be a down-to-earth way of making sure something earthy and fine does not vanish from the planet.

These are spectacles which have already lasted "forever." Whether they last for a few more moments which are the "forever" of modern man's terms, is up to the phenomenon Homunculus, twentieth-century vintage. He has opportunities given to none before him. He will be able to leave his own kind of Utopia and travel to a place that is not paradise but might afford him intimations of Elysium. It is a world fresh and fragile; it is as it was in the beginning.

BIBLIOGRAPHY

This selection lists only the more prominent and recent writings on African wildlife.

ELEPHANTS

Buechner, H. K.; Buss, I. O.; Longhurst, W. M.; and Brooks, A. C. 1963. Numbers and Migration of Elephants in Murchison Falls National Park, Uganda. *J. Wildl. Mgmt.* 27.

Buss, I. O., and Savidge, J. M. 1966. Change in Population Number and Reproduction Rates of Elephants in Uganda. *J. Wildl. Mgmt.* 30.

Field, C. R. 1971. Elephant Ecology in the Queen Elizabeth National Park, Uganda. *E. Afr. Wildl. J.* 9.

Glover, J. 1963. The Elephant Problem at Tsavo. *E. Afr. Wildl. J.* 1.

Glover, P. E., and Sheldrick, D. L. W. 1964. An urgent Research Problem on the Elephant and Rhino Populations of the Tsavo National Park in Kenya. *Bull. Epiz. Dis. Afr.* 12.

Hanks, J. 1971. The Elephant Problem. Morges: World Wildlife Fund.

Harris, L. D. 1968. Population Dynamics of the African Elephant in the Mkomazi Game Reserve, Tanzania, East Africa. M.Sc. thesis, Michigan State Univ., unpublished.

Harthoorn, A. M. 1966. The Tsavo Elephants. *Oryx* 14.

Holman, D. 1967. *The Elephant People.* London: John Murray.

Lamprey, H. F.; Glover, P. E.; Turner, M. I. M.; and Bell, R. H. V. 1967. Invasion of the Serengeti National Park by Elephants. *E. Afr. Wildl. J.* 5.

Laws, R. M.
1969a. Aspects of Reproduction in the African Elephant. *J. Reprod. Fert.,* Suppl. 6.
1969b. The Tsavo Research Project. *J. Reprod. Fert.,* Suppl. 6.
1970. Elephants as Agents of Habitat and Landscape Change in East Africa. *Oikos* 21.

Laws, R. M., and Parker, I. S. C. 1968. Recent Studies on Elephant Populations in East Africa. *Symp. Zool. Soc. Lond.* 21.

Laws, R. M.; Parker, I. S. C.; and Johnstone, R. C. B. 1970. Elephants and Habitats in North Bunyoro, Uganda. *E. Afr. Wildl.* 8.

Lawton, R. N. and Gough, M. 1970. Elephants or Fire—Which to Blame? *Oryx* 10.

McCullagh, K. 1969. The Growth and Nutrition of the African Elephant, *E. Afr. Wildl. J.* 7.

McCullagh, K. G., and Lewis, M. G. 1967. Spontaneous Arteriosclerosis in the Wild African Elephant: Its Relation to the Disease in Man. *Lancet* 2.

Napier-Bax, P., and Sheldrick, D. L. W. 1963. Some Preliminary Observations on the Food of Elephant in Tsavo Royal National Park (East) of Kenya. *E. Afr. Wildl. J.* 1.

Parker, I. S. C. 1964. The Galana Game Management Scheme. *Bull. Epiz. Dis. Afr.* 12.

Parker, I. S. C., and Archer, A. L. 1970. The Status of Elephants, Other Wildlife and Cattle in Mkomazi Game Reserve. Nairobi: Wildlife Services.

Petrides, G. A., and Swank, W. G. 1966. Estimating the Productivity and Energy Relations of an African Elephant Population. *Proc. Int. Grassl. Conf.* 9.

Pienaar, U. de V.
1967. Operation "Khomandlopfu." Koedoe 10.
1969. Why Elephant Culling is Necessary. *Afr. Wild Life* 23.

Pienaar, U. de V., and Fairall, N. 1969. The Influence of the African Elephant on the Vegetation of the Kruger National Park. *Koedoe* 12.

Sikes, S. K.
1968a. The Elephant Problem in Africa. *Afr. Wild Life* 20.
1968b. Observations on the Ecology of Arterial Diseases in the African Elephant in Kenya and Uganda. *Symp. Zool. Soc. Lond.* 21.

Watson, R. M., and Bell, R. H. V. 1969. The Distribution, Abundance and Status of Elephant in the Serengeti Region of Northern Tanzania. *J. Appl. Ecol.* 6.

Watson, R. M.; Parker, I. S. C.; and Allan, T. 1969. A Census of Elephant and other Large Mammals in the Mkomazi Region of Northern Tanzania and Southern Kenya. *E. Afr. Wildl. J.* 7.

Wing, L. C., and Buss, I. O. 1970. Elephants and Forests. *Wildl. Monogr.* 19.

RHINOCEROS

Allbrook, D. B.; Harthoorn, A. M.; Luck, C. P.; and Wright, P. G. 1958. Temperature Regulation in the White Rhinoceros. *J. Physiol.* 143.

Carter, B. H. 1965. *The Arm's Rhinoceros.* London: André Deutsch.

Goddard, J.
1967. Home Range, Behavior and Recruitment Rates of Two Black Rhinoceros Populations. *E. Afr. Wildl. J.* 7.
1970a. Age Criteria and Vital Statistics of a Black Rhinoceros Population. *E. Afr. Wildl. J.* 8.
1970b. Food Preferences of Black Rhinoceros in the Tsavo National Park. *E. Afr. Wildl. J.* 8.

Guggisberg, C. A. W. 1966. *S.O.S. Rhino.* London: André Deutsch.

Hamilton, P. G., and King, J. M. 1969. The Fate of Black Rhinoceroses Released in Nairobi National Park. *E. Afr. Wildl. J.* 7.

King, J. M. 1969. The Capture and Translocation of the Black Rhinoceros. *E. Afr. Wildl. J.* 7.

Schenkel, R. 1969. *Ecology and Behavior of the Black Rhinoceros.* Hamburg: Paul Parey.

HIPPOPOTAMUS

Field, C. R. 1970. A Study of the Feeding Habits of the Hippopotamus in the Queen Elizabeth National Park, Uganda, with Some Management Implications. *Zool. Afr.* 5.

Laws, R. M. 1968. Interactions between Elephants and Hippopotamus Populations and Their Environments. *E. Afr. Agric. For. J.* 33.

Laws, R. M., and Clough, G. 1965. Observations on Reproduction in the Hippopotamus. *Symp. Zool. Soc. Lond.* 15.

Pienaar, U. de V. 1967. The Field-Immobilization and Capture of Hippopotamus in Their Aquatic Element. *Koedoe* 10.

Pienaar, U. de V.; Van Wyk, P.; and Fairall, N. 1966. An Experimental Cropping Scheme of Hippopotami in the Letaba River of the Kruger National Park. *Koedoe* 9.

Thorton, D. D. 1971. The Effect of Complete Removal of Hippopotamus on Grassland in the Queen Elizabeth National Park, Uganda. *E. Afr. Wildl. J.* 9.

BUFFALO

Grimsdell, J. J. R. 1969. Ecology of the Buffalo in Western Uganda. Ph.D. thesis, Cambridge University, unpublished.

Pienaar, U. de V. 1969. Observations on Developmental Biology, Growth and Some Aspects of the Population Ecology of African Buffalo in the Kruger National Park. *Koedoe* 12.

Sinclair, A. R. E. 1970. Studies of the Ecology of the East African Buffalo. D.Phil. thesis, Oxford University, unpublished.

GIRAFFE

Dagg, H. J. 1962. The Role of the Neck in the Movements of the Giraffe. *J. Mamm.* 43.

Foster, J. B. 1966. The Giraffe of Nairobi National Park: Home Range, Sex Ratios, the Herd, and Food. *E. Afr. Wildl. J.* 4.

Spinage, C. A. 1968. *The Book of the Giraffe.* Boston: Houghton-Mifflin.

ANTELOPE

Ables, E. D., and Ables, J. 1969. Home Range and Activity Studies of Impala in Northern Kenya. *Trans. 34th N. Amer. Wildl. Conf.*

Buechner, H. K.; Morrison, J.; and Leuthold, W. 1966. Reproduction in Uganda Kob with Special Reference to Behavior. *Symp. Zool. Soc. Lond.* 15.

Cloudsley-Thompson, J. 1971. The Tricks of Desert Living. *New Scient.* 51.

Dowsett, R. J. 1966. Behavior and Population Structure of Hartebeest in the Kafue National Park. *Puku* 4.

Estes, R. D.
    1966. Behavior and Life History of the Wildebeest. *Nature* 212.
    1967. The Comparative Behavior of Grant's and Thomson's Gazelle. *J. Mamm.* 48.
    1969. Territorial Behavior of the Wildebeest. *Zeit. f. Tierpsych.* 26.

Gosling, L. M. 1969. Parturition and Related Behavior in Coke's Hartebeest. *J. Reprod. Fert.,* Suppl. 6.

Hanks, J.; Price, M. S.; and Wrangham, R. W. 1969. Some Aspects of the Ecology and Behavior of the Defassa Waterbuck (*Kobus defassa*) in Zambia. *Mamm.* 33.

Hvidberg-Hansen, H., and De Vos, A. 1971. Reproduction, Populations and Herd Structure of Two Thomson's Gazelle Populations. *Mamm.* 35.

Kiley-Worthington, M. 1965. The Waterbuck in East Africa: Spatial Distribution, a Study of the Sexual Behavior. *Mamm.* 29.

Leuthold, W.
    1966. Homing Experiments with an African Antelope. *Zeit. f. Saug.* 31.
    1970. Observations on the Social Organization of Impala. *Zeit. f. Tierpsych.* 27.

Schenkel, R. 1966. On Sociology and Behavior of Impala. *E. Afr. Wildl. J.* 4.

Spinage, C. A.
    1969. Waterbuck Management Data. *E. Afr. Agric. For. J.*
    1970. Population Dynamics of the Uganda Defassa Waterbuck (*Kobus defassa ugandae* Neumann) in the Queen Elizabeth National Park, Uganda. *J. Ecol.* 39.

Stewart, D. R. M. 1971. Food Preferences of an Impala Herd. *J. Wildl. Mgmt.* 35.

Talbot, L. M., and Talbot, M. H. 1963. The Wildebeest in Western Masailand, East Africa. *Wildl. Monogr.* 12.

Taylor, C. R.
    1968. The Minimum Water Requirements of Some East African Bovids. *Symp. Zool. Soc. Lond.* 21.
    1969. The Eland and the Oryx. *Scient. Amer.* 220.

Taylor, C. R., and Lyman, C. P. 1967. A Comparative Study of the Environmental Physiology of an East African Antelope, the Eland, and the Hereford Steer. *Physiol. Zool.* 40.

Taylor, C. R.; Spinage, C. A.; and Lyman, C. P. 1969. Water Relations of the Waterbuck, an East African Antelope. *Amer. J. Physiol.* 217.

Walther, F. R.
    1969. Flight Behavior and Avoidance of Predators in Thomson's Gazelle. *Behavior* 34.
    1970. On Territoriality and Migration of Thomson's Gazelle in Serengeti National Park. In press.

Watson, R. M. 1969. Reproduction of Wildebeest in the Serengeti Region, and Its Significance to Conservation. *J. Reprod. Fert.,* Suppl. 6.

ZEBRA

Estes, R. D. 1967. Trials of a Zebra Herd Stallion. *Natural History* 76.

Klingel, H.
    1968. Investigations on the Social Organization and Population Ecology of the Plains Zebra. *Zool. Afr.* 4.
    1969. Reproduction in the Plains Zebra: Behavior and Ecological Factors. *J. Reprod. Fert.,* Suppl. 6.

WARTHOG

Bradley, R. M. 1971. Warthog Burrows in Nairobi National Park. *E. Afr. Wildl. J.* 9.

Child, G., and Roth, H. H. 1968. Reproduction and Recruitment Patterns in Warthog Populations. *Mamm.* 68.

Clough, G., and Hassam, A. G. 1970. A Quantitative Study of the Daily Activity of the Warthog in the Queen Elizabeth National Park, Uganda. *E. Afr. Wildl. J.* 8.

HYRAXES

Bartholomew, G. A., and Rainy, M. 1971. Regulation of Body Temperature in the Rock Hyrax. *J. Mamm.* 52.

Coe, M. J. 1962. Notes on the Habits of the Mount Kenya Hyrax. *Proc. Zool. Soc. Lond.* 138.

Sale, J. B.
    1965. The Feeding Behavior of Rock Hyraxes in Kenya. *E. Afr. Wildl. J.* 3.
    1970a. The Behavior of the Resting Hyrax in Relation to Its Environment. *Zool. Afr.* 5.
    1970b. Unusual External Adaptations in the Rock Hyrax. *Zool. Afr.* 5.

Turner, M. I. M., and Watson, R. M. 1965. An Introductory Study on the Ecology of Hyrax in the Serengeti National Park. *E. Afr. Wildl. J.* 3.

NAKED MOLERAT

Jarvis, J. U. M. 1969. The Breeding Season and Litter Size of the African Mole Rats. *J. Reprod. Fert.,* Suppl. 6.

PLANTS AND HERBIVORE FEEDING HABITS

Agnew, A. D. Q. 1968. Observations on The Changing Vegetation of Tsavo National Park (East). *E. Afr. Wildl. J.* 6.

Anderson, G. D., and Talbot, L. M. 1965. Soil Factors Affecting the Distribution of the Grassland Types and Their Utilization by Wild Animals on the Serengeti Plains, Tanganyika. *J. Ecol.* 53.

Bell, R. H. V. 1970. The Use of the Herb Layer by Grazing Ungulates in the Serengeti. In *Animal Populations in Relation to Their Food Resources,* ed. A. Watson. Oxford: Blackwell Scientific Publications.

Brynard, A. M. 1968. The Influence of Veld Burning on the Vegetation and Game of the Kruger National Park. *Ecol. Stud. in S. Afr.*

Casebeer, R. L., and Koss, G. G. 1970. Food Habits of Wildebeest, Zebra, Hartebeest and Cattle in Kenya Masailand. *E. Afr. Wildl. J.* 8.

Darling, F. F. 1960. An Ecological Reconnaissance of the Mara Plains in Kenya Colony. *Wildl. Monogr.* 5.

Devos, A.
    1968. The Need for Nature Reserves in East Africa. *Biol. Cons.* 1.
    1969. Ecological Conditions Affecting the Production of Wild Herbivorous Mammals on Grasslands. *Adv. Ecol. Res.* 6.

Field, C. R. 1968. A Comparative Study of the Food Habits of Some Wild Ungulates in the Queen Elizabeth Park, Uganda: Preliminary Report. *Symp. Zool. Soc. Lond.* 21.

Glover, P. E. 1968. The Role of Fire and Other Influences on the

Savannah Habitat, with Suggestions for Further Research. *E. Afr. Wildl. J.* 6.

Glover, P. E.; Glover, J.; and Gwynne, M. E. 1962. Light Rainfall and Plant Survival in Dry Grassland Vegetation. *J. Ecol.* 50.

Greenway, P. J., and Vesey-Fitzgerald, D. F. 1969. The Vegetation of Lake Manyara National Park. *J. Ecol.* 57.

Heady, H. F. 1966. Influence of Grazing on the Composition of *Themeda triandra* Grassland, East Africa. *J. Ecol.* 54.

Hedberg, I. and O. 1968. Conservation of Vegetation in Africa South of the Sahara. *Acta. Phytogeogr. Suec.* 54.

Phillips, J. 1965. Fire as a Master and Servant: Its Influence in the Bioclimatic Regions of Trans-Saharan Africa. Fourth Annual Tall Timbers Conference.

Pienaar, U. de V. 1968. The Use of Fire as a Tool in Wildlife Management in the Kruger National Park. In *A Practical Guide to the Study of Larger Herbivores,* ed. F. B. Golley and H. K. Buechner. I.B.P. Handbook 7.

Pratt, D. J.; Greenway, P. J.; and Gwynne, M. D. 1966. A Classification of East African Rangeland. *J. Appl. Ecol.* 3.

Stewart, D. R. M., and Stewart, J. 1970. Food Preference Data by Faecal Analysis for African Plains Ungulates. *Zool. Afr.* 5.

Swart, E. R. 1963. Age of the Baobab Tree. *Nature* 198.

Talbot, L. M.; Talbot, M. H.; and Lamprey, H. F. 1961. An Introduction to the Landscape: A Guide for Field Trips. I.U.C.N./C.C.T.A.

Vesey-Fitzgerald, D. F.
1960. Grazing Succession among East African Game Animals. *J. Mamm.* 41.
1965. The Utilization of Natural Pastures by Wild Animals in the Rukwa Valley, Tanganyika. *E. Afr. Wildl. J.* 3.
1970. The Origin and Distribution of Valley Grasslands in East Africa. *J. Ecol.* 58.

Watson, R. M., and Kerfoot, O. 1964. A Short Note on the Intensity of Grazing in the Serengeti Plains by Plains Game. *Zeit. f. Saug.* 29.

West, O. 1965. Fire in Vegetation and Its Use in Pasture Management, with Special Reference to Tropical and Subtropical Africa. Farnham: Commonwealth Agricultural Bureau,

LIONS

Makacha, S., and Schaller, G. B. 1969. Observations on Lions in the Lake Manyara National Park, Tanzania. *E. Afr. Wildl. J.* 7.

Rudnai, J. 1971. Feeding Habits of the Lion in the Nairobi National Park. In press.

Schaller, G. B. 1969. Life with the King of Beasts. *Ntnl. Geog. Mag.* 135.

Schenkel, R. 1966. Play, Exploration and Territoriality in the Wild Lion. *Symp. Zool. Soc. Lond.* 18.

LEOPARDS

Myers, N. 1972. The Leopard. In press.

Turnbull-Kemp, P. 1967. The Leopard. Cape Town: Howard Timmins.

CHEETAH

Eaton, R. L.
1970a. Hunting Behavior of the Cheetah. *J. Wildl. Mgmt.* 34.
1970b. Group Interactions, Spacing and Territoriality in Cheetahs. *Zeit. f. Tierpsych.* 27.

Graham, A. 1966. East African Wild Life Society Cheetah Survey; Extracts from the Report by Wildlife Services. *E. Afr. Wildl. J.* 4.

Hildebrand, M. 1959. Motions of the Running Cheetah and the Horse. *J. Mamm.* 40.

Schaller, G. B. 1968. Hunting Behavior of the Cheetah in the Serengeti National Park, Tanzania. *E. Afr. Wildl. J.* 6.

WILD DOGS

Estes, R. D., and Goddard, J. 1967. Prey Selection and Hunting Behavior of the African Wild Dog. *J. Wildl. Mgmt.* 31.

Kuhme, W. 1965. Communal Food Distribution and Division of Labor in African Hunting Dogs. *Nature* 205.

HYENAS

Kruuk, H.
1966a. Clan-System and Feeding Habits of Spotted Hyenas. *Nature* 209.
1966b. A New View of the Hyena. *New Scient.* 30.
1970. Interactions between Populations of Spotted Hyenas and Their Prey Species. In *Animal Populations in Relation to Their Prey Species,* ed. A. Watson. Oxford: Blackwell Scientific Publications.

CROCODILES

Cott, H. B.
1961. Scientific Results of an Inquiry into the Ecology and Economic Status of the Nile Crocodile in Uganda and Northern Rhodesia. *Trans. Zool. Soc. Lond.* 29.
1968. Nile Crocodile Faces Extinction in Uganda. *Oryx* 9.

Graham, A. D. 1968. The Lake Rudolf Crocodile Population. M.Sc. thesis, University College, Nairobi, unpublished.

Modha, M. L. 1968. Crocodile Research Project, Central Island, Lake Rudolf: 1967 Breeding Season. *E. Afr. Wildl. J.* 6.

Parker, I. S. C., and Watson, R. M. 1970. Crocodile Distribution and Status in the Major Waters of Western and Central Uganda in 1969. *E. Afr. Wildl. J.* 8.

PREDATORS IN GENERAL

Bourliere, F. 1963. Specific Feeding Habits of African Carnivores. *Afr. Wildl.* 17.

Eaton, R. L. 1971. Evolution of Social Systems in Lions and Cheetahs. Intl. Symp. on World's Cats. In press.

Estes, R. D. 1967. Predators and Scavengers. *Natural History.*

Hirst, S. M. 1965. Ecological Aspects of Big Game Predation. *Fauna and Flora* 16.

Kleiman, D. G. 1967. Some Aspects of Social Behavior in the Canidae. *Amer. Zool.* 7.

Kruuk, H., and Turner, M. 1967. Comparative Notes on Predation by Lion, Leopard, Cheetah and Wild Dog in the Serengeti Area, East Africa. *Mamm.* 31.

Mitchell, B.; Shenton, J.; and Uys, J. 1965. Predation on Large Mammals in the Kafue National Park, Zambia. *Zool. Afr.* 1.

Myers, N. 1972. Spotted Cats: In Danger—Or in Danger of Danger? Intl. Symp. on World's Cats. In press.

Pienaar, U. de V. 1969. Predator-Prey Relationships amongst the Larger Mammals of the Kruger National Park. *Koedoe* 12.

Schaller, G. B., and Lowther, G. R. 1969. The Relevance of Carnivore Behavior to the Study of Early Hominids. *Southwestern J. Anthrop.* 25.

Wright, B. S. 1960. Predation of Big Game in East Africa. *J. Wildl. Mgmt.* 24.

PRIMATES

Altmann, S. A., and Altmann, J. 1970. *Baboon Ecology*. New York: Karger.

Devore, I., ed. 1965. *Primate Behavior*. New York: Holt, Rinehart and Winston.

Gartlan, J. S. 1969. Sexual and Maternal Behavior of the Vervet Monkey, *Cercopithecus aethiops. J. Reprod. Fert.,* Suppl. 6.

Hall, K. R. L., and Gartlan, J. S. 1965. Ecology and Behavior of the Vervet Monkey on Lolui Island, Lake Victoria. *Proc. Zool. Soc. Lond.* 145.

Jay, C, J., ed. 1968. *The Primates*. New York: Holt, Rinehart and Winston.

Rowell, T. E. 1966. Forest Living Baboons in Uganda. *J. Zool.* 149.

Struhsaker, T. T.
  1967a. Behavior of Vervet Monkeys (*Cercopithecus aethiops*). U.C. Publications in Zoology. Berkeley: University of California Press.
  1967b. Ecology of Vervet Monkeys (*Cercopithecus aethiops*) in the Masai Amboseli Game Reserve, Kenya. *Ecology* 48.

Washburn, S. L., ed. 1961. Social Life of Early Man. *Viking Fund Publs.* 3.

BIRDS

Angwin, J. 1969. Birds of the Nairobi National Park. M.Sc. thesis, University College, Nairobi, unpublished.

Brown, L. H.
  1959. The Mystery of the Flamingoes. *Country Life*, London.
  1963. Observations on East African Birds of Prey. *E. Afr. Wildl. J.* 1.
  1971. The Flamingoes of Lake Nakuru. *New Scient.* 51.

Kahl, M. P. 1966. A Contribution to the Ecology and Reproductive Biology of the Marabou Stork in East Africa. *J. Zool.* 148.

Kruuk, H. 1967. Competition for Food between Vultures in East Africa. *Ardea* 55.

Lawick-Goodall, J. van, and Lawick, H. van. 1966. Use of Tools by the Egyptian Vulture. *Nature* 212.

Moreau, R. E. 1966. *The Bird Faunas of Africa and Its Islands*. New York: Academic Press.

Williams, J. G. 1963. *A Field Guide to the Birds of East and Central Africa*. Boston: Houghton-Mifflin.

FISH

Ray, C. 1968. Marine Parks for Tanzania. Conservation Foundation.

Smith, J. L. B., and Smith, M. M. 1963. *The Fishes of Seychelles*. Grahamstown, Union of South Africa: Rhodes University Press.

WILDLIFE NUMBERS, BIOMASS, ETC.

Bourliere, F. 1965. Densities and Biomasses of Some Ungulate Populations in Eastern Congo and Rwanda, with Notes on Population Structure and Lion/Ungulate Ratios. *Zool. Afr.* 1.

Field, C. R., and Laws, R. M. 1970. The Distribution of the Larger Herbivores in the Queen Elizabeth National Park, Uganda. *J. Anim. Ecol.* 7.

Foster, J. B., and Coe, M. J. 1968. The Biomass of Game Animals in Nairobi Park, 1960–66. *J. Zool.* 155.

Lamprey, H. F.
  1963. Ecological Separation of the Large Mammal Species in the Tarangire Game Reserve, Tanganyika. *E. Afr. Wildl. J.* 1.
  1964. Estimation of the Large Mammal Densities, Biomass and Energy Exchange in the Tarangire Game Reserve and the Masai Steppe in Tanganyika. *E. Afr. Wildl. J.* 2.

Petrides, G. A., and Swank, W. G. 1965. Population Densities and the Range-Carrying Capacity for Large Mammals in Queen Elizabeth Park, Uganda. *Zool. Afr.* 1.

Stewart, D. R. M., and Stewart, J. 1963. The Distribution of Some Large Mammals in Kenya. *J. E. Afr. Nat. Hist. Soc.* 24.

Turner, M. I. M., and Watson, R. M. 1964. A Census of Game in Ngorongoro Crater. *E. Afr. Wildl. J.* 2.

Watson, R. M., and Turner, M. I. M. 1965. A Count of the Large Mammals of the Lake Manyara National Park. *E. Afr. Wildl. J.* 3.

Watson, R. M.; Graham, A. D.; and Parker, I. S. C. 1969. A Census of the Large Mammals of Loliondo Controlled Area, Northern Tanzania. *E. Afr. Wildl. J.* 7.

PREHISTORY AND EMERGENCE OF MAN

Bigalke, R. C. 1968. The Contemporary Mammal Fauna of Africa. *Quart. Rev. Biol.* 43.

Bishop, W. W., and Clark, J. D., eds. 1967. *Background to Evolution in Africa*. Chicago: University of Chicago Press.

Clark, J. D. 1970. *The Prehistory of Africa*. New York: Praeger.

Cole, S. 1964. *The Prehistory of East Africa*. London: Weidenfeld and Nicolson.

Cooke, H. B. S. 1968. The Fossil Mammal Fauna of Africa. *Quart. Rev. Biol.* 43.

DeVore, P., ed. 1965. The Origin of Man. New York: Wenner-Gren Foundation.

Dolhinow, P., and Sarich, V. M. 1971. *Background for Man*. Boston: Little, Brown.

Howell, F. C., and Bourliere, F., eds. 1963. *African Ecology and Human Evolution*. Chicago: Aldine.

Isaacs, G. L. 1971. Chronology and the Tempo of Cultural Change in the Pleistocene. In *Calibration of Hominoid Evolution*, ed. W. W. Bishop and J. Miller. Edinburgh: Scottish Academic Press.

Keist, A. 1968. The Southern Continents as Backgrounds for Mammalian Evolution. *Quart. Rev. Biol.* 43.

Leakey, L. S. B. 1965. *Olduvai Gorge, 1951–61*. Cambridge: Cambridge University Press.

Lee, R. B., and DeVore, I., eds. 1968. *Man the Hunter*. Chicago: Aldine.

Martin, J. S. 1967. *Pleistocene Extinctions: The Search for a Cause*. New Haven: Yale University Press.

Moreau, R. E. 1966. Vicissitudes of the African Biomes in the Late Pleistocene. *Proc. Zool. Soc. Lond.* 141.

Sarich, V. M., and Wilson, A. C. 1967. An Immunological Time Scale for Hominid Evolution. *Science* 158.

WILDLIFE MANAGEMENT

Boyd, J. M.
  1965. Research and Management in East African Wildlife. *Nature* 208.
  1966. The Changing Image of the National Park. *New Scient.*, April 28th, 1966.
  1968. Towards a Grand Plan for the Management of Wildlife in East Africa. *E. Afr. Agric. For. J.* 33.

Curry-Lindahl, K. 1969. The New African Conservation Convention. *Oryx* 10.

Darling, F. F. 1969: The Park Idea and Ecological Reality. *Natl. Parks Mag.* 43.

Davis, R. K. 1968. Prospects for Joint Production of Livestock and Wildlife on East African Rangeland: The Case of Kenya. Dar es Salaam: Bureau of Resource Assessment and Land Use Planning 4.

Devos, A. 1968. Problems in National Parks Management in East Africa. *Unasylva* 22.

Dirschl, H. J. 1966. Management and Development Plan for the Ngorongoro Conservation Area. Dar es Salaam: Ministry of Agriculture, Forestry and Wildlife.

Dodds, D. G., and Patton, D. R. 1968. Wildlife and Land-Use Survey of the Luangwa Valley. Rome: F.A.O.

Harthoorn, A. M. 1970. *The Flying Syringe*. London: Bles.

Harthoorn, A. M.; Kanwisher, J.; and Tomkins, N. 1970. Radio-telemetry as a means of Assessing Adaptations to Environmental Conditions. *Zool. Afr.* 5.

Longhurst, W. M., and Heady, H. E. 1968. Report on a Symposium on East African Range Problems. New York: Rockefeller Foundation.

Olindo, P. M., ed. 1969. First Wildlife Conference for Eastern Africa. Nairobi: Kenya National Parks.

Pienaar, U. de V. 1969. Why the Culling of Wild Animal Populations Is an Essential Management Practice in National Parks and National Reserves. *S. Africa Natl. Parks.*

Pratt, D. J. 1968. Rangeland Management in Kenya. *Ann. of the Arid Zone* 7.

Riney, T. 1967. Conservation and Management of African Wildlife. Rome: F.A.O.

Russell, E. W. 1968. Management Policy in the National Parks. Arusha: Tanzania National Parks.

Saibull, S. A. o/e. 1968. Ngorongoro Conservation Area. *E. Afr. Agric. For. J.* 33.

Savory, C. A. R. 1969. Crisis in Rhodesia. *Oryx* 10.

Western, D.
  1971. Amboseli—New Perspectives. *Animals* 13.
  1971. The Human-Animal Equation. *Afr. Wildlife Leadership Foundation Newsletter* 6.
  1969. Proposals for an Amboseli Game Park. Nairobi: Inst. Dev. Studies, University College.

World Bank. 1967. Report on a Project to Develop the Murchison Falls Area of Uganda. Washington, D.C.

GAME CROPPING

Bindernagel, J. A. 1968. Game Cropping in Uganda. Uganda Game Dept.

Brown, L. H. 1968. Animals and Land Use in Kenya. *Anim. Prod. Soc. Kenya* 1.

Casebeer, R. L. 1968. Applying Wildlife Management to Pastoral Land Management. *E. Afr. Agric. For. J.* 33.

Denney, R. M. 1968. The Case for Intensive Wildlife Management. *E. Afr. Agric. For. J.* 33.

F.A.O. 1970. Wildlife Management in Kenya. Rome.

Ledger, H. P. 1968. Body Composition as a Basis for a Comparative Study of Some East African Mammals. *Symp. Zool. Soc. Lond.* 21.

Parker, I. S. C.
  1968. The Commercial Exploitation of Wildlife. *Anim. Prod. Soc. Kenya* 1.
  1969. The Marketing of East African Wildlife Products. *Anim. Prod. Soc. Kenya* 2.

Parker, I. S. C., and Graham, A. D. 1970. The Ecology and Economics of Game Ranching in Africa. *Brit. Ecol. Soc. Symp.* In press.

Sachs, R., and Glees, A. 1967. Preservation of Wildlife, Utilization of Mammals and Processing of Game Meat in Tanzania. Bonn: Dept. of Technical Aid, German Foreign Ministry.

Savory, C. A. R. 1965. Game Utilization in Rhodesia. *Zool. Afr.* 1.

Skinner, J. D.
  1967. An Appraisal of the Eland as a Farm Animal in Africa. *Anim. Breed. Abstr.* 35.
  1970. Game Ranching in Africa as a Source of Meat for Local Consumption and Export. *Trop. Anim. Hlth. Prod.* 2.

Skinner, J. D., and Van Zyl, J. H. M. 1969. Reproductive Performance of the Common Eland in Two Environments. *J. Reprod. Fert.,* Suppl. 6.

Steel, W. S. 1968. The Technology of Wildlife Management and Game Cropping in the Luangwa Valley, Zambia. *E. Afr. Agric. For. J.* 33.

Talbot, L. M.; Payne, W. J. A.; Ledger, H. P.; Verdcourt, L. D.; and Talbot, M. H. 1965. The Meat Production of Wild Animals in Africa: A Review of Biological Knowledge. Farnham: Commonwealth Agricultural Bureau, Tech. Comm. 16.

DEVELOPING AFRICA

Kenya Government
  1967. Family Planning in Kenya. Nairobi: Ministry of Economic Planning and Development.
  1970. Development Plan, 1970–74. Nairobi: Government Printer.

Latham, M. C. 1965. Human Nutrition in Tropical Africa, with Special Reference to East Africa. Rome: F.A.O.

Likimani, J. C., and Russell, J. J. 1971. *Kenya—A Country Profile.* New York: Population Council.

Morgan, W. T. W., and Shaffer, M. 1966. *Population of Kenya: Density and Distribution.* Oxford: Oxford University Press.

Myers, N. 1971. Wildlife and Development in Uganda. *BioScience* 21.

Tanzania Government. 1969. Tanzania Second Five-Year Plan, 1969–74. Dar es Salaam: Government Printer.

Uganda Government. 1971. Third Five-Year Plan, 1971–76. Entebbe: Government Printer.

W.H.O. 1968. Nutrition Survey in Kenya, 1964–68. Nairobi.

MASAI

Brown, L. H. 1971. The Biology of Man as a Factor in Conservation. *Biol. Cons.* 3.

Davis, R. K. 1970. A Proposal for a Socioeconomic Analysis of Group Ranching Development in Kenya Masailand. Nairobi: Inst. Dev. Studies, University College.

Glover, P. E., and Gwynne, M. D. 1961. The Destruction of Masailand. *New Scient.* 249.

Jacobs, A.H.
  1966. African Pastoralists: Some General Remarks. *Anthrop. Quart.* 38.
  1968a. *A Chronology of the Pastoral Masai.* Nairobi: East Africa Publishing House.
  1968b. Masai Marriage and Bridewealth. Nairobi: Society and Law Workshop, University College.

Maloiy, G. M. O., and Heady, H. F. 1965. Grazing Conditions in Kenya Masailand. *J. Range Mgmt.* 18.

Naveh, Z. 1966. The Development of Tanzania Masailand: A Sociological and Ecological Challenge. *Afr. Soils* 11.

TOURISM

Clarke, R., and Mitchell, F. 1968. The Economic Value of Hunting and Outfitting in East Africa. *E. Afr. Agric. For. J.* 33.

Mitchell, F. 1968. The Economic Value of Game Viewing as a Form of Land Use. *E. Afr. Agric. For. J.* 33.

Pienaar, U. de V. 1968. The Ecological Significance of Roads in a National Park. *Koedoe* 11.

Tanzania Government. 1968. Tourism Statistics for Tanzania, 1968. Dar es Salaam: Government Printer.

GENERAL

Brown, L. H. 1965. *Africa: A Natural History.* New York: Random House.

Cloudsley-Thompson, J. L. 1969. *The Zoology of Tropical Africa.* New York: W. W. Norton.

I.U.C.N. 1963. Conservation of Nature and Natural Resources in Modern African States. New Series Publ. 1. Morges.

Owen, D. F. 1966. Animal Ecology in Tropical Africa. London: Oliver and Boyd.

Pearson, J., ed. 1969. *Wildlife and Safari in Kenya.* Nairobi: East Africa Publishing House.

Peterson, J. C. B., and Casebeer, R. L. 1971. A Bibliography Relating to the Ecology and Energetics of East African Large Mammals. *E. Afr. Wildl. J.* 9.

Simon, N. 1963. *Between the Sunlight and the Thunder.* Boston: Houghton-Mifflin.

Spinage, C. A. 1963. *Animals of East Africa.* Boston: Houghton-Mifflin.

Sydney, J. 1965. The Past and Present Distribution of Some African Ungulates. *Trans. Zool. Soc. Lond.* 30.

INDEX

Note: Page numbers appearing in italics refer to photographs and their accompanying captions.